THE SCIE

THE SCIENTIFIC LADY

For Stephen

Patricia Phillips

THE SCIENTIFIC LADY

A Social History of
Women's Scientific Interests
1520–1918

Weidenfeld and Nicolson
London

George Weidenfeld and Nicolson Ltd
91 Clapham High Street, London SW4 7TA

ISBN 0 297 82043 5

Printed in Great Britain by Butler & Tanner Ltd,
Frome and London

Contents

Illustrations

Acknowledgements

I should like to acknowledge the assistance of the staff of the British Library; the Public Record Office, London; the Royal Institution; the Bodleian; the Public Record Office, Oxford; and the English Faculty Library, Oxford. I would like to thank the Librarian, Mrs Gwen Hampshire, who offered considerable practical help and support.

I owe a special debt of gratitude to my husband, Stephen Mills.

Introduction

George Eliot studied chemistry with Michael Faraday, 'revelled' in astronomy and mathematics, and jauntily acknowledged the 'slight zoological weakness' that had precipitated her long-term relationship with the naturalist, G.H. Lewes.

Samuel Taylor Coleridge's daughter, Sara, resorted to geology and botany to alleviate the distress of poor health after the birth of her children. Maria Edgeworth, the Irish novelist, preferred scientists to literary men, relished astronomy and confessed to a zany 'taste for mechanics'.

Lord Byron's daughter, Ada, Shelley's first wife, Harriet Westbrook, Mrs Gaskill's daughter, Meta, and numerous other women all shared the same fascination and enthusiasm for the study of different branches of the sciences. Nor were they the first ladies to do so. Early stirrings of this interest were already evident before 1600. By the mid-nineteenth century it was taken for granted.

The Scientific Lady explores this apparently unlikely manifestation of the intellectual inclinations of women. It is not a history of science nor a history of great women scientists, but an investigation of the interest in science and mathematics cultivated by unexceptional and usually unambitious British women, most of them from the leisured classes.

This feminine predilection for science was partly the result of the general exclusion of women from classical studies. For centuries an education in the classics was considered by the universities and by society in general to be an intrinsically masculine avocation, to constitute the only worthwhile field of scholarship and, furthermore, to confer the essential stamp of gentle birth and good breeding.

The pursuit of science, on the other hand, was tainted by its too intimate involvement with mechanical and menial matters – unde-

sirable on both scholarly and social grounds. Yet, while many gentlemen, members of the privileged élite, repudiated science as too
contemptible and too trivial to warrant their own attention, some
thought these very demerits made it unobjectionable as a study for their
ladies. The operations of the laboratory, after all, were not dissimilar to
those of the kitchen, and scrutinizing lower forms of life through a
microscope was more womanly than vain attempts to master the complexities of Latin and Greek.

In due course, other qualities, all appropriate to the improvement of
the female sex, were attributed to the study of science: that it induced
reverence and modesty; that it encouraged domesticity and curtailed
flightiness; that it offered a harmless hobby, a curative for depression
and a corrective to the evils rife in society.

Not all ladies accepted this condescension meekly. On the contrary,
some vigorously refuted the implication that scientific pursuits were
best suited to inferior intellects. These progressive ladies summarily
dismissed the traditionally prestigious classics as irrelevant and
outdated. Consciously at odds with prevailing opinion on the relative
values of ancient and modern, they argued that women were naturally
scientific in their inclinations precisely because their isolation from the
burden of the past had left them free to develop an innate originality
and a modern outlook, qualities they chose defiantly to highlight as
praiseworthy.

Further elaborations justified the study of science by women on the
grounds that it could contribute to a new sense of their self-worth and
self-realization; or, perceptively, insisted that science studies might open
the way to greater social and political opportunities.

Thus it was that two opposing interpretations of femininity, one
encouraging submission, the other ambition, combined to sustain the
scientific curiosity that was awakening in women.

This theorizing coincided with the expansion of various initiatives to
popularize science throughout the kingdom during the seventeenth
and eighteenth centuries. Women benefited from these initiatives in
particular ways – often inadvertently but sometimes designedly. Books
were written for them; lectures were tailored with their inadequate
education in mind; science was even injected into poetry and con-
scripted into popular magazines and journals to capture the feminine
imagination. Instruments were specially made for them. Women and
girls who so chose could also avail themselves of science teaching, either
from private tutors or in one of the schools with strong scientific

curricula that were in existence from the late seventeenth century onwards.

Ladies indulged in science as a form of recreation, and scientific tourism became fashionable among new generations of travellers eager to experience the delights of the Black Country and the industrial areas of Europe.

If many women treated the subject simply as a hobby, as not a few gentlemen amateurs were content to do, there were others who pushed their interest some way into the realms of research. In the early nineteenth century, women enjoyed a brief spell as welcome members of the growing scientific community. They did so on the strength of the long female scientific tradition which was recognized, with some surprise, during the 1860s in the first government report on the education of middle-class girls.

A very few women, notably Caroline Herschel and Mary Somerville, achieved something like professional status. In this book, however, it is not so much their contributions to the history of science, in any case already well documented, that are of concern, but their early struggles and setbacks as students, which mirror the efforts of less ambitious women.

In due course, the systematic and well-organized campaign to persuade the educational establishment, the universities of Oxford and Cambridge, to open their doors to women gained momentum. Its eventual victory was to mean that women finally won the right to study the classics, still the acme of academic excellence. In the process, however, the long tradition of women's bias towards science had to be jettisoned, for science still bore the blemish of workshop and factory floor. By the end of the nineteenth century, those women aspiring to share the cultural inheritance long denied them, and to be accepted in the higher reaches of the academic world, came to reject the study of science, just as most of the privileged men they were emulating had always done.

Simultaneously, the gradual swing towards professionalism in the sciences was getting under way. In view of the greater commitment and higher standards that were then necessary, the exclusion of women, whose schools remained poorly funded, may have followed inevitably. But in some measure they themselves connived in this exclusion by switching to the traditional educational formula. Thus was born the belief, still so widely held, that the female mind is constitutionally unscientific. Ignorant of a three-centuries-old tradition, most girls today choose to drop science after the preliminary stages and many women continue to collude with the myth that to be scientific is to be unwomanly.

In laying out the themes of the book, it has not always been possible to follow a strict chronology. It was also necessary to telescope the events and personalities of three hundred years, if some sense of the tradition was to emerge. In the interests of length, I have had to exclude many references, most typically those that simply noted the name and interests of some forgotten provincial lady. I hope the result avoids serious distortion. I have used the word 'science' in its modern meaning, specifying various branches when relevant. The contemporary term was usually 'natural philosophy'. I have treated women's interest in mathematics, in both simple arithmetic and accounting as well as more advanced mathematics, as part of their scientific curiosity. Although mathematics was part of the classical curriculum, many gentlemen thought accounting skills too demeaning and pure mathematics too arcane, so the willingness of women to tackle these subjects was another indication of their intellectual boldness.

I am aware that many scientists were often university-educated men, indeed not unusually clergymen, but I believe that in the eyes of society they were often considered as a group apart and their preoccupations frequently criticized as reprehensible.

I do not suggest that women in general were interested in science. For the most part they were too busy coping with pregnancies and domestic life to have any time to spare for the luxury of personal study. By way of comparison, however, it is worth noting that it was only a small minority of male amateurs that was open to the fascinations of scientific pursuits. When I refer to 'women' in the following pages, I use the term for convenience to indicate not all females, but those particular individuals who at any one time were displaying an interest in science. Nor do I mean to imply that these women pursued their interest much beyond the level of recreation. Some – indeed a surprising number – did, but most were content to indulge their curiosity at an elementary level. This low level of achievement was due not only to the limited efforts of the women themselves, but to their own modest expectations and the rigid social circumscription of their ambitions. And yet, such limitations notwithstanding, there is something courageous in the way in which these women, busy and ever mindful of their duties to family and friends, still endeavoured to snatch their morsel of intellectual freedom through the medium of science.

The four chapters that make up Part I concentrate mainly on the seventeenth century and describe the low intellectual prestige of women and their exclusion from the classics; their reactions to this; how and why they made the choice of science as an alternative; the women, British and continental, whose scientific activities made them influential models to imitate; and the theories of equality or superiority that female interest in science generated.

Part II covers the period from the seventeenth to the end of the eighteenth century. It describes the media through which science was conveyed to women, and those who enjoyed and those who produced these media; the formal or informal education in the sciences that some women were lucky enough to experience; some of the scientific recreations in which women participated; and the complex arguments that were evolved to justify their interest in science.

Part III moves into the nineteenth century, recounting the activities of women in the newly founded Royal Institution and in the British Association for the Advancement of Science. Some participants in these bodies are discussed at greater length. Attention is then drawn to the central place of science in the minds of those who spearheaded the influential movements that had begun to upgrade and further the education of middle-class women. The science education of women of the lower classes is discussed by way of contrast. Chapter 8 is devoted to the findings of the government report, known as the Taunton Commission, which corroborated the tradition of women's interest in science.

The conclusion, indicating the demise of the tradition that encouraged women to seek their intellectual self-fulfilment in science, points the way into the twentieth century.

PART I

The Development of Science as a Female Interest

Introduction

During the seventeenth century, the classics were accepted as the essential reading not only of scholars, but also of gentlemen. A man's intellectual and social status could be defined by the extent of his knowledge of the languages and culture of ancient Greece and Rome. No other section of society was permitted access to these intellectual privileges.

Women, in particular, were excluded because they were considered incapable of any intellectual effort of substance. This incapacity was usually attributed to what was seen as the divinely ordained inferiority of the female of the species, which was further revealed in the psychological deficiencies in the intellectual make-up of women.

For many reasons, women ceased to be so tolerant of this misanthropic view of their abilities during the century. They began to counter all arguments relating to their shortcomings with ones that emphasized their advantages. In this new rationale of female superiority, the prestige offered by kinder interpretations of the Genesis story, that Eve was perfection because created last, had an important place. The qualities of a woman's mind were redefined and accorded a new value. Similarly, the freedom of women from the burden of the past and their consequent originality and inventiveness was frequently emphasized.

New educational theories, particularly those of the famous European pedagogue Jan Amos Comenius, laid great stress on the value of science and the strict necessity to educate all alike, men and women, rich and poor. Comenian theories achieved popularity in England where they were instrumental in beginning the slow improvement in education for women.

An interest in the past achievements of women, especially those who had pursued some aspect of scientific study, provided interesting and imitable role models for English women who were concerned to improve their lot.

CHAPTER 1
Classics: A Gentleman's Subject

When that inveterate traveller, Captain Gulliver, landed up on the floating island of Laputa he made one of his startling socio-anthropological discoveries. He found not the bellicose midgets or the benign giants of his earlier voyages, but an even stranger race. Devoid of any appreciation of what Gulliver perceived as reality, these laughable beings applied themselves exclusively to scientific study and research. Shut away from all contact with nature's simple laws, behind the walls of the Grand Academy of Lagado, they devoted themselves to vain attempts to extract sunbeams from cucumbers, build houses roof first, or produce cheaper and ready-dyed silks by feeding brightly coloured flies to house spiders. In Gulliver's eyes, these remote and ridiculous mandarins seemed more enthralled by the labyrinthine nature of their own mental meanderings than motivated by a real desire to improve the quality of life.[1]

When later in his explorations Gulliver meets Aristotle, he finds that the greatest natural philosopher of the Classical Age shares his low opinion of these benighted scientists. The father of all learning, casting a wise and experienced eye over these modern pretenders to deeper and more profound explanations of man and matter, dismisses them as enthusiasts captivated merely by the extravagant fads of fashion. Lacking any solid basis in true wisdom, their new ideas and theories 'would flourish but a short period of time, and be out of vogue when that was determined'.[2]

Gulliver's dismissive attitude to science reflected, of course, the opinion of his creator, Jonathan Swift, an opinion that continued to influence educational and social thinking in England for centuries. Some of the criticisms of science were blunter than Swift's amusing satire. Like a good journalist, Joseph Addison was only articulating popular feeling when, in 1711, he made one of the earliest known attacks on modern science and the practice of vivisection. He accused scientists both of a fondness for torture and mutilation and a foolish obsession with trivia. According to him, these

> innumerable Retainers to Physick ... amuse themselves with the stifling of Cats in an Air Pump, cutting up Dogs alive, or impaling of Insects upon the point of a Needle for Microscopical Observations; besides those that are employed in the gathering of Weeds, and the Chase of Butterflies; Not to mention the Cockleshell-Merchants and Spider-Catchers.[3]

To its tradition-bound critics, scientific research and experimentation could never produce that humane and civilized society that should be the goal of all thoughtful men. This was because science concerned itself with the seemingly petty details of matter while remaining indifferent to the great and immutable truths of human existence. The deluded and misguided zeal of scientists was the subject of many disparaging attacks. That by Nicholas Malebranche (1638–1715), a reputable, widely read and often quoted philosopher, was typical:

> Men came not into the World to be *Astronomers*, or *Chymists*, to spend their whole Life at the end of a *Telescope*; or labouring at a Furnace, to deduce trifling Consequences from their painful Observations ... It perhaps, has set them up in Reputation with the World: but if they would reflect upon it, they would find that Reputation did but increase their Bondage.[4]

According to Malebranche, man's most important task was to know himself: 'The finest, the most delightful, and most necessary *Knowledge*, is undoubtedly that of *Ourselves*' (sig. a2v). To uncover the secrets of moral, not natural philosophy was the great human task. Without such a goal all man's endeavours could be dismissed as fruitless. Alexander Pope, one of Swift's friends and a fellow satirist put it this way:

> Go, wondrous creature! mount where Science guides,
> Go, measure earth, weigh air, and state the tides;
> Instruct the planets in what orbs to run,
> Correct old Time and regulate the Sun; ...
> Go, teach Eternal Wisdom how to rule–
> Then drop into thyself, and be a fool![5]

To assist him in his search for truth, the gentleman of the seventeenth century had the works of the great ancients as his guide. Ever since their recovery during the Renaissance these literary masterpieces, the works of Aristotle, Homer and Virgil, had been considered the highest achievements of which man was capable. In comparison with this source of enlightenment, the new sciences, as Aristotle remarked to Gulliver, had little that was of true importance to offer.

The great humanists of the sixteenth century, men of the calibre of Matteo Palmieri, Erasmus and Juan Luis Vives, had ensured the continuation and reputation of classical scholarship. In *De Ratione Studii*, Erasmus had written authoritatively that 'within these two literatures are contained all the knowledge which we recognise as of vital importance to mankind'. The humanists had also implanted a contempt for the apparently trivial preoccupations of science. The study of nature, they argued, might well be laudable in some ways, but compared with 'the supreme task of solving the problem of how to live' it was 'of the minutest interest'.[6]

Thus it was that generation after generation of English schoolboys was obliged to confront an unchanging syllabus devoted solely to the study of Latin and Greek. Their parents and schoolmasters and, most importantly, the university authorities remained convinced that the classics were the single most efficacious way in which to inculcate a rigorous moral and intellectual training. It was always taken for granted that the best minds were those that had derived the greatest benefit from their long years of classical application.

This is not to say that this opinion, although prevalent, was never challenged. Many interested bodies attempted to broaden the basis of culture and education. As early as 1561, the sea-captain Sir Humphrey Gilbert, Sir Walter Raleigh's step-brother, suggested that the children of the noblest families in England should be taught mathematics, geography, physics, surgery and modern languages as well as the usual subjects of moral philosophy, Greek, Latin and Hebrew. Their teachers were to occupy their own leisure time in translating foreign works of science and scholarship, performing experiments and writing up their results. 'By erecting this Achademie', Gilbert suggested, 'there shal be hereafter, in effecte, no gentleman within this Realme but good for some what, Whereas now the most parte of them are good for nothing'.[7]

As late as the last quarter of the nineteenth century, the Department of Science and Education was still trying, with great difficulty, to allay the suspicion of science still strong among parents and school authorities. To persuade the parents and pupils of England's great public schools that a scientific curriculum would lower neither educational nor moral standards was a task which, some would say, has not yet been achieved.[8]

The years in between witnessed regular exhortations from scientists and leaders of industry, commerce and navigation to improve the education of gentlemen by introducing science into the curriculum. The change did come eventually, but painfully slowly – and long after other social groups, the lower orders and the Dissenting minorities in particular, had seen the necessity of introducing science into mainstream education.

The classics continued to maintain their superior status until well into the twentieth century. This was due not only to the belief that they were the single best way in which to train the minds of the ruling classes. There was another reason, equally significant and no less influential. Since custom and privilege had long enshrined the classics as the intellectual preserve of the most distinguished in society, a classical education, however inadequate, came to symbolize the breeding deemed essential to the gentleman. The classics marked out, as nothing else could, not so much the scholar as the gentleman.

An easy familiarity with the classics might well be thought to denote refined sensibilities and intellectual capacity, but, for many people, it was more likely to be employed as a yardstick to determine class and social status. Not to have had a classical education was to be for ever exiled beyond the pale of polite society. The experience of Richard Lovell Edgeworth (1744–1817), the inventor, who found his social origins called into question, was typical. As the son of an Irish landowner he had, in fact, had the classical education befitting a gentleman. It was just as well because when he began to involve himself in designing agricultural machines and travelling vehicles, he drew doubt on his pedigree – so much so that even a liberal man like Dr Erasmus Darwin betrayed his deep-seated social prejudices when they first met in the 1770s. They had sought each other out, drawn by a mutual interest in the improvement of carriage design. Darwin took it for granted that the young man who brought him such detailed and practical drawings must be an artisan. It was only when the supposed carriage builder's classical knowledge became evident that the good doctor realized he had mistaken the young man's social rank. Edgeworth recalled the process of detection and identification:

We talked upon other mechanical subjects, and afterwards on various branches of knowledge, which necessarily produced allusions to classical literature; by these he discovered that I had received the education of a gentleman. 'Why! I thought', said the Doctor, 'that you were only a coachmaker!'[9]

Another devout adherent to classical education, Thomas Gaisford, at Oxford in 1800, put the rationale for the tradition of Latin and Greek in its simplest terms: 'The advantages of a classical education are two-fold – it enables us to look down with contempt on those who have not shared its advantages, and also fits us for places of emolument, not only in this world, but in that which is to come.'[10] Believing this, and knowing others shared their belief, was sufficient to persuade parents and sons to continue to follow the tradition without question.

In these circles, a familiarity with scientific knowledge was a very doubtful recommendation. It implied too close an acquaintance with the artisan or industrial classes, which in turn cast doubts on a man's social and intellectual status. It did not seem to matter much that science and the classics often co-existed comfortably in several eminent men. Indeed the early Fellows of the Royal Society tended to be ordained clergy and products of Oxford and Cambridge. In the popular mind of polite society, it was known that gentlemen knew their classics, while those who occupied themselves with hand-soiling tasks were artisans. The exclusive and symbolic nature of the classics was clarified by Lord Chesterfield in his usual pithy and cynical fashion. In a letter to his son he wrote, 'Classical knowledge is absolutely necessary for everybody, because everybody has agreed to think and call it so.'[11]

Notes

1. Jonathan Swift, *Travels into Several Remote Nations of the World. By Captain Lemuel Gulliver. Part III: A Voyage to Laputa, Balnibarbi, Glubbdubdrip, Luggnagg and Japan* (1726).

2. *Gulliver's Travels*, pp. 359–64.

3. *Spectator*, no. 21 (1711). See also *Tatler*, no. 216 (1709).

4. *Father Malebranche. His Treatise Concerning the Search after Truth*, trans. by T. Taylor (1700), sig. a3r.

5. Alexander Pope, *An Essay on Man* (1733–4), Epistle II, ll. 19–30 in *The Poems of Alexander Pope*, ed. by John Butt (1963), pp. 516–17.

6. William Harrison Woodward, *Studies in Education during the Age of the Renaissance 1440–1600* (1924), pp. 76, 123, 162–3 and *passim*.

7. *Early English Text Society. Extra Series VIII* (1869), pp. 1–17, quoted in G.H. Armytage, *Four Hundred Years of English Education* (1964), pp. 2–3. See also A.G. Debus, *Science and Education in the Seventeenth Century. The Webster–Ward Debate* (1970).

8. See below, pp. 238–42.

9. *Memoirs of R.L. Edgeworth, Esq.* (1820), I, pp. 164–5.

10. Quoted in Armytage, *English Education*, p. 66.

11. *Letters*, ed. by Lord Mahon (1892), V, p. 511.

CHAPTER 2

Female Rationality: Seventeenth-Century Views

For three hundred years or so, unanimity on the unrivalled superiority of the classics as the only possible education for a gentleman remained fairly constant. By general consent, classical studies were upheld both for the rigorous intellectual training they imparted and for their significance as the expression of the greatest culture yet known to men. By studying the great authors in boyhood, a gentleman was reputed to develop a familiarity with them and the societies that produced them which would stand him in good stead during his active adult life as a leader of men.

Despite their superior reputation for intellectual gravity, it was recognized that the classics were a product of a very different era and that some of the habits of thought embedded therein, particularly in matters of religion, morals and politics, were inappropriate in a seventeenth-century context. For the most part, it seems to have been taken for granted that the mental resources of a gentleman could distinguish and discount the temptations inherent in a literature that depicted a pre-Christian world of dubious moral integrity and political virtue. Not so the lower orders.[1]

It seemed self-evident that the study of the classics was inimical to the coarser grained in society. Inferior social groups were credited with neither the inherent mental dexterity nor the careful intellectual cultivation of the gentleman. The intellectual content alone made such studies irrelevant to the 'hewers of wood and drawers of water'. Paradoxically, it was also recognized that to permit or encourage this intellectual trespass could lead to catastrophic social consequences. At best, artisans or peasants might begin to look above their station in life; at worst, they could well find the inspiration for developing subversive and rebellious ideas.[2]

It was equally obvious that the study of the classics was unbecoming in the fair sex, whatever their station in life, on grounds not dissimilar to the objections that applied to the lower classes. The female mind, being deficient in rational powers, was unfit for the necessary mental effort required to study the classics. Nor was it necessary that women be so stretched since their sphere of activity was firmly circumscribed within the kitchen, sickroom and nursery, where skills of a manual and practical nature were all that was required.

It was particularly important, too, to shield the congenital weakness of women from the grosser aspects of the classical writers. It was an article of faith that women were easy to corrupt. Feminine commitment to the Christian faith was always thought to be tenuous. Women's immoral inclinations were legendary and would presumably have been encouraged, even authorized, by much of what they might have read in Homer and Virgil. And that other unacceptable predeliction of women, their unreasonable and unfeminine interest in political intrigue, would also find undesirable stimulation in the classics.[3]

This complex justification for excluding women from participating in the education of gentlemen was part of that ancient and formidable legacy of misogyny that pervaded English society. This legacy was an understandable by-product of countless decades of conflict. On the one hand there were continuous attempts to confine women strictly to their biological function, and on the other there were the counter measures taken by women to subvert what they saw as a unilateral and unjust interpretation of their destiny. In the mid-seventeenth century those cornerstones of society, the Church, the Law and the Universities, still brooded on what appeared to be the disharmony between the importance of women's essential and unique purpose on earth and the intellectual and moral shortcomings of the individuals who had been chosen to fulfil it.

Women were continually upbraided: they were unworthy of their destiny and, paradoxically, their disinclination to submit to it was unseemly. It was usually agreed that much of the trouble stemmed from the very origins of Woman. It was a common exercise sedulously to trace female intractability to the well-known imperfections inherent in the creation of the first of all women, mother Eve. One version pointed out that she had been created from a rib, 'a crooked thing', and therefore women were to be excoriated for ever as 'crooked by nature'.[4]

Not only was the bone deformed, it was dispensable – an inessential part of that perfect being, Adam. So it was often deduced that Eve, too, was deficient and superfluous – a being in every way less than the perfection of the noble male. The sole purpose of this dubious creation was to facilitate the mechanics of Adam's perpetuation and to augment those pleasures of the flesh that had been divinely contrived for his exclusive enjoyment. Only very liberal and independent souls would have disagreed with the way in which one author summed up woman's destiny: 'I affirm that the Female is so frail and variable ... it seems that Nature hath only framed her more for the perpetuation of mankind, and pleasure of man, than for any individual perfection in that Sex.'[5]

But it was not only Eve's inferiority that exercised the minds of the fathers; it was the greater threat she represented, as the instrument, of Adam's fall and the conduit through which evil infects mankind. What was regarded as a fatal female combination of wickedness and weakness haunted many a sermon writer. The French author translated by Richard Bancke even managed to draw up a catalogue of female perfidy so comprehensive that it had to be organized on alphabetical principles. Its range was masterful – each letter indicated a noxious vice. Thus B stood for the 'Bottomless Abysse of Bestiality', the natural habitat of the female. Other letters designated the various diabolical roles that women have adopted: 'Contrivers of Malice', 'Increasers of Sin' and 'Ruiners of Realms' being just a few of the options.

That women, if not strictly reined in, would advocate anarchy over order and that their power over men was such that they could plunge the whole of society into disarray was a prevailing anxiety. A shiver of horror convulsed polite society when, in the spring of 1693, it was reported that a young bride had refused to include 'honour and obey' in her marriage vows (*Athenian Gazette*, no. 14, 1693). Popular journals seized on this stereotype with enthusiasm. It made good reading. The *Jovial Mercury*, one of the many 'rags' of the 1690s, asserted in a good-humoured way that women were monsters with only 'some small glimmerings of Rationality' and would be unable to enter the Kingdom of Heaven 'until they have been metamorphosed into men, as the Nobler Sex' (no. I, 1692/3).

Whether cheerful or chilling, attacks such as these never ceased. Even Parliament itself eventually joined in when, in 1770, on the eve of the French Revolution and the Romantic Age, a statute was passed to curb the perfidy of women. It declared that

all women of whatever age, rank, profession or degree, whether virgin, maid or widow, that shall from and after such Act, impose upon, seduce, and betray into matrimony any of His Majesty's subjects by means of scent, paints, cosmetics, washes, artificial teeth, false hair, Spanish wool, iron stays, hoops, highheeled shoes, or bolstered hips, shall incur the penalty of the law now in force against witchcraft and like misdemeanours and that the marriage upon conviction shall stand null and void.[6]

The intellectual inferiority of women

Although prelates, parliamentary representatives and pamphleteers were prompt to credit women with sexual powers of an almost diabolical strength, they were, however, less ready to allow them a similar strength of intellect. Proofs of female inferiority were gleaned from other sources besides the Bible. Even the sciences of psychology and physiology were mined to furnish yet more evidence of a woman's mental shortfall. Still in their infancy and heavily in debt to their classical, patristic and medieval antecedents, these disciplines yielded up the necessary confirmation of female inadequacy. Nicholas Malebranche, ironically a particular favourite among women readers, endorsed the commonly accepted belief in the unequal mental powers of the sexes. Couching his arguments in the psychological terms then current, he described the inadequacies of the female mind. According to him, their soft and weak bodies are an accurate mirror of the soft and yielding consistency of their brains.[7]

He was quite ready to concede that his generalization ignored the many examples of individual women of sterling mental ability, but he maintained its universal application nonetheless. He was adamant that women were capable of understanding nothing more demanding than the harmless superficialities of taste and fashion, and that their enjoyments were strictly limited to the peripheral material luxuries of life. If they wished to exercise their small mental powers, it was acceptable to permit them to arbitrate on the harmless topics of etiquette and dress. It was only on such simple matters that they might be secured from the injury that more strenuous mental effort would inflict on their fragile and sensitive brains:

> All things of an abstracted Nature are Incomprehensible to them. They cannot employ their Imagination in disentangling compound and perplex'd Questions. Their consideration terminates on the surface and outside of things; and their Imagination has neither Strength nor Reach enough to pierce to the bottom of them, and to make a Comparison of their parts, without distraction … In short,

the Mode and not the Reality of things, is enough to take up the whole Capacity of their Mind. [p. 54]

David Abercromby, the eminent seventeenth-century physician, was another influential supporter of the view that women 'have not received from God so perfect Souls as Men, because by God's special appointment they are to obey and Men to command'.[8] In his opinion this divinely ordained inferiority is confirmed by their lack of mental facility. Their thinking processes are clumsy and they are generally incapable of employing any powers of selection or discernment, being completely at the mercy of 'a mutable and confused Imagination or Fancy' (p. 32).

The impossibility of ever training a woman to rein in her wild 'feminine' imagination and to curb it by developing her critical powers exercised the wits of countless writers. A favourite method of highlighting a woman's irredeemable mental flightiness, particularly with writers aiming to entertain, was to take a literary peep into various period versions of the 'room of one's own'. Inevitably, what was discovered was neglect, poverty, dirt and disarray. Naturally, this unedifying condition was supposed to mirror accurately the penurious mental state of the occupant. In one version entitled *Sylvia's Revenge* (1688) there was nothing to be seen in the woman's study but the shabby disorder of 'a box of Marmalade, Culpeppers Midwifery, a Prayer-Book and two or three Plays'.[9]

In another somewhat later version, in the *Spectator*, Joseph Addison pictured the literary lady 'Leonora' sitting among a greater wealth of possessions, but a similar confusion. She had all the latest in seventeenth-century romances, a general assortment of books of devotion and conduct, some classics in contemporary translations, the current bestsellers and, what rather took the curious male observer aback, a complete collection of the works of Sir Isaac Newton. In view of what will become evident later in this book, that was not so surprising, but for the moment suffice it to note that Addison permitted himself the scathing observation that they were in Latin, implying thereby that the good Leonora would be incapable of reading them (*Spectator*, no. 37, 12 April 1711).

Whatever was the true nature of Leonora's efforts, whether earnest study, frivolous escapism or fashionable pretension, one thing was certain: she need not have looked for much sympathy from those among the leading male intellects of the time who remained convinced of the immutability of women's inferior status and who resented fiercely any efforts that might be made to improve it. Alexander Pope, justifiably the greatest poet of that classical age, spoke for most of his friends when he quipped:

> Tho' *Artimesia* talks, by Fits
> Of councils, Classicks, Fathers, Wits;
> Reads *Malbranche, Boyle,* and *Locke*;
> Yet in some Things methinks she fails
> 'Twere well if she would pare her Nails
> And wear a cleaner Smock.[10]

Pope's poetical method underlines the meaning. Artimesia's intellectual interests, which read like a hectic, ill-assorted shopping list, are linked by rhyme with madness. By contrast Pope's own opinion, expressed in the final two lines, is a model of the measured sanity and common sense that Pope would claim characterized the well-trained masculine intellect.

Counter arguments in women's favour

This venerable and ancient tradition of assuming the spiritual and mental inferiority of the female, of dismissing her feeble pretensions with all the authority and power of ages, came under a prolonged and at least partially successful attack during the later seventeenth century.

Seventeenth-century women (or at least a group of them that compensated for its smallness by its vociferousness), aided and abetted by numbers of sympathetic males, began to demand a reappraisal of their position. Why there should have been such a concerted effort at that time, often taking form in pamphlets and articles demanding educational improvements, rebutting vituperative attacks or asserting women's rights and the need for greater recognition of those rights, can only be conjectured. But it was a time when new ways of thought, social, political and pedagogic, were hastening the splintering of old traditions.

The new moves to improve literacy so as to enable both men and women to come to a personal understanding of the Word of God contributed to the better education of women. A fascination with doctrine and exegesis generated a wealth of sermons, which was gratefully received by willing listeners. (For many decades, writing sermons down from memory remained a favourite pastime for intelligent young girls on a Sunday afternoon.) The growing strength of Puritanism improved the condition of women in other ways too, for although it vigorously enforced the received Pauline view of women, it also exalted the virtue of family life and the special role of the mother as educator and guardian of the developing minds of her children. As a complement to this new dignity of womanhood there was also a novel insistence on the duties of men towards women.

There were new roles for women to play, too, in the religious sects that began to flourish in the mid-seventeenth century. Now for the first time, women in these groups adopted the authoritative stance of preacher. By and large these women drew nothing but the abhorrence of society on themselves, as in the pamphlet, *A Discoverie of Six women preachers, in Middlesex, Kent, Cambridgeshire and Salisbury* (1641), a goading attack which took as its text 1 Cor. 14:34–5, 'Let your Women keep Silence in the Churches'). But these female preachers made their mark nonetheless, not least in the virulently feminist sermons that some chose to deliver to their flocks. One such diatribe was *The Woman's Advocate* (1697) in which the author, one M.M., proclaimed herself a second Messiah on the grounds that God had already tried a male and found him wanting (p. 2). Another woman preacher rebuked the chief of all misogynists, St Paul himself. In 'Good News to the Good Women' (1700), she presented a vision of a redeemed world in which sexual inequality, being incompatible with scripture and the divine plan, would cease to exist.

A not unimportant factor in this new assertiveness among women was the impact of the Civil War on their restricted lives. War often has the effect of pushing women into roles of greater independence, an independence that clings to them even when the soldiers come home. The heroism of the women at the siege of Lyme in Dorset was celebrated by James Strong in 1645 in a poem bearing the informative title, *Joanereidos: or Feminine Valour: Eminently discovered in Westerne Women: As Well By defying the merciless Enemy at the face abroad, as by fighting against them in Garrison Townes; sometimes carrying stones, anon tumbling of stones over the Works on the Enemy, when they have been scaling them, some carrying powder, others charging of Peeces* [sic] *to ease the Souldiers, constantly resolved for generality, not to think any one life deare, to maintaine that Christian quarrell for the PARLIAMENT. Whereby, as they deserve commendations in themselves, so are they proposed as example unto others.*[11]

Then again women had begun to evince an interest in the history of their own sex. In fact, it seems to have been a subject of general appeal. By the time Jeremy Collier published his history of famous women in *The Great Historical, Geographical and Poetical Dictionary* (2nd edn, 1701), there was already an impressive bibliography of authoritative works that gave space to biographies of women.[12] These lists most often broadcast the names of women of virtue and renown.[13] But the glorious reputation of good queen Bess still lingered in the memory, and increasingly another image of woman, that of the female intellectual, began to be noted and her feats inside and outside the universities at home and abroad were widely reported.

None of the arguments that denigrated women went unanswered.[14] The traditionalists were challenged on all counts, often with enchanting and surprising ingenuity. Everything, from woman's supposedly inferior beginnings as the rib of Adam to the contemporary psychological justifications of her inadequate intellectual resources, was examined and refuted.

The conflict was as old as Plato himself, and the women who wrote on their own behalf or who were vindicated by male champions had just as impressive an arsenal of argument and invective to draw on as their challengers. Plato's case for the equality of the sexes in the *Republic* made regular appearances throughout the seventeenth century and beyond, in one guise or another. One popular variant, presented to a receptive audience by a woman, went thus 'a she Ape is as full of, and as ready at Imitation as a He; a Bitch will Learn as many Tricks in as short a time as a Dog; a female Fox has as many Wiles as a Male'.[15]

Other Platonic references offered women a less earthy affirmation of female value: 'Plato ... affirmeth that woman's society hath made ciuill the more outrageous condition of men's lives: yea, such as naturally have been barbarous and enemies to their own kinde.'[16]

This last was to become a potent, if equivocal, factor in the rationale of a 'woman's worth', for to claim for women the dignity of being an agent of civilization was to lay a whole new set of restrictions on them. But, for the moment, it was a welcome change. Men of influence, as diverse as Jonathan Swift and Samuel Johnson, extolled the refining effect of the intellectual woman on the more barbaric male, and the eighteenth century was to witness the introduction of the ladies' *salon* or drawing room, the ultimate expression of the civilizing feminine influence.

Other eminent authorities, among them Valerius Maximus, Plutarch and Boccaccio, were also quarried for the arguments which were to become so familiar. The early humanists were another productive, if paradoxical, source. Erasmus and Juan Luis Vives had averred a belief that women must be educated and their status improved, but only because this was the most efficacious way in which to weaken their proclivity to evil. This, too, became a powerful argument to muster the grudging support of those who doubted the usefulness of learning to women. If it was going to deter her from sinfulness, then it became more acceptable.[17]

The greatest reference book of all for the female polemicists, itself a compendium of many earlier arguments, was undoubtedly *De Nobilitate et Praecellentia Foeminei Sexus*. Addressed to Margaret of Austria and Burgundy, it was written by the German-born Henricus Cornelius Agrippa and published in Antwerp in 1529. The book was translated into English at least three times during the sixteenth century, and most of its arguments and examples were subsequently plagiarized for many years.[18]

Agrippa's version of the Genesis story, for example, furnished women with a much more supportable account of their origins. As he saw it, Adam embodied the characteristics of the gross material (the 'slime and dung' as one author unflatteringly put it), of which he was fashioned. On the other hand Eve exemplified life. She had been created last, the final act of the Divine Maker, in Paradise itself, out of divinely animated material. She was beautiful, biologically more significant and excelled man in that gift that sets human above brute creation, the power of speech.[19]

The guilt of the original sin was also redistributed. Agrippa suggested that the culpability rested fairly and squarely on the shoulders of Adam. Eve's failing was in allowing herself to be deceived. It was Adam who sinned and suffered for it. Agrippa noted that the ancient Jewish ritual of circumcision constituted the rite of atonement traditionally endured by the male sex only. The final and most telling evidence of male inferiority was that Christ expatiated the sins of mankind through the ultimate humiliation of assuming manhood.

Agrippa's treatise also provided women with valuable arguments by which they could not only defend their much maligned physical weakness, but also exploit it to their advantage. In the version of Agrippa published in England as *The Nobylyte of Wymen* in 1559, during the first year of Elizabeth's reign, the author, Wyllm Bercher, wrote:

> Ye knowe right well that Philozophye maketh an argument of the wysedome of the mynde by the constytucon of ye bodye and sayethe that creaturs endewid soft and tendr fleshe have ye better wysedome and understandynge. Whearby it cannot be doubted but wymen havinge moste soffte and delycate fleshe muste nedes have better wyttes and be more apte to speculacun then men. [p. 97]

Accordingly, that agglomeration of singular attributes so often quoted to prove a woman's inherent mental weakness could now be manipulated to demonstrate her unique cognitive skills. In an age which accepted that all knowledge derived from sense impressions, it had to be conceded that the more sensitive those faculties were, the more knowledgeable one was likely to become.

Inevitably this sort of theorizing became the stuff of journalism. One of its most interesting applications on this level appeared much later in the *Lady's Journal* (October 1693). Significant for its unique position as the first magazine written for and by women as well as for its radical stance on the position of women (only a single issue appeared), its central essay, 'That Women may apply themselves to the Liberal Arts and Sciences', develops the theme that the superiority of a woman's mental faculties can be measured by the degree in which her physical faculties excel those of the male.[20] And, of course, the physical constitution of a woman is demonstrably unrivalled. The head alone indicates the greater intellectual potential:

> The Physiognomy of Women is generally more promising than that of Men; their Forehead is generally high, rais'd and broad, which is the usual token of an ingenious and inventive person; and accordingly, Women have a great deal of Vivacity, Imagination and Memory.[p. 336]

In those respects in which they were not superior, the author argued that women were the equal of men, for 'the Mind act[s] in the same Manner in both Sexes' and is 'equally able to effect the same thing in either' (p. 335).

The point of the essay is to demand that women be excluded no longer from the education that men enjoy, so that they too may be admitted to the 'honourable and profitable employment' which would then be open to them, this being 'the chief end of most men's study'.[21]

In claiming the equal rights of women to the education received by men, the anonymous author of the essay in the *Lady's Journal* declared herself to be of the party that wanted women to win their equality by competing on equal terms with the men. By no means all women shared this view, but it was always a powerful rallying point in the struggle for the intellectual parity of women. In the seventeenth century its most influential apologist was the young Dutch woman, Anna Maria von Schurmann (1607–78).

Von Schurmann was living proof of the reality of the learned woman. Her sex notwithstanding, she had become a scholar in the traditional sense. She was an accomplished classicist and had added the languages needed for biblical exegesis to her studies. Her reputation was such that her home in Utrecht became a meeting place for the greatest minds of the day. Queen Christina of Sweden and other travelling royals all paid her court. Descartes, Gassendi, Voët and Spanheim were all close friends. At that time all that was new and exciting in philosophical and scientific theory was fermented in Holland. The systems of Descartes and Spinoza both evolved in that heady intellectual climate.

Among intellectuals von Schurmann was held in high esteem. She was allowed to attend lectures at the University of Utrecht, albeit discreetly screened behind a curtain. In 1636, as the best Latinist in the city, Anna was requested by the rector, Gisbert Voët, to write some verses for public declamation to celebrate the inauguration of the new university. The results were said to have entranced the public, and Anna's prestige grew accordingly. She became known as the 'Sappho of Holland' and was acclaimed as the unofficial poet laureate of Utrecht.[22]

When she decided to throw her weight behind the women's cause, she was heard with considerable respect. Her publication was entitled *De Ingenii Muliebris ad Doctrinam et Meliores Literas Apitudina* and appeared in 1641. Its standard English title was that of its first English translation by Clement Barksdale, *The Learned Maid or Whether a Maid may be a Scholar* (1659).

Part of the book's enormous influence in European and English intellectual circles was due not only to the author's fame and impeccable classical credentials, but to its success in reaching a wide and scholarly audience. Von Schurmann achieved this by writing in Latin and by couching her argument in the classical form of the syllogism or exercise in logic. Men who would not have read such a book in the vernacular enjoyed it in its classical format. Her name, more than any other woman's, became the one most often quoted by men who wrote on women's matters during the following decades.

The argument of the book was that women should have the freedom to study whatever they wished. They should not be deflected either because they could never put such studies to use or because academic subjects had no direct relevance to a woman's domestic existence. Von Schurmann pointed out that it was illogical to argue that women should be excluded from study because the life plan imposed by tradition and convention permitted few opportunities for them to utilize such knowledge. If that was so for women, it was just as much the case for men whose studies were often quite irrelevant to their later careers. Yet no man was ever debarred from education for that reason.

Von Schurmann's position on education was a conservative one. She accepted the humanist tradition of scholarship as the only acceptable educational system. It was therefore natural for her to suggest that 'the study of *letters*, that is the knowledge of Tongues and Histories' should constitute the ambitions of the learned woman. It also seemed self-evident that educational opportunities should be permitted only to women of rank, wealth, intelligence and leisure. Furthermore, even these women should never allow their academic pursuits to take precedence over their more serious tasks of saving their souls and looking after children and husband.

Von Schurmann headed a tradition which certainly allowed some women to achieve very real success in their classical studies. These eminent women were usually accorded a real, if grudging, admiration. The exceptional nature of their achievement was always stressed, and the wiser women among them balked criticism by cultivating some distinctively feminine and public art. It was the proudest boast of Elizabeth Carter, the translator of Epictetus and friend of Samuel Johnson, and one that her biographer ensured was duly passed on to later generations, that she was never without her sewing. She deemed the skill essential in a woman.[23]

But the very acceptance by some women of the superiority of classical education always raised a question as to the value of the alternative systems of education that many other women proposed to devise for themselves. Educational reformers recognized that von Shurmann's programme was retrograde, and she was criticized by leading feminists of the day both for her approval of the exclusive classical curriculum and for her élitist approach to education.[24]

However, despite the shortcomings of her traditional views, Anna Maria von Schurmann did inspire more radical followers. She had, after all, insisted that women had the right to regard the whole body of knowledge as accessible to them. She also made the curious suggestion that some women ought to contemplate more active roles in society. They should apply themselves not only to the classics, but to science, to the law and to military strategy. In that way they would prepare themselves for future careers at the Bar, in both Church and University, and even be ready to take their places in the highest positions in government. These demands were to become a constant feature of feminist doctrines during the eighteenth and nineteenth centuries.

'Unlearned' and 'original' woman

Meanwhile, not many women sought to prove their equality by braving the male preserve of the classics. Long custom had made their mastery too daunting or too undesirable. Already in the seventeenth century many women felt they should employ themselves on better things and that their very exclusion from the classics was not so much a handicap as a positive blessing. These ideas constituted that other strand in the evolution of women's crusade for equality – a desire to turn away from the burdensome classical tradition and to formulate in its place an education more suitable to the needs and interests of women. This process was closely interwoven with the ideas of those who wished to update education in general.

Peter Motteux summed up feminine disdain for the classics in the preface which he contributed to the *Lady's Journal*. He underlined the significance to women of their non-classical education. Far from being a drawback, it meant that their innate intelligence remained unfettered by the harsh bridle of academic tradition, permitting them thereby a free and unreined originality and inventiveness. He thought these qualities should be regarded not as the negative side of their character, as was often claimed, but as their natural and enviable good fortune. With such creative temperaments it was clear that they made finer authors and thinkers than the supposedly better educated and superior male.

A man's education, or so claimed Motteux, constrained and restricted all his mental facility so that his intellectual landscape resembled a desert where what grew naturally was only what was thorny and unappealing. His only hope was to cultivate the hothouse techniques of tradition and precedent, for he would never be able to equal the happy and inspired enterprise of the thoughtful woman. Motteaux regretfully compared the laboured and custom-ridden efforts of himself and other men with the inspired and artless writings of women. He summed up the difference in an image which contrasts the vegetation of the infertile wasteland with the easy blessings of nature in a productive soil:

> But most of our Sex with all their Art vex in vain a Stubborn Soil, their own barren Minds, productive indeed sometimes, but 'tis of luxuriant Weeds and thorny Conceptions. They would be witty at any cost; but their Wit, like forc'd Flowers, more due to Art than to Nature, generally fails of the perfection of their [women's] easy and unaffected Productions. [p. 325]

Thus encouraged, many women in the second half of the seventeenth century turned to literary work. Some wrote for money, some because they envied the men their coveted role as authors. All assumed that their newly accredited wealth of originality and inventiveness would be an adequate substitute for the classical frame of reference readily available, and thought essential, to a serious male author.

Many did acquire popularity and some, lasting fame, but critics of the conservative school, who felt the well-being of culture was safe only in their hands, reacted predictably. They saw to it that these 'petticoat authors' would be discredited on both personal and professional grounds.

It was soon a commonplace that the general deterioration not only of moral but of literary standards was due to the unwelcome trespass of women in the demesne of letters. One lady noted dolefully that there was 'scarce a more reproachful Name than Poetess'.[25] There was general agreement that these 'She-Authors' might be tolerated in the frivolous literary forms of the lyric or the romance, but if they dared attempt the serious classical genres of epic or tragedy, they ran a gauntlet of vituperation.[26] Not only was their lack of literary skill and talent upbraided, but their moral and physical shortcomings as well. So, although many women took to writing and were indeed soon supplying the rapidly growing market in light literature, it was not a profession to be undertaken carelessly. Even if they succeeded in extracting payment for their work, their reputations were always at risk. Successful writers of certifiable respectability did preserve their honour, but such was the stigma that hung about the profession for many years that most women writers, and indeed some men, preferred to publish anonymously rather than court the contumely of the public.

In any case, writing was a profession that appealed only to certain sorts of women. The others, who simply wished to develop their minds and understandings, cast about for areas in which they would be permitted to study, discover and learn. For many, science was the perfect alternative.

Notes

1. J.A. Comenius, the educational reformer who was invited to England in 1641 to advise on educational matters (see below, pp. 30–33), heartily disapproved of the paganism and the debauchery of classical writers. See *The Great Didactic* (1657), p. 193.

2. The 'Sedition and Rebellion' of the late 1660s was attributed to the tendency of country grammar schools to draw pupils from the lower classes. Thomas Hobbes was one who held such élitist views. See Armytage, *English Education*, p. 40.

3. The volubility of women and their unseemly interest in politics was often censured. See, for example, *Spectator*, nos. 81, 128 and 247.

4. Joseph Swetnam, *The Arraignment of Lewd, Idle, Froward and Unconstant Women* (1637), p. 1.

5. [Mr Richard Bancke], *A Discourse of Women, Shewing their Imperfections Alphabetically, Newly translated out of the French into English* (1673), p. 10. Other similar attacks on the character of women were *The Ape-Gentle-woman, or The Character of an Exchange-wench* (1675); *The 'Miss' displayed; with all her wheadling* [sic] *Arts and Circumventions* (1675); *Love given over: or a Satyr against the Pride, Lust and Inconstancy, etc. of Women* (1686).

6. Quoted in Ralph Wardle, *Mary Wollstonecraft* (Kansas, 1951), p. 136.

7. Father Malebranche, *His Treatise* (1700), p. 65.

8. *A Discourse of Wit* (1685), pp. 214–15. The legal position of women as *sub potestate viri* is described in *A Treatise of Feme Coverts, or the Lady's Law* (1732), which demonstrates that the Old Testament could be invoked in court cases to prove that a women 'is disabled to make any Grand Contract or Bargain, without the Allowance or Consent of her Husband', p. 179 and *passim*.

9. [Richard Ames], *Sylvia's Revenge, or; a Satyr against Man in Answer to the Satyr against Woman* (1688), 'Epistle Dedicatory', unpaginated.

10. *Artimesia* (written before 1709) in *The Poems of Alexander Pope*, ed. by John Butt (1963), p. 13.

11. The poem was a popular one and appeared in print adorned with many other congratulatory verses. It had a second expanded edition in 1674. Another woman who distinguished herself, this time on the Royalist side, was Lady Anne Halkett (1622–99, who claimed to have assisted the escape of the young Duke of York and to have nursed the soldiers after the battle of Dunfermline: *Autobiography*, ed. by J.G. Nichols (1875).

12. Collier noted Boccace Betussi, Peter Paul de Ribera, Francis Serdonati, Augustin della Chiesa, Philip de Bergamo, Scardeoni, Caesar Capacio, Pinot, Hilarion de Costa, Brantome, Bayle, Scaliger and Menagii as authorities on the history of women.

13. A typical example of the defences of women that concentrated on their virtue is *The Illustrious History of Women, or a compendium of the many virtues that adorn the Fair Sex represented, not only in lively discourses grounded upon Reason, but in sundry examples of virtuous Love, Piety, Prudence, Modesty, Chastity etc. with other examples of Women Skilled in the most curious Arts, to which are added, The Example of Warlike Women: with the prophesies and Predelictions of the Sybills* [sic] *in relation to our Blessed Saviour; and the Character of a Virtuous Woman in all her Capacities* (1686).

14. Some of these defences of women are *The Woman's Sharpe Revenge* (1640); *Now or Never: or A New Parliament of Women assembled And met together near the Popes-Head in Moor-Fields...* (1656); *The Great Advocate and Oratour for Women, or The Arraignment, Tryal and Conviction of such wicked Husbands (or Monsters) who hold it lawful to beat their Wives, or to demean themselves severely and tyranically towards them: where their crafty Pleas are fully stated, and their Objections answered; and the just Sentence of their Condemnation passed against them from the law of Nature...* (1682); *The Female Advocate, or An Answer to a late Satyr against the Pride, Lust and Inconstancy etc. of Women. Really written by a Lady in vindication of her Sex* (1686); *The Lost Maiden-head: or Sylvia's Farewell to Love. A New Satyr against Man* (1691); *Sylvia's Complaint of her Sexes Unhappiness. A Poem, being the Second Part of Sylvia's Revenge, or a Satyr against Man* (1692).

15. Mary Astell, *An Essay in Defence of the Female Sex* (1696), pp. 13–14. Astell is discussed below, pp. 44–5.

16. *A Woman's Woorth* [sic], *defended against all the men in the world Proving them to be more perfect, excellent and absolute in all vertuous actions, than any man of qualitie soever*, written by a French lord, trans. by Anthony Gibson (1599), p. 33.

17. W.H. Woodward, *Studies in Education*, p. 207.

18. The translations were by David Clapam as *A Treatise of the nobilitie and excellencye of woman*

kynde (1542); by E. Fleetwood as *The Glory of Women* (1652), and by Wyllm Bercher as *The Nobylytye off Wymen* (1559). Agrippa's own literary debts are noted in the Roxburghe Club edition of Bercher (1904).

19. Women's vocal powers were more usually denigrated. See, for example, *Spectator*, no. 247 (1711).

20. The *Lady's Journal* was a single issue published by Peter Motteux in place of his monthly *Gentleman's Journal* which appeared fairly regularly between January 1692 and October/November 1694. For a full description of the contents of the *Lady's Journal*, see Patricia Phillips, 'The Lady's Journal (1693)', *Studia Neophilologica*, vol. 53 (1981), pp. 283–92.

21. Similar demands for education were frequent. See François de Fénelon's very influential *Traité de l'Education des Filles* (1687); Nahum Tate, *A Present for the Ladies* (1692); Daniel Defoe, 'An Academy for Women' in *Essay upon Projects* (1697), p. 293. Bishop Gilbert Burnet referred to the issue in the conclusion to his *History of His own Time* (1724). See further, Chapter 3 below.

22. Una Birch, *Anna von Schurmann. Artist, Scholar, Saint* (1909), pp. 50–1.

23. *Memoirs of the Life of Mrs Elizabeth Carter*, ed. by Montagu Pennington (1807), p. 17.

24. See below, Chapter 3, pp. 37–8, and Chapter 4, p. 56.

25. *Artemisa to Cloe. A Letter from a Lady in the Town to the Lady in the Country; concerning the Loves of the Town* (1679), p. 3. When the authoritative French critic René Rapin attacked the literary pretensions of women he found many English supporters: see Henry Barker, *The Polite Gentleman* (1700), pp. 25–6; Charles Gildon, *The Complete Art of Poetry* (1718) 'Dialogue III', *passim*; John Oldmixon, *An Essay on Criticism* (1728).

26. The classical prejudice of the time was so powerful that even successful women writers were affected by it. The playwright Aphra Behn (*c.* 1640–89) resented her lack of a classical education, although by her third play, *The Dutch Lover* (1673), she felt confident enough in her 'Epistle to the Reader' to dismiss it as unimportant.

CHAPTER 3
Science: A Lady's Subject?

During the late seventeenth century, a surge of feminine self-confidence expressed itself in demands for intellectual recognition. There were calls for improvements in the educational opportunities available to women in order to encourage greater parity between the sexes. To some, this simply meant that women too should be permitted to study Latin and Greek and to enter the field of letters. However, more women were shaping their ambitions in accordance with the new and more subtle interpretations of feminine intelligence. Women should be treated by men as their equals, but it should also be accepted that they were different. Many women agreed that they were 'unlearned', which in contemporary jargon meant not having had the benefit of a classical education, but to balance that, they claimed intellectual credentials of equal weight. They were original and unhampered by the burden of the past.

This optimistic assessment of the status of women was part of the anti-classical reaction of the time. The exclusion of women from the classics was reinterpreted as a guarantee of their untrammelled originality, their free and questing intelligence and their cultural purity. Influential voices claimed that, if women were to advance, they should ignore the outworn classical tradition prized by men. In its place they should explore new avenues of intellectual endeavour that would allow them to assert their indifference to the classics and to exploit their own unique intellectual temperament.

'Th' untrodden paths of science to explore'[1]

The most important of these avenues in the mid-seventeenth century was the new science. For many women, science was a preferable alternative to the classics. It had two great advantages. It was a study that demanded serious attention, and yet the student needed no more elaborate preparation than commitment, application and an independent mind. At least that was how contemporary scientists themselves defined the requirements for the study of science. In their efforts to ensure the attention and approbation of the public, they brushed aside all the objections that usually ensured the exclusion of the subordinate classes from intellectual matters. At the same time, they asserted that the dignity and importance of science equalled the prestigious study of the classics. Particular problems that might have daunted the tentative curiosity of the women were also deftly solved.

To confound the attacks of the classical critics, the scientists marshalled evidence to prove their independence from the past and to assert, in the face of considerable censure, their value to the present. Their first serious propagandist, Bishop Thomas Sprat, attacked the opposition on several fronts. In *The History of the Royal Society of London, for the Improving of Natural Knowledge* (1667) he contended forcibly that scientists were not only expanding human understanding of the environment, but also forging a new cultural and literary tradition. Instead of the hackneyed 'Fables and Religions of the Ancient World', they were bringing to the attention of the literary and artistic the value of the 'Arts of Men's Hands' and the inspiration of 'Working Nature' (pp. 413–16). Sprat was aware that neither of these two spheres was highly prized in the classical tradition, but working these seams would infuse a little originality into a sterile literary tradition. His chapter 'Experiments will be beneficial to our Wits and Writers' was a self-assured attempt to cajole those 'Wits and Railleurs' who were undermining scientific work by their dismissive satire to adopt a more positive attitude to science and scientists.[2]

He also revealed to the public the important decisions that had been taken in scientific circles, in particular in the Royal Society, on the reform of the language. Within that body the current state of the vernacular was under attack. For too long, it was claimed, English had been debilitated by the superior reputation of Latin. In the interests of general public understanding, scientists had decided to expunge this unfortunate influence and 'to return back to the primitive purity and shortness, when men deliver'd so many *things* almost in an equal number of *words*'.[3] All scientists were encouraged to put communication and comprehension before style. What they were to cultivate was 'a close, naked natural way of speaking, positive expressions, clear sense, a native easiness, bringing all things as near the Mathematical plainness' as possible. The aim was to replace the esoteric and exclusive style of 'Wits and Scholars' with 'the language of Artizans, Countrymen and Merchants'.

Sprat had put his finger on a growing trend. Despite the powerful and influential lobby that poked fun at science, there were many who appreciated its potential literary resources. These enthusiasts felt liberated by its 'original' and 'unlearned' neutrality. Therein lay the promise of a new intellectual freedom. One young writer among many, John Hughes, described this liberation in *The Ecstasy* (1720). His subject was astronomy and his inspiration, Isaac Newton, whose example as a daring explorer on unknown paths he aspired to emulate. Like that 'great Columbus of the Skies' who had pushed out the horizons of human knowledge, Hughes hoped to expand the universe of poetry by substituting the daring originality of a scientific examination of light and colour for the usual outworn subject matter approved by classical precedent.

Not only Newton but other scientists, from Jacob Bobart, professor of Botany at Oxford in 1711, to the great names of Harvey and Woodward, were all congratulated by the new writers on their sparkling originality and daring ingenuity, and these qualities were extolled as the antidote to the stultifying grasp of the past on the country's intellectual life.[4]

John Norris of Bemerton was another writer who had joined in the abhorrence of the 'overfond and superstitious deference to Authority, especially that of Antiquity'. In his essay, *On the Advantages of Thinking*, a very popular work in the latter end of the seventeenth century, he concluded that nothing 'cramps the parts and fetters the understandings of men' more than the prevailing devotion to the imitation of the past:

> Men are resolv'd never to out-shoot their forefathers Mark; but write one after another, and so the Dance goes round in a Circle; out of which, if some had not the Boldness and Courage to venture, the World would never be the Wiser for being older.[5]

To women seeking an outlet for their intellectual aspirations, the independence and originality of science and scientists must have seemed attractive. In this field, female ignorance of the classics and the originality and unfettered imaginative powers with which women were said to be endowed were positive advantages. In addition, the scientific world rejected the exclusivity of traditional learning. In its place were substituted the values of universal comprehensibility and prosaic communication.

A further incentive to women to take up an interest in science was provided from two sources. These were the crusade for educational reform in the 1630s, which seeded notions that science was particularly appropriate for them, and the new histories of women that provided illustrious illustrations of females who had succeeded in these fields. These worthy models were held up to women as examples of behaviour worthy of imitation and equal in value to the virgins and martyrs, virtuous wives and dutiful daughters, all of whom constituted the traditional roll of feminine honour.

Comenian pedagogy and its significance for the scientific interests of women

Women interested in science profited from the reforms that derived from the ideas of Jan Amos Comenius (1592–1670), Europe's foremost educational consultant. He encouraged women's interest in science and their enthusiasm for change by underlining the importance of scientific study as part of education. He claimed that as an instrument of mental discipline it equalled the classics. He reinforced the connection between women and science by suggesting that it was a subject particularly appropriate to women.

His arrival in England in 1641 was due to the invitation of a group of progressive-minded men who had begun to devise a plan to upgrade and formalize the study of science in the country. They included such famous educationalists as Samuel Hartlib, John Dury and Robert Boyle, and the young mathematician, John Pell (1611–85).[6] Pell had a sister, Bathsua, who found the ideas of Comenius dovetailed with her own interest in science and her concern to improve the educational opportunities of women. In later years she was to put into practice these theories in an educational programme for girls in which science was of central importance.

It is not surprising that Bathsua was influenced by Comenius. Although a religious exile from his native Bohemia, from where he had fled leaving behind wife and children, Comenius's prolific writings on education were widely read and discussed throughout Europe. He travelled extensively all over northern Europe, advising and consulting and often trying to put his visionary proposals into action. Indeed there was a persistent rumour that he had been offered the presidency of Harvard as an inducement to take his ideas to the New World.[7]

Comenius had been summoned to England to address the burning question of the place of science in education, and it was to this issue that he gave most attention. He felt that new social developments called for new educational methods and new subjects of study. He was well aware of the dominating position filled by Latin in the school system and equally aware that the study of the subject rarely lived up to the high ideals claimed by its supporters. Times had changed and much that was relevant was being ignored in the training of young people. Looking back on his own educational experiences, he was convinced that the traditional timetable was greatly wanting: 'At school I was taught one thing only, and that badly, namely Latin. But during the last 200 years much new knowledge has come into existence and it should be taught in schools.'[8]

As far as Comenius was concerned, the study of science should be the foundation of any education system. Beginning in the infant school, children should be taught the groundwork on which to develop those essential techniques of observation and examination. He further insisted that science should be a subject of study for all members for society, without exception, for only by universal participation can universal progress be ensured.

Generally speaking, women have tended to benefit from schemes of universal education. Education for all was the essence of Comenius's programme, as it had been for another religious rebel, Martin Luther, back in the 1520s: 'None ought to be excluded, neither man, nor woman, neither old man, nor child, neither noble, nor ignoble, neither craftsman, nor ploughman etc. For we are all alike, the off-spring of God.'[9] In his plans, women had their rightful place, as is evident from the title of his most famous work on education, published eventually in 1657: *The Great Didactic Setting forth the whole Art of Teaching all Things to all Men or, A certain Inducement to found such Schools in all the Parishes, Towns and Villages of every Christian Kingdom, that the entire Youth of both Sexes, none being excepted shall Quickly, Pleasantly and Thoroughly, Become learned in the Sciences, pure in Morals etc.*

But Comenius's plan for women was more positive than merely including them in a great scheme of universal education. He made it clear to those who sought his advice that women were to be permitted to participate in his great design not simply through default. On the contrary, their rights were equal to men's, their human dignity as noble and their intellectual capacity as great, or possibly greater:

They also are formed in the image of God, and Share in His grace and in the kingdom of the world to come. They are endowed with equal sharpness of mind and capacity for knowledge (often with more than the opposite sex), and they are able to attain the highest positions, since they have often been called by God Himself to rule over nations, to give sound advice to Kings and princes, to the study of medicine and of other things which benefit the human race ...[10]

Comenius attacked the two evils that have constantly inhibited the development of women's education. Even in the twentieth century the view still persists that school for women should mean a training in housekeeping skills or a 'finishing' in the accomplishments and deportment. This seventeenth-century reformer was adamant that limiting the education of women to the purely vocational skills did them as great a disservice as confining them to the triviality of the accomplishments. He believed strongly that women too had the right to share in the pleasure that only intellectual study for its own sake can give. Women should place personal satisfaction above all other goals. This could only be achieved if they were permitted to engage in some worthwhile activity.

Comenius noted many benefits that would accrue from women's studies in science. It could, for example, form 'a suitable introduction to ethics', and, as an educational tool, it had many further advantages. Like the classics, it sharpens the mental faculties and 'stimulates and retains the attention'. Both exercises were vital to improve the fallow brains of women. However, none of these valuable reasons for the study of science should overshadow the most important one, that women would find such a study, quite simply, 'productive of great pleasure'.

Comenius has rightly been called 'the evangelist of modern pedagogy' because of the love for children, the 'inestimable treasure', that permeates his work and because of his two major alterations to the then current curriculum: the use of the vernacular and the study of science.[11] But he has a further claim on our attention. He was the first major voice in the modern period unreservedly to urge reforms in the education of women, not solely to improve their moral and spiritual characters, the traditional justification for the education of women, but for reasons that enhanced their dignity and reinforced their self-confidence.

He insisted on the intellectual equality of women and on their natural inclination to scholarship. He encouraged women to undertake scientific studies and devised an impressive vindication for such studies. He made science palatable by linking a knowledge of science with an understanding of ethics. He advocated science as an efficient instrument of mental training comparable with the traditional classics, and, something that was to inspire many future generations of women, suggested to women that scientific study was one accessible route to intellectual fulfilment. For this far-sighted analysis of the value of science to women, Comenius deserves to be honoured as one of the earliest and most pragmatic evangelists of women's intellectual freedom.

Almost in despite of the continued insecurity of his exile, Comenius retained a determined optimism and an undimmed hope for the well-being of future generations – 'the more candles the greater lights', as he wrote in *A Reformation of Schooles* (1637, p. 28). But with the outbreak of the Civil War looming, he departed for the more salubrious climate of Queen Christina's court in Stockholm. Some of his ideas, at any rate, took firm root in the war-torn land he had left. His defence of women's education and his justification of the usefulness and pleasure that women might derive from the study of science laid sturdy foundations for developing a future rationale for female interest in science.

Among the small candles that he ignited was a small group of reformers who, in furthering his ideas, made no small impact on their own day and later.

Bathsua Makin to Mary Astell: science in girls' education in the seventeenth century

Although there were others who suggested that science should be taught to girls, it was through the efforts of Mrs Bathsua Makin, who knew Comenius through her brother, John Pell, that the theories of Comenius, in a version all her own, reached a later generation of schoolgirls and their parents.[12]

In 1673, towards the end of a long life of what seems to have been struggle and grim determination, Mrs Bathsua Makin entered the debate on women's education, probably not for the first time. In that year she published a prospectus to attract the attention of wealthy parents to her school at Tottenham High Cross. This document was accompanied by a formidable article stressing the necessity of equipping girls for a proper and independent position in life and suggesting that this could be best achieved by a careful scientific education.

Who was Bathsua Makin? Ironically for a woman so distinguished and who received nationwide recognition in her own day for her learning and scholarship, few personal details apart from her married name have survived. Not even the place or date of her birth is known. It is fortunate that the crucial document outlining her ideas on the education of women, together with the curriculum for the school she ran and some snippets of letters, have been preserved.

The lives of her brothers are far more adequately documented, and from those some hints of what might have influenced Bathsua's early life can be surmised. The best known of her brothers was John Pell (1661–85), the mathematician and founding member of the Royal Society and a member of the distinguished group that had invited Comenius to England. He was one of the first people whom Comenius mentions in his early letters home after his arrival in England.[13] He was also closest to Bathsua in interests and, it would seem, in education. Through him she made the two important contacts that were to shape, in part, her own ideas on the education most appropriate for women of the middle and upper classes.

Legend has it that Bathsua was plain and poor. 'She is represented old, without any remains of beauty. I should rather conclude that she never had any, as her figure is remarkably homely', noted James Granger of her portrait.[14] John, on the other hand, had been a fortunate youth. Blessed with great beauty and a large enough income to support the pleasures of young manhood, he appeared to have the makings of genius as well. His education had been carefully supervised too, in hopes of ensuring a successful career. A pupil at the free school in Steyning in Sussex, he progressed so rapidly that he was admitted to Trinity College, Cambridge at the age of thirteen. By the time he was twenty, he had mastered Latin, Greek, Hebrew and Arabic as well as modern languages, and was already regarded as a rising star in mathematics. It was said that Bathsua too was an accomplished linguist and mathematician.

John became part of that circle of scientific and scholarly Europeans in constant correspondence with each other on scientific matters. Among his friends was Sir Charles Cavendish, another well-known mathematician and scientist, who, like many of these men, sympathized with the aspirations of women. Cavendish undertook the scientific education of his young sister-in-law, Margaret, later the famous Duchess of Newcastle but at one time lady-in-waiting at the court of Charles I, where Bathsua was also employed.[15]

As John's reputation grew, he received many offers of academic posts, including the professorship of mathematics in Amsterdam in the 1640s (and later, positions of trust under the government of Oliver Cromwell followed). It must have been while he was in Holland that he met that country's most famous daughter, Anna Maria von Schurmann. Her example and her writings also exercised a major influence on Bathsua's theories. They correspond with each other and it is quite possible that Bathsua, like many seventeenth-century tourists, visited Holland herself.[16] In any case, she remained a lifelong admirer of the Dutch woman and adopted, sometimes critically, the more pragmatic elements of her educational theories in the evolution of her own views.

Bathsua's own reputation was impressive. Charles I had employed her as tutor to his clever daughter, the Princess Elizabeth. Elizabeth proved an apt pupil, and her proficiency in mathematics and in Greek, Latin, French, Italian and Spanish was famous throughout Europe. She had early developed other interests too, particularly in science and medicine, often choosing to be present at dissections. It is likely that this preoccupation stemmed from the scientific interests of her teacher. Later, when the princess went to live in Holland, where she became an intimate friend of Anna Maria von Schurmann, she shared many of the scientific pursuits, particularly the study of anatomy, with her. Her presence in Holland may well have been an additional incentive for Bathsua to visit there.

From letters to her brother, John Pell, in later life, it is clear that Bathsua Makin's scientific interests were long standing. Since he had spent so much time overseas, she appeared to regard him as a most useful channel through which to keep abreast of new scientific developments in Europe. Because his contacts with foreign universities were better than most, she applied to him for information on current research. In one letter she asked to borrow a recent paper from abroad that he had already shown her, so that she might make a copy of it for her own use.[17]

For all his considerable early advantages, John never realized the rich promise of his early career and he died a pauper without ever having published the work of genius that his friends, and probably his sister, continually expected. Prosperity was not to fall to Bathsua's lot either. Not only did she not receive a salary for her royal teaching, but, presumably because of her royalist connections, she also fared badly under the Protectorate. One of her surviving articles describes vividly the horrors of the debtors' gaol. It may be conjectured that the description was based on personal experience, either her own or that shadowy figure, her husband's.[18] But as a very old lady, she was still fighting not only to survive, but to further Comenius's ideas on the importance of science in women's lives.

This, together with the urgent need to improve the education of women, was the theme of the article with which Bathsua Makin prefaced her school prospectus and which was to have critical influence during the last quarter of the seventeenth century. Entitled *An Essay to Revive the Ancient Education of Gentlewomen* (1673), it was tactfully attributed to a 'gentleman' whose interest was supposedly dictated by the need to select a suitable school for his own daughter. Clearly Mrs Makin felt that a gentleman's voice would carry more weight with prospective parents. The need to attract the notice of such parents is evident, too, in the decorous and conservative tone with which the essay begins. This was a style that did not really suit Mrs Makin's naturally acerbic character, and she soon dispensed with it.[19]

As a further sop to parental sensibilities, the putative gentleman-author solemnly declared at the outset that he was not concerned with changing current ideas on women's intellectual stature. Nor was 'he' interested in altering other dearly held beliefs. It may have been the influence of von Schurmann on Makin, or simply the acceptance of the aristocratic imperatives of exclusiveness and rank, that motivated the apparently frank acknowledgement that only girls possessed of rank, wealth and leisure could be considered suitable subjects for a training of any intellectual pretensions. For whichever reason, a similar caution is evident in the 'gentleman's stated belief that the primary aim of education for women should be a preparation for their spiritual salvation, followed by the secondary goal of making them capable of giving sound instruction of their children. To the uncritical eye, the opening paragraphs of the *Essay* seemed to imply that Mrs Makin's school would be in the traditional mould.

But the studied pose of the urbane, rather old-fashioned gentleman-parent is soon discarded and Mrs Makin's own very different views on the nature, content and importance of women's education take over. The time-honoured platitudes disappear in a wave of anger and irritability that seemed to overwhelm the author for the rest of the essay. Mrs Makin had no time for the socially acceptable ideal of womanhood, the metamorphosis of modest girl to decorous wife. She had discovered, through experience and observation, that the ignorance in which girls were confined in the interests of this ideal secured not their protection, but their exploitation. Marriage, the only goal that was freely permitted to women, offered least security of all.

At the same time she had come to understand that women have their own considerable resources of power and strength. The resolution of some women in the adversity of the Civil War, responding to the challenges that had been thrust upon them, defending children and property, fighting for their rights and holding their own in the law courts in the legal confusion of the war's aftermath, would not have been unknown to her. Their experiences and her own had convinced her that the key to the improvement of the lot of women lay in upgrading the standard and type of education on offer to them.

So Mrs Makin put her point bluntly. If men want women solely to satisfy their basest needs, then they would be better off with whatever services monkeys could provide, for surely God would never have created the fine intelligence of women if he had not had in mind for them some grander destiny than the gratification of men:

> Had God intended women only as a finer sort of cattle, he would not have made them reasonable. Bruits [*sic*], a few degrees higher than Drils or Monkies, (which the *Indians* use to do many Offices) might have better fitted some mens Lust, Pride and Pleasure; especially those that desire to keep them ignorant to be tyrannized over.[p. 23]

Naturally, Mrs Makin herself had no doubts on the true value of women. She belonged to the party that vaunted the superiority of women. She permitted herself a sweeping generalization in their support: 'Seeing nature produces Women of such excellent Parts, that they do often equalize, sometimes excel men, in whatever they attempt, what reason can be given why they should not be improved?' (p. 23). And since no reasonable opposition to the proposition has ever been satisfactorily adduced, she proceeds to present her method of improving the female condition.

There were two parts to Mrs Makin's theory on the education best suited to women. On the one hand she appeared to accept a combination of the liberal ideas of Comenius and the humanist principles of Anna Maria von Schurmann. This pact was evident in her suggestion that education should be reserved for the leisured women, who should, however, be permitted to undertake 'the whole *Encyclopedia* of Learning', which she defined as the traditional classical curriculum of trivium and quadrivium. She particularly stressed grammar, rhetoric, logic, the classical languages, primarily Greek and Hebrew, mathematics, geography, music, painting and poetry. She also threw in botany and homeopathy for good measure, because these skills were such an integral part of a woman's traditional training for her obligations to her family and servants (p. 24).

But her real interest, and that to which she devotes most space in the *Essay*, centred on the girl or woman obliged to acquire an education not for the sake of intellectual self-fulfilment, but because it would assist her to become financially independent. Neither Comenius nor von Schurmann had considered such a possibility. But the image of the single woman or single parent was strong in Mrs Makin's mind, and the curriculum she devised for such women was emphatically scientific.

Before elaborating this curriculum, Mrs Makin counted the advantages that the well-educated and independently minded woman enjoyed. She would be accustomed to think and decide for herself, no longer the willing and ignorant dupe to empty flattery and specious promises. Although she would have to fend for herself, she could command immediate financial and commercial advantages. An unmarried but well-educated girl is in a much better position to elicit not only self-respect, but the respect of potential employers. Furthermore, not even marriage, the undoubted goal of most young women, should pre-empt the need for a good education. Properly educated, a wife and mother may not only play a valuable role as her children's first teacher, but can also participate with advantage in her husband's trade or profession (pp. 26–8).

Mrs Makin's knowledge of Holland had taught her admiration for the woman of that country who joined with their husbands in equal partnership to manage their business and commercial interests. In that country nothing less was expected of a wife. In England, she suggested women could gain greatly by following their example and learning more about the methods of earning a living.[20]

When Mrs Makin came to discuss in greater detail the sort of curriculum that would be appropriate for the woman she had in mind, she reverted to Comenius's suggestions for reform of the timetable and forcibly rejected the study of letters as advocated by von Schurmann: 'Was all Learning in *English*, as it is now in *French*, I think those dead Languages would be of little use, only in reference to the Scriptures' (p. 34). What women needed was an education emphasizing technical and practical subjects. In words too closely reminiscent of Bishop Thomas Sprat to be coincidental, she declared, 'My opinion is, in the educating of Gentlewomen, greater care ought to be had to know things, than to get words. If one must be neglected, it's better to neglect Tongues than Arts; though it is best where both may be had' (pp. 34–5). By 'Arts' she meant what Sprat, the apologist for the Royal Society, had meant: practical and scientific subjects. In her opinion it was these subjects that were essential for the women 'whose condition calls them to business'; the liberal studies of languages might be left to the self-indulgence of ladies of leisure.

To illustrate her point she resorted to the usual method of the homily, that of selecting a woman of biblical or Christian fame in order to delineate a virtue worthy of emulation. Her choice was the wife of King Solomon, and this shadowy lady was presented to seventeenth-century readers in the novel guise of the hard-working, practical scientist/technician. This would seem to be the first categorical statement in the history of women's education in England that, if education is to be of any use, it must be solidly scientific rather than classical, and that, for the most part, only a scientific education can prepare a woman for her particular career demands:

> To buy Wooll and Flax, to die [*sic*] Scarlet and Purple, requires skill in Natural Philosophy. To consider a Field, the quantity and quality, requires knowledge in Geometry. To plant a vineyard, requires understanding in Husbandry: She could not merchandize, without Knowledge in Arithmetick: she could not govern so great a Family well, without Knowledge of Politicks and Oeconomicks: She could not look well to the wayes of her Household, except she understood Physick and Chirurgery: She could not open her Mouth with Wisdom, and have in her Tongue the Law of Kindness unless she understood Grammar, Rhetorick and Logick. [p. 35]

In fact, as Mrs Makin herself hastened to confirm to her readers, 'This seems to be the description of an honest, well bred, ingenious, industrious Dutch-woman' (p. 35).

In the last paragraph of the *Essay*, Mrs Makin addressed a peroration to women exhorting them to rebut the slurs and abuses heaped on them and to develop powers of self-assertion and the will to self-improvement:

> I hope some of these Considerations will at least move some of this abused Sex to set a right value upon themselves, according to the dignity of their Creation, that they might, with an honest pride and magnanimity, scorn to be bowed down and made to stoop to such Follies and Vanities, Trifles and Nothings, so far below them, and unproportionable to their noble Souls, nothing inferior to those of Men, and equally precious in Christ, in whom there is neither Male nor Female. [pp. 41–2]

Following the *Essay* came the prospectus for the school at Tottenham High Cross. Bearing in mind that Mrs Makin was only too bitterly aware that 'the less anything of solidity is taught' the more popular a school is likely to be, and that her aim in publishing her prospectus was to advertise her school and attract patronage, it comes as no surprise that the actual curriculum of the school appears, on first sight, to be less daring than the accompanying *Essay* would have led one to believe. But, just as in that article, Mrs Makin concealed the unusual nature of what she was offering behind a more conventional format.

Accordingly, half of the timetable was apparently to be devoted to the standard female accomplishments of needlework, handicrafts, dancing, music, singing, writing and arithmetic. During part of the remaining time, girls were offered the unusual opportunity of lessons in the classics and modern languages. It may well have been, in the light of Mrs Makin's earlier remarks on the type of woman who should be permitted to indulge in such studies, that she had hopes of attracting girls from the highest ranks in society. Her experience as a royal tutor might have left her sufficiently well connected to hope for some pupils from the upper ranks.

It was in the variations that she inserted into this timetable that Mrs Makin revealed her scorn for convention. Here, too, the influence of Comenius and the English scientific movement is clearly seen. For example, Mrs Makin approved of Comenius's theory that a child should be introduced to science by being encouraged to study her immediate environment from an early age. Accordingly, Mrs Makin offered a group of special subjects. Her young ladies could avail themselves of the opportunity to study something of the natural landscape about them: they could learn 'the Names, Natures, Values and Use of Herbs, Shrubs, Trees, Minerals, Juices, Metals, and Stones'. In this brief statement Mrs Makin outlined a curriculum strong on botany, geology, metallurgy and other scientific topics that was to find general acceptance among those who wanted a reform in women's education. Indeed, in variations ranging from academic to trivial, this format became the standard in a great number of girls' schools up to the end of the nineteenth century.

Mrs Makin also made provision for those children whose parents would countenance a more comprehensive education for their girls. In addition to what has gone before, they would also be encouraged to study astronomy, geography, arithmetic and history.

Finally, and as some indication of how particularly appropriate science studies were felt to be for girls, Mrs Makin assured those parents who doubted the value to girls of any education that mirrored, even remotely, the liberal studies of a boy's education that their daughters could receive a purely scientific education at her school. It is evident that to opt for this scientific curriculum was considered an acknowledgement of the overall inferiority of that field of studies and its consequent suitability for girls. The point was clear. A female might be incapable of studying language, but science was within her grasp: 'Those that think one Language enough for a Woman may forbear the Languages and learn only *Experimental Philosophy*' (p. 43).

Viewed overall, Mrs Makin's school aimed to combine what parents

generally wanted for their daughters, the acquisition of accomplishments, perhaps slightly more useful ones, with the ambitions of the
more liberally minded who would permit their girls to study the same
curriculum as their sons. But it is equally clear that there was to be yet
another option, aimed at the parents and girls who would find the
accomplishments too trivial and the classics too ambitious, and this
was to be a demanding programme of scientific study. In answer,
presumably, to the general demand that women study something
serious but within their intellectual range, Mrs Makin devised the first
scientific curriculum for girls. At her establishment a girl might ignore
the noble study of Latin and Greek, resist the allure of French and
needlework, and, instead, devote herself to experimental science, astronomy, geography, botany, geology, mineralogy, arithmetic and mathematics.

Many of Mrs Makin's ideas found a sympathetic ear among English
readers. Clement Barksdale (1609–87), best remembered for providing
the English public with a translation of Anna Maria von Schurmann's
The Learned Maid, essential reading for all thinking women in the
late seventeenth century, and for his sympathies with the educational
objectives of women, published an interesting letter (12 August 1675)
not long after Mrs Makin's public proposal. He called it *A Letter
Touching A Colledge of Maids; or a Virgin Society*. In it, he proposed, on
the basis of a discussion he had had with some young women of his
acquaintance, that it was time to establish a women's college at Oxford,
or, as he put it, 'A Colledge [*sic*] of Maids' to be modelled on the Halls
of Commoners at Oxford.

Apart from the clause that mentions that fathers could at any time
interrupt their daughters' studies in order to 'dispose of them in marriage when they [the fathers] please', no academic restrictions of any
kind were to limit the curriculum. The aim of the proposal was an up-
to-date and thorough education with a strong emphasis on science. The
school was to be well equipped with appropriate facilities. As well as
all the usual subjects, the girls were to enjoy the use of an extensive
library. Since the main orientation of their education was to be the study
of science, in particular botany and medicine, through the experimental
method, the college was to be provided with a physic garden to permit
practical work.[21]

The feminine fripperies of fashion were to be strictly excluded in this
nursery for early 'bluestockings'. The students were to attire themselves
in a simple uniform. But, this restriction notwithstanding, the Revd
Barksdale was strongly of the opinion that there would be no difficulty

finding enough girls for his college within a radius of 7 miles.

It seems unlikely that there were sufficient numbers of parents willing to participate in the Barksdale experiment. What is interesting is that it was suggested at all, that its originator was a man of the cloth, and that science should have been allocated so much importance.

The Revd Barksdale's plans were for the education of 'well-to-do young ladies. Mrs Makin's *Essay*, although also written to improve the education of 'Gentlewomen', had taken into account women who were obliged to fend for themselves. There was already a strong feeling in some parts of society that women, at least among the lower classes, must somehow be assisted to become self-supporting. Again, Holland offered a powerful example in this area. Many English travellers were impressed by how the Dutch did things. Often the result seemed to be a vision of Britain as a nation of female shopkeepers. Sir Josiah Child (1630–99), a merchant who had made a fortune and been rewarded with a baronetcy, was one major source for information on Dutch society, and his opinions were influential. In 1665 he wrote *A Discourse about Trade*, which perpetuated a compelling image of the Dutch business woman that endured long after the main point of the essay, the lowering of interest rates, had been forgotten. It made an enormous impact on women, both during his lifetime, when there were five editions alone, and subsequently. Keen lady entrepreneurs were still taking his advice in the early 1800s.[22]

Among the reasons he gave for fhe Dutch success in commerce was the startling fact that both sexes received a careful training in mathematics and that women were expected to be just as career orientated as men. He noted that once women were given the chance they showed a distinct aptitude for mathematics: 'the well understanding and practice whereof, doth strangely infuse into most that are the owners of that Quality, of either Sex, not only an Ability for Commerce of all kinds, but a strong aptitude, love and delight in it' (1690 edn, pp. 4–5).

Dutch business prospered because of the absence of snobbery and the continuity in the workplace that a mixed workforce ensured. The Dutch merchant could hold on to and consolidate his business, knowing that his wife was sufficiently competent to take over as managing director even in the event of his death. In England, on the other hand, all a man of business could look forward to was the depressing 'unexperience and unaptness' of a wife who neither expected nor was allowed to apprise herself of these matters.

It were wise for English industry and English women, suggested Sir

Josiah, to adopt new attitudes. To his mind, the female sex would be vastly improved by measured doses of mathematics, for 'it hath been observed in the nature of *Arithmetick*, that like other parts of the *Mathematicks* it doth not only improve the *Rational Faculties*, but inclines those that are expert in it to Thriftiness and good-Husbandry' (pp. 5–6).

Soon after Bathsua Makin published her prospectus, another woman's voice echoed not only Mrs Makin's thoughts on the independence of women, but also Sir Josiah's admiration of Dutch ladies. Her pamphlet, although directed not at ladies but at the women of the commercial classes, is, nevertheless, a splendid and very early exhortation to women to break out of the confines of tradition and seek the sort of employment that will be to their true financial advantage. These ladies were entreated to throw aside their needlework, a hopelessly unprofitable and arduous way in which to make a living, and to concentrate on improving their mathematics, an art that would certainly ensure their future prosperity.

The pamphlet cost 6d. and was published in 1678. As its title indicated, it proposed a revolution in the education and attitudes of women: *Advice to the Women and Maidens of London; shewing that, instead of their usual Pastime, and Education in Needle-work, Lace and Pointmaking, it were far more necessary and profitable to apply themselves to the right understanding and practice of keeping Books of Accounts; whereby either single or married they may know their Estates, and carry on their Trades; and avoid the Danger of a helpless and forlorn Condition; incident in Widows.*

The author remained anonymous. The pamphlet carried one advertisement, however, for a school run by one Mr Randolph in Mugwell Street near the Chirurgeons Hall, which specialized in mathematics. It seems likely that the author was either the enterprising wife or daughter of Mr Randolph.[23]

The aim of the author was to persuade women of the use that a knowledge of mathematics could be to them. To begin with, 'she' asserts that any woman who is suitably fortified with a sound and well-trained mathematical understanding need have no fear of the vagaries of fate, which, in most cases, would be the dreaded destitution of widowhood. If a woman has had the foresight to study mathematics, she will be able to continue in business singlehandedly, and without the wasteful and inefficient assistance of a manager. Women should urgently begin to consider numeric skills as more important to them than the usual domestic crafts. An incompetent cook will never cause as much havoc in a family as a woman who cannot do her accounts. The author counsels women to farm out their burden of needlework to the poor, to allow themselves more time to develop their mathematical skills.

To the objectors, those who maintained that mathematics is too difficult for women, that its acquisition undermines a woman's necessary and heaven-ordained meekness, that women should not be taxed with anything more demanding than needlework patterns, or that women are destined only to sew or launder for a living, the author offers short shrift: 'Having in some measure practised both Needlework and Accounts, I can aver, that I never found this Masculine Art harder or more difficult than the effeminate achievement of Lacemaking, gum-working or the like' (p. 2). The author was especially irritated by the charge that skills in mathematics or similar subjects made women arrogant. She pointed out that it had never yet occurred to anyone to claim that the unremunerative but exceedingly skilful arts of needle-work could have the same effect, presumably because those domestic arts had the support of convention and custom.

It is clear that, in the closing decades of the seventeenth century, the notion that the study of science and mathematics was of importance to women was becoming firmly established. Many writers, like the author of this pamphlet, insisted that those subjects were well within the grasp of even the most domesticated women. In due course, the suggestion was offered that these subjects were, in fact, typically and appropriately feminine. It found expression most influentially in the writing of Mary Astell (1668–1731).

In Astell's *Defence of the Female Sex* (1696), the ideals of Bathsua Makin were recommended to the nation by a worthy champion. Astell was herself a well-known and respected intellectual, and her work on women's education was one of the most notable contributions to the subject in the late seventeenth century. In the *Defence*, she contrasts the traditional allocation of a privileged education to men with the inferior provision made for women.[24] Her counter attack is to make an unequivocal claim for the superior educative value of science. As far as she was concerned, women would find all they needed in the new knowledge of science. Furthermore, she suggested that they might discover their intellectual salvation precisely in their exclusion from the male preserve of the classics. She compared the two systems and found nothing positive to say for the traditional one. It was her contention that, while a boy was obliged to spend his entire academic career coping with a monstrous, and largely irrelevant, diet of philology and grammar, a woman could reap the many benefits that came from an education designed on modern principles and in touch with her own experience of nature and truth. A boy never gets the opportunity to delve into the secrets of nature or learn the workings of the universe, the true test of education. Instead he is restricted to a one-sided and often most inadequate linguistic training that induces nothing better than a crabbed and warped pedantry of mind and spirit, and results, as often as not, not in a liberation, but in a bondage of spirit.

The 'unlearned' curriculum, which was by then, according to Astell, a fact in girls' education, had more positive results. Because science, the study of things rather than words, opens up their eyes to nature, 'the great Book of Universal Learning', girls acquire an early maturity and the development of their personality in all its aspects – intellectual, spiritual and moral – is realized more completely and effectively.

The other great advantage of girls' education is the common use of the mother tongue. Mary Astell, like her predecessors Makin and Comenius, could see little benefit in restricting children to a study of the dead languages of long-gone cultures: 'I have often thought that the not teaching Women Latin and Greek, was an Advantage to them, if it were rightly consider'd and might be improv'd to a great height' (p. 57). This classical innocence does not prevent their access to the most significant scientific works, quickly available in English, but ensures that their minds, free and original as they are, need not be continually limited and harassed by the useless harness of antiquity: 'I am confident they would find no such need of the assistance of Languages as is generally imagin'd. Those that have of their own, need not graft upon Foreign Stocks' (p. 57).

When she went on to put her case for the superiority of women, Mary Astell also resorted to some of the ideas current in psychology and physiology to strengthen her argument. Like other writers who had employed these ideas, she was willing to attribute many beneficial effects to women on the grounds of their physical structure: 'the very Make and Temper of our Bodies shew that we were never designed for Fatigue; and the Vivacity of our Wits, and readiness of our Invention (which are confess'd even by our Adversaries) demonstrates that we were chiefly intended for Thought and the Exercise of the Mind' (p. 18).

Such female superiority demanded a realignment of the traditional distribution of labour, in Mary Astell's opinion. She suggested that, as the more intellectual, if sedentary sex, women should be encouraged to take over the clerical and bureaucratic operations of the country. To men, the coarser, less imaginative sex, might be left manual tasks which simply required thoughtless strength and uncreative purpose.

The poet and writer, Mary Lady Chudleigh (1656–1710), forwarded

these ideas into the eighteenth century. She, too, reiterated the relationship between women's intellectual inclinations and science and, like
Makin and Astell, recalled the words of Bishop Sprat:

> What I would advise myself and others in relation to a course of
> Study should be to endeavour to get an insight into the useful Parts
> of Learning, and to attend more to Things, than Words ... Let
> Languages be left to the Grammarians, and let the Rhetoricians
> contend about the niceties of style; and, while they are quarrelling
> about the Husk, the Shell, the superficial worthless Part, let us be
> solicitous only for the Substance; be industriously striving to make
> such things ours, as will prove real accomplishments to our Minds,
> true and lasting Ornaments to our souls.[25]

But the energy with which she urged women to liberate themselves
through personal effort and self-improvement, although reminiscent of
Bathsua Makin, gave new point to the argument. Like many reforming
women of the period, Mary Chudleigh was acutely conscious that
some women connived in their inferior status in order to indulge their
indolence and dislike of responsibility.[26] Their lives were 'parcell'd out
between the *Glass*, and the *Table*, the *Park* and the *Play-house*, unnecessary *Visits* and expensive *Games*, those merciless Wasters of our little
Stock, our small Pittance of Leisure'. A scientific education could shake
women out of the torpor in which many of them willingly languished,
by encouraging them to 'reflect seriously' and to 'pry into the secret
Labyrinth, the shady, the obscure Recesses' within themselves, there
to find '*the Embrio's* of Science, the first Rudiments of Virtue, the
Beginnings of all useful *Knowledge*' (p. 6).

Many contemporary sources were offering encouragement for this
new departure in women's attitudes to themselves by uncovering lives
of women of the past as evidence of the sort of female superiority
prescribed by Makin, Astell and Chudleigh. In this, their own history,
usually presented to them by sympathetic men, women were able to
find suitable models of emulation to inspire their newly accredited
intellectual ambitions. It is striking how frequently these women of the
past were found to have linked a lively scientific interest with an urgent
desire for improvement in women's status.

Notes

1. J. Fortescue, DD, Science (1750), p. 15.
2. In classical terms the most elevated kinds of poetry were the representation of noble actions

and the doings of good people related in epic or tragedy. See Aristotle's *Theory of Poetry and Fine Art*, trans. by S.H. Butcher (1895), ch. IV, p. 17.

3. See 'Their Manner of Discourse' in *Critical Essays of the Seventeenth Century*, ed. by J.A. Spingarn (1908–9, reprinted 1957), II, pp. 117–18.

4. For poems in praise of scientists see Patricia Phillips, *The Adventurous Muse: Theories of Originality in English Poetics 1650–1760* (1984), pp. 46–8.

5. *A Collection of Miscellanies* (1678, 4th edn 1706), p. 115.

6. See G.H. Turnbull, *Hartlib, Dury and Comenius* (1947), pp. 350–70.

7. See Turnbull, p. 368.

8. See M.W. Keatinge, *The Great Didactic of John Amos Comenius* (1896, 1931), p. 9.

9. *A Reformation of Schooles* (1637), trans. by Samuel Hartlib (1642), p. 59.

10. *The Great Didactic*, ed. by M. W. Keatinge (1931), p. 43.

11. *The School of Infancy* (1633), p. 1.

12. Adolphus Speed proposed a school for young women in 1648 in which only 'useful' subjects would be taught; Dorothea Moore, who was related to Robert Boyle the scientist and acquainted with the Cavendishes (see below, pp. 56–67) had rigorous notions on the kind of education best suited to the needs of women. See G.H. Turnbull, *Hartlib, Dury and Comenius* (1947), pp. 237, 260–1.

13. R.F. Fitzgibbon Young, *Comenius in England*, letter dated 8/10 October 1641 (1932), p. 64.

14. *A Biographical History* (1779), 3rd edn, II, p. 392.

15. Mary Astell. See below, pp. 44–5.

16. Von Schurmann published her letters to Bathsua in her *Opuscula* (1653). At least two other English women, Elizabeth Mackenzie and Dorothea Moore, who later married John Dury, wrote to her. Sir Simonds D'Ewes the MP visited her. See Una Birch, *Anna Von Schurmann* (1909), pp. 100–1.

17. British Library. Add. Mss. 4279, f. 103.

18. 'The malady ... Remedy of Vexations and Unjust Arrests and Actions', 24 September 1646 in *The Female Spectator*, ed. by M.R. Mahl and Helene Koon (1977), pp. 118–24.

19. Writing to his wife in 1657, Pell remarked of his sister, 'You know that she is a woman of great acquaintance and so small impatience. She will not strike to rail at me and you, where ever she comes.' See *The Female Spectator*, p. 116.

20. For the prestige of Holland see below, pp. 42–3.

21. Oxford's Physic Garden was established in 1632; the President of Harvard informed Robert Boyle in 1672 of his intention to provide that college with a large garden and orchard as well as a laboratory and an 'ergasterium': Robert Boyle, *Works*, VI, p. 653.

22. See below, pp. 224–8.

23. Not the least interesting aspect of the pamphlet is the author's breakdown of her household expenses for the year. Most of the budget was spent on clothing (£70 12s.) and meat (£62 1s.). Food, rent and taxes were the other main items of expenditure.

24. Many of her ideas are reflected in the writings of Peter Motteux, Daniel Defoe and others, suggesting their topicality.

25. *Of Knowledge* (1710), p. 24. See also below, p. 121.

26. Women often worried about other women's penchant for laziness. See Elizabeth Carter, *Rambler*, no. 100.

CHAPTER 4

'More Candles ... Greater Lights': Scientific Ladies set an Example

Anna Maria von Schurmann's work was an important milestone in marking the claims of women to intellectual equality. With the help of Comenius and others, Bathsua Makin and Mary Astell modified and expanded her narrow interpretation of the 'learned' woman. They suggested that science was a more fitting area of study for a woman: Makin because science was the best training for a woman's vocational needs; Astell because science provided a more complete mental training than the classics. All three offered a very real inspiration to many women seeking to satisfy their intellectual and vocational needs. Their contributions were recognized and appreciated, and their names became passwords of progress in the writings of many later reformers. Such was their reputation that it was even suggested that medals should be struck to honour their singular efforts.

The proposal was made by the diarist, John Evelyn (*Numismata*, 1697, p. 265). He had long sympathized with, appreciated and encouraged the work of these and other women engaged in improving the lot of their sex. He was one of several historians towards the end of the seventeenth century who concentrated on resuscitating the vigorous tradition of the learned woman as an example to contemporary ladies. Although patterned on the traditional catalogues in which the lives of virtuous women were used as examples of piety and self-sacrifice, the women selected tended to have distinction over and above the once favoured female virtues of passive suffering and martyrdom. Among the three dozen or so English women noted by Evelyn as deserving of the special recognition of a medal were the warlike Boadicea and the unconventional Juliana Barnes.[1]

One group of learned ladies given particular prominence by these early historians were the distant ancestresses of contemporary scientific ladies, those who in far-off classical times had been 'Disciples of Pythagoras and others of the Philosophers'. Readers of Evelyn's tome and the other works on the subject would have been introduced to the scientific activities of such women: of Aspasia who taught Socrates, of Aristippius's early teaching from his mother, and of the women who attended Plato's school (*Numismata*, p. 285).

They would also have learned something of the lives of less distant women, those whose work had ensured the continuation of the tradition of the scientific woman: of Anna Comnena, the eleventh-century prodigy who studied mathematics, astronomy, medicine and military technology, of the Italian students of science and mathematics during the Renaissance, Tarquinia Molza, Costanza Calenda and Christiana Eleonora Bosia, of the university women of Padua, such as the learned doctor Helena Cornaro or Lucretia Marinellos, of the Polish astronomers Maria Cunitz and Elizabeth Korpman, of the French astronomer Jean Dumée and of the heroic adventures of the fearless Dutch entomologist Maria Merien (1647-1717), who travelled to Surinam to study, catalogue and draw indigenous invertebrates, sometimes accompanied by her young daughters.[2]

Among this well-packed pantheon of illustrious women selected for the edification and gratification of more ordinary ladies in the last years of the seventeenth century, there were three, apart from Anna Maria von Schurmann, Bathsua Makin and Mary Astell, who made a particular impact on English women. These have been singled out for a more detailed investigation of their ideas and activities. They not only studied one or more scientific subjects in an exemplary way, but linked their interest in science to a concern for the intellectual equality of the sexes. Two of them went further and attacked the pernicious discrimination against women in all the important areas of life. From the numbers of times they were quoted or referred to by writers during the succeeding years, it is clear that their words and deeds had considerable power to fire the imagination. They were Margaret Roper, Marie le Jars de Gourney and Margaret Cavendish.[3]

Margaret Roper

Margaret Roper (1505-44) was the daughter of Sir Thomas More, Henry VIII's Lord Chancellor. The most retiring of the ladies under review, her life and work set an example nonetheless positive for later generations of women, for she was the first woman intellectual in England known to have formally studied a scientific subject. Her reasons for doing so were twofold. Her father believed that the sexes should be educated equally, and both his son and daughters were taught the same classical curriculum. The best tutors were employed and More kept a close check on the girls' progress, writing them long letters when away from home and expecting a daily letter, in Latin, from them. Margaret, being a perfectionist, had chosen to study the full classical syllabus, which included astronomy and mathematics.

But she had another reason for her interest in these subjects, over and above their classical respectability. Both astronomy and mathematics were rapidly becoming modern disciplines. The scientific world was on the brink of new and revolutionary discoveries. It was not to be until 1543 that Copernicus put the sun at the centre of the solar system and set the earth in motion around it in the first comprehensive heliocentric theory of the universe, but already, like other informed people, Margaret was conscious of the intellectual movements of her time and wanted her studies to keep pace.

More was ambitious for all of his children, but particularly for Margaret. He had hopes that she would specialize in divinity and medicine, the most advanced scientific field of the day, but when, in 1521, she turned to the study of astronomy, he promptly engaged a tutor, one Mr Nicolas, for her. Perhaps he remembered his own misunderstanding with his father, who had neither understood nor appreciated his enthusiasm for 'new' subjects while he was at Oxford. His education there, a detailed and intensive study of Latin, had been typical of the young Renaissance man. He spoke and wrote that language with facility, but his great enthusiasm was for Greek, still a new subject of doubtful accreditation. His father never changed his mind about Thomas's regrettable interest in this new intellectual fashion.

Of scientific expertise More had little, but as a parent he was enormously conscious of the importance to the next generation of the accelerating movement of discovery in these new fields of knowledge. Some of this excitement he conveyed to his children in the letters they exchanged on such matters. He believed firmly that every branch of knowledge, however new, should be taught to young people. In his opinion, the study of a scientific subject, such as astronomy, was as valuable as the study of a classical one, for as he said, 'by this kind of learning our judgements are either gotten, or certainly much helped thereby' (Foster Watson, *Vives and the Renaissance Education of Women*, 1912, p. 193).

Margaret's reaction must have been immensely gratifying. She decided that she must be extra diligent in her study of the new subject in order to make up for lost time. More was delighted with her resolution, pointing out in supportive letters that, although it was a difficult task, she had youth on her side and her tutor was reckoned to be one of the best. In one letter in particular, which must be the first missive from a father expressly encouraging his daughter to excel in scientific study, More's playful encouragement took the form of persuading her that, in science alone of all subjects, it was permissible for her to attempt to outclass her young husband (William Roper (1496–1578) whom she had married in 1525): 'and whereas I am wont always to counsel you to give place to your husband, now on the other side, I give you licence to strive to master him in the knowledge of the sphere' (*Vives and the Renaissance Education of Women*, p. 194).

The studious bliss of Margaret's life was shattered by her father's imprisonment and subsequent execution in 1535. Her bravery and heroic devotion to his memory became a matter of legend. Although the combination of filial piety and intellectual brilliance which she embodied was sufficient to ensure her a place in the feminine hagiology of later times, it was her interest in astronomy and mathematics that endeared her to women anxious to embark on their own scientific studies in the late seventeenth century.

Marie le Jars de Gourney

When Marie le Jars de Gourney (1565–1645) died on 14 July 1645, she left an impressive reputation as a professional author and *savante*. Her fame was such that public notice was given to the obsequies performed in her honour at the church of St Eustache in Paris. By the time of her death, her renown had attracted the attention not only of European intellectuals, but of those from England as well. John Evelyn, in Paris in the early 1640s, courting his future wife, was just one of the many visiting Englishmen to be drawn to her salon to sit at her feet. Almost half a century later, he acknowledged his admiration by honouring her in his history of women (*Numismata*, p. 287).

De Gourney's lasting and surprising claim to eminence was her editorship of the works of Michel de Montaigne, the foremost philospher and essayist of his day. Hardly less provoking for her contemporaries were her own writings on the issues of class and sexual equality, which were far in advance of the time. A further novelty in the life of this astonishing woman which set her apart was the long period she spent pursuing chemical and alchemical interests.

Her scientific interests had developed in a most unexpected way. There was nothing in de Gourney's background to prepare her for the life of cerebral activity she chose. The eldest child of a petty French aristocrat, with no education except what she could glean in despite of her mother's avowed opposition, she initiated a platonic and intellectual friendship with the eminent Montaigne which appeared to satisfy both of them. On his death in 1593, his widow requested her to prepare and edit Montaigne's work for publication. Over the next forty years, eleven editions appeared under her editorship. It was an enormous undertaking for anyone, not least for an autodidactic young woman from a provincial French village. But her efforts succeeded in impressing her critical contemporaries, and even posterity has conceded that her work was well done according to the standards of the time. It certainly made her name in literary and political circles in Europe. She was invited on the sixteenth-century equivalent of the lecture tour and so, in 1597, she travelled to Flanders and the Low Countries where Montaigne was particularly popular. Met by municipal bands, wined and dined by local dignitaries and sought after by the intelligentsia of each city she visited, she received all the honour that an illustrious and distinguished personality might expect, and gleefully recorded all in her autobiography.[4]

The experience persuaded her to opt for a career as a professional woman of letters. She betook herself to Paris, penniless and unprotected, for there she hoped to attract the attention of the intellectual and social élite and, more importantly, the eye of the King, whose occasional but generous pensions to deserving authors was known to be the best way of securing the future.

The ambitious hopes of this budding intellectual for success and the recognition of her peers suffered a severe setback when her meagre funds ran out. It was then that Marie resorted to alchemy. Part science, part magic, alchemy embraced many of the constituents and methods that were to produce modern chemistry. The practice of alchemy combined chemical experimentation with an arcane legacy of mystery, rhetoric, occult symbols and the lure of gold. At times and with different individuals, this latter aspect tended to dominate. Certainly it was what had attracted the opportunist hopes of Marie in the first instance. But in the long run, it was the experimental aspects of the subject that came to fascinate her. Long after she had given up the idea of 'wealth creation' in an alchemical sense, she pursued her experiments for their own sake and spent a further seven years (*c.*1598–1608) in thoughtful chemical research. She would have used quantities of gold, copper, lead, iron, tin and mercury, would have learnt the constituents of these metals together with the properties of the corrosive salts, mostly the vitriols, alums and the chlorides of sodium and ammonia, and would have acquired some knowledge of the mineral acids, nitric, sulphuric and hydrochloric, which had been discovered by alchemists in the thirteenth century. It was an expensive pursuit, and in her earnest application to her research in the early days Marie let her small resources dwindle away. She was lucky in that a helpful friend arranged that she might have access to the furnace in a glass factory near her home on the Rue des Haudriettes (near the present Archives Nationales) in Paris in order to perform her experiments.[5]

It was possible to make a living from such work at the time. The man who probably introduced Marie to alchemy, Jean d'Espagnet, former president of the Bordeaux parliament and her escort when she travelled to Bordeaux to meet Montaigne's family in 1595, was an accomplished alchemist and had published several books on the subject. He is known to have become a very rich man, whether because of, or in spite of, his researches is not clear. But, like other practitioners, he was happy to combine his abstruse experiments with more practical projects and was known to promote experiments with materials that could be used to replace certain of the dangerous pharmaceutical and cosmetic preparations then in vogue. One of his books contains a recipe for the preparation of talcum powder, a less noxious substitute for the notorius Blanc d'Espagne then in use.[6]

It is not known whether Marie le Jars de Gourney had such entre-preneurial ambitions. By the mid-seventeenth century there were said to be women making a living supplying the lucrative cosmetics market. John Dury's wife, Dorothea, was rumoured to be supporting her family in that way. The available evidence suggests that Marie le Jars de Gourney pursued her work in the spirit of intellectual enquiry recommended to women by Comenius. Certainly she appeared to derive a great deal of pleasure from her studies. However, she was conscious that she needed to defend such interests against charges that they were not normal for a woman in the society of the day. As to why she did what she did, she explained in her autobiography that it was just for the pleasure of finding out: 'pour voir sous les degrés d'une très belle décoction, ce que deviendtra la matière que je tiens sur le feu, curiosité naturelle et saine [to see from the proportions of a very pretty decoction, what the substance I have on the fire will become, which is a natural and normal curiosity]'.[7]

The cautious note that can be detected in de Gourney's defence of her chemical studies is understandable in the context of contemporary attitudes to alchemy. As an attempt to interfere with control of the source of wealth it was politically suspect and socially subversive. There were many records of royal disfavour falling on the heads of alchemists whose claims had become too bold. More alarmingly for a woman, such secret activities could also be connected with witchcraft. Independently minded women who chose to dabble in what few understood took a serious risk. Over 400 women were executed as witches in the province of Bordeaux alone, in the spring of 1610.

Marie was aware of the danger into which her scientific curiosity might lead her. She defended herself with some vigour: 'our most illustrious kings and those of recent date have practised alchemy, as have the most intelligent and best qualified men in France.'[8] She might have added other names, for alchemy had always exercised a fascination for many scientific minds. From the bizarre Paracelsus and the staider Van Helmont to Robert Boyle himself, 'the father of modern chemistry', and the greater Isaac Newton, there were few scientists, either before or after Marie, who were unable to refrain from devoting some hopes, time and thought to alchemical studies.

What was good enough for the best qualified men in France and elsewhere was good enough for Marie le Jars de Gourney, for one of the cornerstones of her philosophy was her conviction that men and women are equal in everything, except opportunity. The dignified and reticent claims put forward on behalf of women by other sixteenth-century intellectuals were seized on by Marie with a frank directness to be echoed by later feminists, notably Bathsua Makin. Her assessment of the supposed differences between the sexes was uncompromising and forthright and certainly Platonic in origin: 'rien n'est plus semblable au chat sur la fenêtre, que la chatte [nothing looks so much like a cat on a window sill as a female cat]'.[9]

Her theories on the equality of the sexes are to be found mainly in the two publications she devoted to the subject, *Égalité des Hommes et des Femmes* (1622) and *Grief des Dames* (1626), both of which were extended and republished in 1634 and again in 1641. They were read everywhere. She brought to her theme complete conviction and considerable talents as a polemicist. Her wide reading, as well as her bitter experiences as a woman in a man's world, had furnished her with all the evidence she needed of the invidious nature of a woman's subjection. It was apparent to her that such subordination could be due neither to the will of God nor to nature, but simply to the ruthless arrogance of men who had restricted and regulated the environment, habits and permitted occupations of women in order to perpetuate their eternal inferiority. It was an abiding irritant with her that a man of the stature of Plato had had no difficulty in according women total intellectual and social equality, whereas the half-baked courtiers and pseudo-intellectuals, 'le vulgaire des lettres', with whom she was surrounded were in a position to patronize or ridicule the work of an author infinitely more gifted than they, simply because of her sex.[10]

It should also be noted that, like some of the most visionary intellects of her time, Marie linked the ideal of sexual equality with the greater ideal of general democracy: 'tous les hommes [sont] nés sous les lois de l'égalité'.[11] According to her, there ought not to be any difference between the ruler and the ruled. The office of prince carried with it the responsibility of good government, but the prince and his people were equal in every other way.[12]

Marie de Gourney fashioned an impressive reputation for herself during her long life. As Montaigne's first editor and as the writer of many articles and prefaces on the French language and poetry, on education and on political and civil events, the reputation was well deserved. Her significance for later women centred on her unusual scientific interests and on her forward-looking theories of sexual equality. For many years she was to be honoured for her pioneering role in both these fields and for the impulse to change that she engendered in other women. Anna von Schurmann was one of her most devoted disciples. The younger Dutch woman had read de Gourney's works and had applauded her stance on behalf of women. In letters and laudatory poetry she promised the 'noble Gornacence', that she would follow her example in fighting the great cause of women's equality. Her *Learned Maid* was conceived as an addendum to de Gourney's efforts.[13]

In the event, Madame de Gourney was affronted by being associated with the élitist notions of the Dutch classicist. In her usual forthright way she informed her younger admirer that, in laying so much emphasis on the learned languages, she had missed the point. If women were to further their cause, they must turn to the opportunities that science offered them. Anna Maria von Schurmann was nonplussed. Her letter to Paris in reply was a very subdued defence of her love of languages.[14]

It could be said, however, that Marie le Jars de Gourney's influence extended through Anna Maria von Schurmann to the last woman under discussion here, Margaret Cavendish. A comparatively short time after the publication of *The Learned Maid*, Margaret Cavendish came to live in Holland, there to develop her scientific interests and to elaborate notions on the position of women in society.

Margaret Cavendish, first Duchess of Newcastle

'The whole story of this lady is a romance, and all she doth is romantic', confided Samuel Pepys to his *Diary* in May 1667. The rare but dazzling appearance in London of Margaret, first Duchess of Newcastle (?1624–74), had sparked off the enthusiasm of the celebrity-hungry Londoners. Her visit to court, her night at the theatre, her rides in the park acquired the status of spectator sports. Her clothes, her looks, what she said or did not say, where she went and what she did, furnished London gossips handsomely during her six weeks in town. Pepys was one of the crowd. The *Diary* records his hectic quartering of the fashionable sections of London as he and his friends, in company with hundreds of others, worked hard to catch a glimpse of their outlandish quarry.

What it was that attracted the throng, in addition to her 'antic dress' and noble rank, was the Duchess's well-known interest in science. Even more notorious, she was the only known English woman to have written and published several books of her scientific opinions.[15] So when the Duchess let it be known that she expected an invitation to a meeting of the Royal Society, there was anticipation on all sides. The members were bewildered and very embarrassed. How to answer the invitation provoked a heated and energetic debate in the Society. Some were in favour of the visit, aware of the value of ducal patronage; others warned of the dire consequences of such rashness. Pepys was sure the ballad-mongers would be pleased, which was what worried the Society, already the butt of the ridicule of the wits. If the members were known to have invited a woman, and such a woman, to participate in their unconventional activities, they could expect little mercy.

But the Duchess's influence and wealth had their way. The required invitation was sent and the stars of Gresham House prepared the show. It was one of the best attended sessions in the Society's existence. On the day, 30 May 1667, Pepys took the afternoon off from the office. He had not been to a meeting of the Royal Society since the previous January. The increasing complexity of his domestic life as well as the growing demands of his job in the Navy Office left him little time for scientific pursuits. But the Duchess's presence was an irresistible attraction.

All the Fellows were excited. There was an expectant tension in the room, but the Duchess was late. It proved very difficult to proceed with the ordinary business of the Society while all ears strained for the arrival of the ducal carriage. At last, at the sound of wheels in the courtyard of Arundel House, where the meeting had been arranged, Lord

Brouncker, the President, seized the mace and rushed to the door to welcome the noble lady and her entourage. The noble guests all crowded in eagerly and took their seats, all except someone's little boy who ran about the room noisily.[16]

The Honourable Robert Boyle, with the assistance of the Secretary of the Society, Robert Hooke, began the programme they had devised for the Duchess's benefit. First they weighed a quantify of air. Next, and more spectacularly, they demonstrated the 'experiment of mixing colours'. Boyle always considered the chemistry of colour a subject particularly suitable to stimulate the interest of women.[17] He had discovered during the many introductions to chemistry that he had offered ladies of his acquaintance that this was one display guaranteed to excite them. So what he demonstrated to the Duchess were probably the two experiments which he had described in his book on experiments with colours. He deftly produced from two transparent liquids, sulphuric acid and aniseed oil, the startling result of 'Heat and Smoak [*sic*] and a Blood-Red colour'. She was delighted and equally enthralled when he made a glass of hock turn 'a lovely green' by adding a few drops of a 'steel' solution to it. After these absorbing sights, the Duchess was further enchanted by two cold liquors being 'by mixture made hot' and a piece of roast mutton being transformed into 'pure blood' by being dipped into a bath of sulphuric acid. Even Pepys enjoyed this: 'very rare', he noted in the *Diary*. For his final demonstration, Boyle displayed a lodestone weighing some 60 pounds, which had been presented to the Society by the Bishop of Exeter. It produced fluctuations in a compass held 7 feet away. The Duchess was so intrigued that she rose to her feet to get a better look. A short while later, accompanied by her ladies, she left, showering praises on all she had seen and leaving her hosts to their cheerful, if somewhat self-conscious ridicule of her.

To them, as to many, she was 'Mad Madge of Newcastle', or as Pepys put it without a trace of self-irony, 'a mad, conceited, ridiculous woman'. Her own sex was scarcely more charitable. Dorothy Osborne, soon to be the wife of William Temple, thought one could find saner people in Bedlam. John Evelyn's prim wife, Mary, put her finger on the reasons for the general antagonism. It was felt that the Duchess gave herself airs, not social airs but intellectual ones. When she ought to have known better, she persisted in discussing 'science, difficulties, high notions', subjects which no one believed that she, a mere woman, should admit to knowing anything about. Mrs Evelyn may have been having her leg pulled. The Duchess once wrote, possibly mischievously, that the best way to get rid of stupid women visitors was to brag of oneself at great length.[18] Undoubtedly, she lacked that essential quality, womanly modesty, and its absence excited the envy of some of her contemporaries who revenged themselves in ridicule.

There is no doubt that she brought much of the ridicule on herself. Put simply, she was an eccentric, a freak. Her attire, her conversation, but above all her audacious wish to write on scientific subjects and to publish her views on science and on the equality of the sexes, went far beyond what society was prepared to accept. But she did have her admirers too. Her husband was thoroughly supportive of her scientific work and encouraged her in it. His brother, Sir Charles Cavendish, took great pains to educate his sister-in-law. In the course of her prolific career, members of both universities and other eminent men found time to write her letters of admiration and encouragement.[19] John Evelyn was a particular fan and, perhaps partly through his praise of her 'extraordinary fanciful habit, garb and discourse', later generations of women came to admire and respect 'this writing lady'.[20]

Until Margaret developed her scientific interests, she had not had a very eventful life. Her childhood was as one of a large family, a comfortable if clannish existence. She surprised her widowed mother and elder siblings by demanding to be allowed to become a maid-in-waiting to Queen Henrietta Maria, wife to the ill-fated Charles I. On the outbreak of the Civil War (1642), she fled with the court to France, where after two unhappy years she made an unlikely match with 'my lord, the Marquis of Newcastle'. He was twice her age, a widower with a grown-up family, very grand but almost penniless. No one approved of the match, least of all Newcastle's royal friends, but after a whirlwind courtship the pair married and appear to have lived happily after.

He seems to have found a willing listener, an adoring admirer and an acute and useful manager of his chaotic business affairs. She acquired a tutor and a guide into a new world of science which was to inspire the dozen large folio volumes that comprised a sizeable proportion of her prolific output. In the course of her writing life, she addressed herself to scientific theory and opinion; she created a new form of science fiction in which women figure in exotic and commanding roles, as scientists, explorers, military commanders, scholars and governors (fictionalized versions of Anna Maria von Schurmann's plans for women); and she wrote poems and plays, as well as a very fine example of biography.

There had been nothing at all in Margaret's early education to prepare for her unlikely metamorphosis. As a child all she had been taught were the 'accomplishments', and her mother placed little value on even these skills. Margaret herself had had no interest in self-improvement. Her sole inclination was to construct fantasy worlds and to play out imagined roles. Her happiest hours had been spent not in a precocious search for knowledge, but in a passion for the extravagance of dressing-up: 'for I always took delight in a singularity, even in accoutrements of habits'.[21]

Educationally, her brothers did not fare much better. Only her middle brother, the future Lord Lucas, had evinced an academic disposition. He was another founding member of the Royal Society, and later in life the Duchess, as she then was, accorded him partial credit for having stimulated her interest in the study of natural philosophy. But, as a youngster, he had spent his time with his brothers occupied in field sports and exercise. The Duke of Newcastle, Margaret's husband, was likewise poorly educated. Margaret described the process that was typical of all gentlemen:

> His education was according to his birth; for as he was born a Gentleman, so he was bred like a Gentleman. To School-learning he never shew'd a great inclination; for though he was sent to the University, and was a Student of St. John's Colledg [*sic*] in Cambridg [*sic*], and had his tutors to instruct him; yet they could not persuade him to read or study much, he taking more delight in sports, than in learning; so that his Father being a wise man ... suffer'd him to follow his own Genius. [*The Life of William Cavendish*, 1667, p. 141]

Later in life, however, though not a scholar himself, he liked to patronize those who were. Descartes, Van Helmont, Thomas Hobbes, all the top minds in Europe, were entertained at his home in exile in Antwerp. Here Cavendish compiled an enviable collection of optical glasses. Even at this early stage, the mechanics of science fascinated the amateur.[22]

When scientific men gathered in the Cavendish household, after-dinner conversation often lingered on the fashionable topics of new stars and space exploration as well as on other scientific subjects, and Margaret was always present, a silent but avid listener.[23] After the boredom of court life, she was dazzled by these displays of erudition, always loyally seeing her husband as the inspiration of these fascinating thoughts. In fact, as her disingenuous account of their education showed, it was not William but his brother Charles who was the true scientist in the family.

Charles was a gentleman scientist. He had had a good mathematical training and was keenly interested in the most recent developments in astronomy and the latest technical advances. Indeed, he himself had tried his hand at improving the quality of the telescope and was in close correspondence on these and other matters with the leading scientists of the day.[24] It was he who was to encourage Margaret's budding interest in current scientific theory, although she always attributed her education to her husband.

Margaret received her scientific instruction when she and Charles were obliged to return to England together in 1651 in order to try and negotiate with the Cromwellian government for the return of their confiscated property. As exiled Royalists, they had forfeited their rights. It was hoped, however, that after the execution of the King in 1649 at least some non-combatants might be permitted to buy back family estates on the payment of an extortionate fine. The offer clearly did not apply to William who had fought loyally for the King, but Charles and Margaret hoped to salvage something from the ruins of the family fortunes.

While the lawyers examined the legal niceties of the case, Margaret was obliged to hang about London for almost a year, putting up with uncomfortable lodgings, separation from her beloved husband and the blatant unfriendliness of the supporters of the new regime. It was during this long waiting time that Margaret received some instruction in science from Charles. Through these conversations she gained her first serious insight into current scientific theories, gradually moved to a deeper appreciation of this way of looking at the world and was eventually able to put together for herself a coherent and well-defined natural philosophy.

Initially, she appeared to condone the usual gentlemanly attitude to science, which one is tempted to believe may have borrowed something from her husband's approach to the subject: 'Natural Philosophy is to be used as a Delight and Recreation in Men's Studies, as Poetry is, since they are both Fictions, and not a Labour in Man's life' (*The World's Olio*, 1665, p. 161).

To pass the long solitary hours she turned what she had learned of current scientific theory from these conversations with Charles into verse. She then took the unusual step of publishing her work as *Poems and Fancies* in 1653 with a dedication of gratitude to her brother-in-law.[25] Although the content of *Poems* is almost wholly scientific, the Duchess felt obliged to appease 'the Natural Philosophers' among her readers by assuring them that she used the subject as though it was merely fantasy, and that fantasy was a peculiarly feminine weakness to which she had resorted as a harmless solace in an unwelcoming city.

Regardless of the reasons she gave to her public, it was evident that the Duchess had found scientific thought most interesting. Despite her disavowal of the seriousness of her intentions, she showed in the book that she had managed to assimilate 'and reproduce a well-argued system of natural philosophy handling themes and ideas much discussed at the time. The basis of her system at this early stage of her scientific career was Gassendian atomism, clearly derived from her brother-in-law's enthusiasm for the ideas of his friend, Pierre Gassendi.

But Margaret's early introduction to scientific theory was comprehensive. She demonstrated a familiarity with the work of Thomas Hobbes, also a friend of the family and a man whose influence on her would grow in time. She was aware, as were all interested people, of the current debate on Harvey's theory of the circulation of the blood, which since it had been propounded in the 1620s had exercised many minds. She had gleaned a considerable amount of information on the newest technical advances in navigation, the use of the lodestone, chart and compass. Other scientific questions, such as the nature of meteors, the movements of tides and the salinity of the sea, were all given some attention. By the time she had guided her first published volume through the press, she had made a momentous decision to carry on as an 'effeminate Writer' and to take up science as a serious vocation.[26]

She was already finishing a second volume, which had been conceived in the greatest haste. In all, it had taken her three weeks and was the most compact work she was ever to produce. It was called *Philosophical Fancies* (1653), and in it she showed the growing independence of mind that was to characterize all her future productions. She had decided to reject the atomic theory as deficient. In a later work she described why she had changed her mind: 'And as for atoms, after I had Reasoned with myself, I conceived that it was not probable that the universe and all the creatures therein could be created and disposed by the dancing and wandering and diverse motions of atoms' (*Philosophical Opinions*, 1655, 2nd edn 1663, sig. c2r). In its place she elaborated a mechanistic interpretation of the universe stemming from Galileo through the medium of Thomas Hobbes. It was the theory which, with some expansion and refurbishment, she continued to expound for the rest of her life.

Hobbes was also responsible, presumably, for the strongly atheistical tone that increasingly coloured her writing, an uncommon but not unique attitude in a woman. She frequently spurned those who attempted to combine the two very different attitudes inherent in religion and science. As far as she was concerned matters of faith should be kept strictly apart from scientific questions. She conceded that God existed, but contended that he had no role in nature, which was 'altogether Material' and open only to scientific scrutiny:

> Nor am I of the opinion of our Divine Philosophers, who mix Philosophy with Divinity, Faith and Reason, together and count it Irreligious, if not Blasphemy, to assert any other Principles of Nature, than what they ... draw out of Scripture, especially out of Genesis, whereas *Moses* doth only describe the Creation of this World, and not of Infinite Matter. But, as Pure Natural Philosophers do not meddle with Divinity, or things Supernatural; so Divines ought not to entrench upon Natural Philosophy. [*Observations upon Experimental Philosophy*, 1666, 2nd edn 1668, p. 333]

It was views like this that ensured the Duchess's notoriety. Although she may only have been putting into words what many were thinking, most people were more cautious. When Isaac Newton produced his new and original theories, he wrote in Latin and carefully censored his words in order to avoid any confrontation with Church or State. The Duchess's flamboyant disregard for the proprieties of life and her supposed or real atheism were very provoking. In dubbing her Newcastle's 'illustrious whore' and the 'Great Atheistical Philosophraster', John Stainsby, friend of the antiquary and collector Elias Ashmole, summed up much of the antagonism that this outspoken woman drew upon herself.[27]

She was very lucky that her husband supported her. When she expanded *Philosophical Fancies* to her favourite folio proportions, and published it in 1665 as *Philosophical and Physical Opinions*, she disarmingly claimed this to be her masterpiece. Her husband agreed and wrote a laudatory preface to the work in which he extolled his wife's unusual occupation and singled out for praise her powers of original thought and her choice of subject. To those who criticized her, he was severe. They spoke out of a petty jealousy that inspired criticism of a woman who had accomplished so much: 'But here's the crime, a Lady Writer ... and to intrench so much upon the male prerogative, is not to be forgiven' (*Philosophical and Physical Opinions* 1665, Preface, sig. a3v).

The basis of her new mechanistic theory was hypothesis rather than experiment. In this preference for theory above research she resembled Descartes, whose method was to contemplate the form of a thing and then to guess the motion that may have produced it. This predilection for theory continued to dominate her scientific writings even when she returned to empiric England after the Restoration of Charles II. In this she was hopelessly at odds with the prevailing spirit of English science, heavily influenced as it was by the legacy of Sir Francis Bacon.

When Robert Hooke, the newly appointed Curator of Experiments at the Royal Society, published his *Micrographia* in 1665, she seized this as her moment to attack what she considered to be the unjustifiable reining in of the enquiring scientific spirit by those who espoused the carefully deductive methods of empiricism. The world was informed of her opinion in *Observations on Experimental Philosophy* in 1666. Her argument was that science, which should be an imaginative exploration of matter, was too often restrained by the limitations of the available technology. Seventeenth-century microscopes were clumsy tools which seem to have distorted more than they could ever have revealed. Looking at English science at the time, she saw a slavish dependence on the assistance of 'deluding Glasses and Experiments' instead of an assertion of the true spirit of enquiry which was to be found only in 'rational and judicious observations'. (In fact she had overlooked Hooke's own cautious warnings of the dangers of too many scientists wanting to see the world only through the tunnel vision of the microscope.)

It was this blindness to greater issues that irritated Margaret Cavendish. She argued that many scientists were using experiments in an unscholarly way and that their methods resembled not the discerning procedures of thoughtful men, but the simple and mechanical operations of housewives. In her opinion the work of the laboratory was not a field for the superior intelligence. It suited the limited abilities of lesser creatures, the women who enjoyed such things, and it is they who should undertake the lowly tasks involved in tinkering with 'Fire and Furnace'. The Duchess of Newcastle suggested that women made fine experimental scientists because that work was closely akin to their domestic tasks. If that side of science were left to women, men would be liberated to 'employ their time in more profitable studies than in useless experiments' (p. 104).

Despite her sex, she firmly dissociated herself from this new fashion for 'Experimental or Mode Philosophy, built upon deluding Art' which was attracting so many devotees, both men and women. She preferred the contemplative and rational scientific method whose primary command for her was 'Reason shall be my guide.'

She pronounced on the status of women many times throughout her writing career, and her verdicts were sometimes in favour and sometimes against her own sex. She always tended to see herself as exceptional and above the limitations of more ordinary creatures. But, after her interest in science had been aroused, she became, if not more sympathetic, at least more conscious of the difficulties which inhibited many women. Securely and happily married, adored by her husband and childless, she herself occupied a very privileged position.

In her earliest scribbling days she held the opinions on her sex that might have been expected in the most misogynist circles of the time. She saw no discrepancy in comparing ordinary women of her day with the giants of the Bible or the classics, and no fallacy in her conclusion that men and women could, therefore, be neither physically nor intellectually equal. Quoting a commonly held platitude, she informed her readers that women were like monkeys. The only way they could improve themselves was by aping men, their intellectual betters. This was not a course of action she could countenance either, for it was notoriously true that a half-educated woman was little short of a social disaster. They lost all restraint and resisted the law and order of male society, with a consequent increase in the rate of illegitimacy. Happily, the Duchess was confident that the febrile sex could be controlled: 'Nature, out of love to the Generation of Men, hath made Women to be governed by Men', and male strength and 'authority' would ensure the peace (*The World's Olio*, 1655, sig. A5v–A6v).

On several occasions she noted her irritation with the ,hysical and mental weakness of women. They were, at best, like children, or they resembled 'a yielding vegetable', the willow in contrast to the sturdy masculine oak. In a comparison of beasts and birds, women were like birds 'because they are more Useless Creatures, for most Birds are of no use but to sing and some to Prate; they are neither Useful for Labour nor war as most Beasts are' (*CCXI Sociable Letters*, 1664, p. 37).

As the Duchess developed her interest in science, however, her attitude to herself and to other women changed substantially. As soon as she began to delve into the serious business of natural philosophy, she appeared to realize that she had to unravel the thorny question of women's apparently fundamental incapacity. She had become reluctant to assign the fault to some peculiarly feminine characteristic. Like others at the time, she reached the conclusion that it was the educational system that was at fault. At one stage in her career, she took the interesting step of appealing to the 'Two Universities' to take on their proper responsibility and encourage the intellectual and academic ambitions of women. It had become clear to her, as it would do to those who asked for the same thing two centuries later, that without this encouragement women, for all their endeavour, would never escape the intellectual darkness in which they languished. It is evident that, like Anna Maria von Schurmann and others, she found the continued exclusion of women from all 'Civil and Marshall Affaires' a chaffing irritation:

> thus by an opinion, which I hope is but an erronious [*sic*] one in men [that women lack understanding, knowledge and prudence], we are shut out of all power and Authority by reason we are never imployed [*sic*] either in civil nor marshall Affaires, our counsels are despised, and laught at, the best of our actions are troden [*sic*] down with scorn, by the over-weaning conceit men have of themselves and through a dispisement [*sic*] of us. [*The Philosophical and Physical Opinions*, 1655, sig. B2v]

When she set out to counter the charges of inferiority, the Duchess resorted to the useful doctrine of the originality of women. She agreed that women may certainly suffer from being debarred from education, but maintained that they can compensate for this unjust exclusion by drawing on their own naturally implanted stocks of reason and judgement. The strength of these faculties in women can give them a head start over less well-endowed man, for 'though education doth help natural reason to a more sudden maturity, yet natural reason was the first educator: for natural reason did first compose Common-wealths, invented arts and sciences' (*Philosophical and Physical Opinions*, sig. B2r).

The Duchess was irresistible. She wrote and published her books at her own expense. She was so confident that she was about to change the course of English scientific thought that she made sure that no institute of higher learning, either at home or abroad, nor any individual of intellectual eminence, remained in ignorance of her ideas. Her self-confidence was infectious. When, after her death, her devoted husband gathered together the tributes his wife had received, the result, *Letters and Poems in Honour of the Incomparable Princess, Margaret, Dutchess of Newcastle* (1676), was an impressive memorial to her name and her endeavours. There were letters of gratitude from the University of Leyden, from the Vice Chancellor and Senate of the University of Cambridge, from St John's and Trinity Colleges, Cambridge, from Oxford and from the Bodleian Library, as well as from numerous men of intellectual stature and status, all of whom had received copies of her works, and all of whom paid her lavish compliments.

They were unanimous and fulsome in their praise. Discarding convention and tradition, the Duchess had shown other women a way in which they could improve their lot. Her fine disregard for a woman's domestic duties, her wholehearted enthusiasm for science and her successful career as a writer were all adduced as evidence to persuade others of the value of her lifestyle and interests. (In the preface to *Sociable Letters*, she admitted to her husband her inadequacies as a housewife, but claimed some knowledge of sheep rearing.) Ignoring the dubious streak of atheism in her character and her seditious contempt for the traditional sphere of women, her admirers elevated her as a model worthy of emulation by other lesser women. By following her example, they would learn to reject their inferiority and to relinquish those tokens of their serfdom, their cosmetics, their accomplishments and, most of all, their lady-like silence. Francis Fane, one of the contributors to the festschrift, entitled his poem, 'To the Glory of her Sex … upon her most admirable works'.

> Now let enfranchiz'd Ladies learn to write
> And not Paint white, and red, but black and white
> Their Bodkins turn to Pens, to Lines their Locks
> And let the Inkhorn be their Dressing Box: …
> The *Silent Woman* Famous heretofore
> Has been, but now the writing Lady more. [pp. 162–3]

The ladies took the advice. Many turned to writing, but many more found that science provided them with the possibility of some form of intellectual self-fulfilment. Their success was to be so conspicuous that, although not many of them could lay claim to the fame and reputation of the Duchess, they inspired a mood of self-confidence in many women. This led to a vein of feminist writing which was to be as radical as anything since produced.

Feminism and science in the eighteenth century

A 'Lady of Quality', writing in 1721, yoked the scientific avocations of women with a new self-image which she heralded as 'Woman Triumphant'. In *Woman Triumphant: or, the Excellency of the Female Sex; asserted in opposition to the Male*, she conveys an impression of a ferment of scientific activity among women at this time. She describes how her contemporaries, avid for these new opportunities of learning, crowd into all available courses in 'Mathematicks and Experimental Philosophy', and do all in their power to compensate for their exclusion from the universities. She was also deeply impressed by such novel expressions of women's interest in science as the *Ladies Diary*, the first scientific publication exclusively for women, and particularly by those women, veritable 'Sphinx's', who displayed their mathematical erudition in its pages.[28] The 'lady' was clear that such unusual developments demanded a new assertiveness among women:

> I think it is high time to look about Us, and to vindicate Our Sex;
> to let them know the value we ought in Justice to set upon ourselves;
> to rouze up our courage, and fire our Breast with a worthy Indig-
> nation, and Resentment against such inhumane Treatment as we
> daily meet with, that we may no longer give Pre-eminence to such
> vain, thoughtless, and ungovernable Animals, as Men of what
> Denomination soever. [p. 111]

The essence of her argument is a complaint that women, their abilities
notwithstanding, are still restricted to the tight and age-old domestic
boundaries. She used what had, by then, become almost an adage, that
'Woman as far exceeds Man, As Animals do Inanimates, or as *Organized
Bodies* are preferable to senseless *Clods*' (p. 3), to launch an attack on
the injustice of restricting girls to vocational training. While girls are
persuaded to confine themselves merely to what will be of use to them
in their combined roles as wife, housekeeper and parent, young men
enter university and a way of life that secures them freedom to develop as
thinking individuals, 'a relax from all other Affairs'. This untrammelled
access to a liberal education, in turn, ensures their future in 'Posts of
Honour and Trust, both in Church and State' (p. 18).

It is this situation that the writer would change. Girls must be
permitted the same opportunities as boys even to the level of university
education. The touch of militancy that appears in a poem appended
to the pamphlet perhaps explains why it took another two hundred
years or so for this to come about:

> So let our Sex be unto 'Learning' bred,
> Like you in Liberal Sciences be read;
> In one short Age the Press from our keen Wit,
> Should out-shine All that Men have ever Writ,
> As Woman now so Men should truckle then,
> Beneath the Lashes of each Female Pen. [p. xv]

The attenuated education permitted to female children and the
exclusion of women from both education and the professions rankled
all during the eighteenth century and was the inspiration for several
radical essays. Two of the most outspoken were by the anonymous
author 'Sophia'. Who she was and how she dared produce such virulent
arguments remains an intriguing but unsolved mystery.

Her first essay was *Woman Not Inferior to Man: or a Short and Modest
vindication of the natural Rights of the Fair Sex to a perfect Equality of Power,*

Dignity and Esteem with the Men (1743).[29] Undoubtedly this is the most dramatic and fully developed argument for the greater social and intellectual emancipation of women to appear in the first half of the eighteenth century. Given the restrictions, both professional and social, under which women then laboured, this analysis of the wrongs of women and the justification of their ambitions, although still groping for true expression, is a worthy forerunner of the better known feminist writings from later in the century.

Sophia repeats much of the by then not unfamiliar thesis proving not only the superiority of women, but their originality and their scientific bent as well. Where she goes further is in her perceptive analysis of contemporary society, dominated as it is by men, and her criticism of many of the notions that men hold dear. Religion, for example, is dismissed as nothing more than an amalgam of worn-out opinions that time has made acceptable. Racial prejudice also is adduced as evidence of unthinking male irrationality, as is the illogicality of the class structure: 'The very inequality of stations, which pride, ambition, and other like causes have introduced among Men, had deceived multitudes of them into a notion that the same inequality is in Men themselves' (p. 6).

Among these 'vulgar errors' which Sophia lays at the door of the men is, it need hardly be said, the supposed inferiority of women. Only the illogical male could fail to see that women's unique biological role, if nothing else, should guarantee their superiority, since the continuation of the human race rests with them.

Why women should have been excluded from learning, given that the souls of the sexes must be equal and that women have more acute senses than men, can only be due, she insists, to a conspiracy of repression practised against women for many centuries. To uphold this repression men have resorted to an ideology that enshrines the roles of 'divine providence and their own sovereign sense', and the result has been that these male usurpers have 'debarr'd us of sciences, government and public offices'. When this conspiracy succeeded in ensuring the subjection of women, that very state of unnatural subjugation was itself added to the reasons for maintaining the status quo. The result, she declared, has been the unanswerable circular argument: 'Why is *learning* useless to us? because we have no share in public offices. And why have we no share in public offices? because we have no *learning*' (p. 28). This arrogance and insolent illogicality pushes Sophia to revolutionary fervour:

But let truth speak for once: why are they so industrious to debar us that learning, we have an equal right to with themselves, but for fear of our sharing with and outshining them, in those public offices they fill so miserably? The same sordid selfishness which urges them to engross all power and dignity to themselves, prompts them to shut up from us that knowledge which wou'd have made us their competitors. [p. 25]

The usurpation of the rightful place of women in society has been achieved by 'violence, shameless injustice and lawless oppression', and is accepted only because it bears a timeworn seal awarded by those evangelists of prejudice, the 'drivellers' and 'half-thinking pedants' of former times. As Anna Maria von Schurmann had suggested a century earlier, Sophia argues that, since the Bible only forbids one career, the Church, to women, this means that all others must be open to them. She claims that it is obvious to all right-thinking persons that a woman has a place in the civil and military government of a country. She may lead an army, rule a nation, speak at the Bar, act as a judge in a court of law, or, as a magistrate, be accorded the dignity of being preceded in the street with the sword, mace and other ensigns of authority.

But it is in science and medicine, 'Our sex seem born to teach and practice physic', that a woman can make a unique contribution. Her intellect and her disposition both incline her to science, and her common sense will ensure that she will not fritter away time on the 'fictitious trifles' to be 'found only in their own noddles', which so often preoccupy the limited minds of male academics:

Our endeavour should be to investigate the true nature of things, to understand wherein they related to or differed from us; and by what applications they may become beneficial or noxious; that so we may avoid evil, and obtain all the felicity providence deigns us. [p. 49]

While Sophia was aware that many of the prevailing conventions that restricted women's lives must be altered, she also laid a great deal of the responsibility for change in the hands of women themselves. To step out of the mould that society had decreed they must occupy, they must display determination and strength of character. They are, therefore, 'under a necessity of surmounting the softness they were educated in; of renouncing the pleasure and indolence' in which 'cruel custom' imprisons them, of overcoming 'the external impediments in their way to study', and lastly of resisting the general prejudice entertained by both sexes of 'learning in *Women*' (pp. 44–5).[30]

Sophia's paper provoked an answer, whose virulently misogynist arguments were typical and scarcely need rehearsing.[31] What have women to do with theory? he sneers. Theory is a ground 'too holy for female feet to tread with impunity … no; practice is the boundary of their province' (pp. 80–1). He firmly returns the debate to its more usual lines of biblical and classical precedent and anecdote, thereby unwittingly verifying Sophia's criticism of man's inability to operate outside the limits of received opinion.

Sophia replied with *Proving Woman Superior in Excellence to Man* and her tone was scathing. The major part of this paper is devoted to a realistic appraisal of the situation of women. As she describes it, the existing climate of opinion leaves little room for the sort of rebellion she had appeared to be inciting in her earlier publication. Her assessment of a woman's chances of education left little hope. An education at best snatched in the face of convention, at worst short on content and long on 'finishing', left the women who had the energy to aspire to intellectual pursuits only the opportunities that came by stealth.

What was needed was a radical onslaught on convention. As in her earlier paper, the parallel injustice of racial discrimination comes to mind. It might be possible for women to overthrow their shackles by the activities of some brilliant individuals, just as it would only need a few 'Aethiopian doctors at Oxford or Cambridge' to alter public perception of the intellectual prowess of non-white races. Offering that slim hope for eventual change, she concludes that in the meantime women must carefully cultivate their self-respect.

'Sophia' belongs to a more militant tradition – the scientific tradition of social usefulness, as distinct from the tradition that encouraged women to seek personal satisfaction through study. She addressed herself to women as a social group, hoping to make them more aware of themselves as rational, even naturally scientific, beings. Her aim was to fire them with an enthusiasm not for the development of the self, but for public office – which they would achieve through a programme of scientific study. Her particular preoccupation was with the exclusion of women, as a class, from all career opportunities and reasonable standards of education.

These two views of the importance of education to women continued to exist side by side. In one case, however, a splendid exegesis of female emancipation, both concepts are dextrously amalgamated and refurbished. Entitled *Female Rights vindicated, or the Equality of the Sexes Morally and Physically proved* (1758), the anonymous author, 'a Lady', provides the readers with an analysis of history's success in corroborating 'the Imbecillity of the Women', but notes in fairness that women might have done the same had they been given the chance. After reviewing women's innate inclination to scientific study, she presents a list of the studies that are particularly appropriate to women.

Physics tops the list. It is a subject particularly suited to women, for all that is required by way of preparation is close observation, a keen eye for detail, patience and energy – precisely the skills that women who have been obliged to spend hours sewing and embroidering have to excess. Medicine comes next in importance. The author refers to the long tradition of women in medicine and is aware of the not inconsiderable reputation acquired by some female doctors and chemists. Some, indeed, have even received grants from Parliament to fund their researches:[32]

> Their Abilities are not confined to administering the remedies; they are equally fit for discovering them, The World is indebted to our Sex for a Number of medicinal Inventions; and our Country in particular (some of whom have received pecuniary Grants from parliament for their Discoveries) are remarkable for their great Hospitality and Charity to the Sick of all Kinds. [p. 38]

Astronomy and mathematics are also eminently suited to the woman student. Women possess the same powers of sight as man, and need only access to good telescopes to assist them in their perusal of the heavens. Twenty years later Caroline Herschel would prove the point. Similarly, mathematics, like any other subject within the grasp of men, can be understood by women 'since all their Faculties are clearly evinced to be as perfect as those of the Men' (p. 62). This, of course, applies equally to that citadel of masculine knowledge, the classics themselves. Significantly, the author concedes that only by studying the classics will a woman be adequately prepared for a professional career, or, in the more colourful language of the pamphlet, to be 'immersed in the general Combustion of Civil Society' (p. 66).

The case for the equality of the sexes rested on the results that equality of educational opportunity would produce. Many women were not willing to accept that the prevailing mode of education would answer their needs. They sought a programme of study that was appropriate for their particular inclinations. Various feminine qualities – application, curiosity, attention to detail, practicality – persuaded many of the fair sex that the sciences were their natural milieu.

The humanist tradition of the woman scholar, who, while studying the classics in the privacy of her closet, maintained a modest exterior in public, persisted undiminished. But those other, less demure women who insisted that the study of physics and chemistry prepared a woman for nothing less than a position in government, a salary and political and social prestige were never silenced. Indeed it may not be too much to suggest that the women who chose science directed the slow evolution of female emancipation into the public arena in a way that female scholars of Greek or Latin were neither willing nor able to do.[33]

Notes

1. At the end of the seventeenth century Juliana Barnes was popularly supposed to have written the treatise on hawking, hunting and fishing, *The Boke of St Albans* (1486) and to have been prioress of Sopwell Nunnery in Hertfordshire.

2. Apart from *Numismata*, there were M. Christian Juncker, *De Ephemeridibus* (1692), Jeremy Collier, *The Great Historical ... Dictionary* (2nd edn 1701), and early issues of the *Ladies Diary* (1704 ff.). Margaret Alic, *Hypatia's Heritage* (1986) is an excellent modern catalogue of learned ladies.

3. Anna Maria von Schurmann admired Margaret Roper (Birch, p. 77). She knew and corresponded with Marie le Jars de Gourney (Birch, pp. 73–6) and Bathsua Makin. Bathsua Makin's brother John knew the Cavendish borthers very well. Margaret Cavendish lived in Holland for more than a decade at the centre of the intellectual community. In many and various ways these women were acquainted with each other.

4. *L'Ombre de la Damoiselle de Gourney* (1626), pp. 525–6, quoted in M.H. Ilsley, *A Daughter of the Renaissance, Marie le Jars de Gourney, Her Life and Works* (The Hague, 1963), p. 83.

5. *Les Advis ou Les Presens de la Demoiselle de Gourney* (1st edn 1634, 2nd edn 1641), pp. 509, 511, 517, quoted in Ilsley, pp. 87, 96.

6. Alan M. Boase, *The Fortunes of Montaigne* (1938), p. 27.

7. *Advis* (1634), p. 509, quoted in Ilsley, p. 95.

8. *Advis*, p. 509, quoted in Ilsley, p. 96.

9. *Égalité des Hommes et des Femmes* (1622), p. 69, quoted in Ilsley, p. 207.

10. *Grief des Dames* p. 92, quoted in Ilsley, p. 210.

11. *Advis*, p. 455, quoted in Ilsley, p. 209.

12. *Advis*, p. 458, quoted in Ilsley, p. 209.

13. Birch, *Anna Van Schurmann*, p. 75.

14. Birch, pp. 75–6.

15. Thirteen of her books were published during her life, of which six dealt with scientific matters.

16. Thomas Birch, *History of the Royal Society* (1756), II, p. 176; S.I. Mintz, 'The Duchess of Newcastle's visit to the Royal Society', *Journal of English and German Philology* (1952), pp. 168–76.

17. Robert Boyle, *Experiments and Considerations touching Colours* (1664), sig. A3v–A4r.

18. *CCXI Sociable Letters* (1664), p. 243.

19. After her death, her husband published this collection of compliments in *Letters and Poems in Honour of the Incomparable Princess* (1676).

20. *The Diary of John Evelyn*, 6 vols, ed. by E.S. De Beer (Oxford, 1955), III, p. 478.

21. 'A True Relation of my Birth, Breeding and Life' in *Nature's Pictures* (1656), p. 387.

22. Douglas Grant, *Margaret the First* (1957), p. 93.

23. *CCXI Sociable Letters*, pp. 223–5; *The Life of Willilam, Duke of Newcastle* (1667), pp. 145–6.

24. Jean Jacquot, 'Sir Charles Cavendish and his Learned Friends', *Annals of Science*, no. 8 (March 1952), pp. 13–27.

25. Some of her work predating 1653 was collected and eventually published as *The World's Olio* in 1655. In this book she deals with questions such as the breathing mechanism of humans compared with fish and discussed as a certainty the imminent inventions of 'speaking tubes' for long-distance communication.

26. 'To all Writing Ladies' in *Poems and Fancies*, p. 162.

27. D. Grant, *Margaret the First.* (1957), p. 199.

28. p. 15. For the *Ladies Diary* see below, pp. 98–103.

29. A second edition in 1751 bore the title, *Beauty's Triumph: or, the Superiority of the Fair Sex invincibly proved. Wherin The Arguments for the natural Right of Man to a Soverign Authority over the Woman are fairly urged, and undeniably refuted; and the undoubted Title of the Ladies, even to a superiority over the Men both in Head and Heart, is clearly evinced; shewing Their Minds to be as much more beautiful than the Mens as their Bodies; and that, if they had the same Advantages of Education, they would excel their Tyrants as much in Sense as they do in Virtue.*

30. Sophia was aware of the work of many of her contemporaries, e.g. Elizabeth Carter, Elizabeth Rowe and Constantia Grierson. See p. 44.

31. *Beauty's triumph, Part II. Being an Attempt to refute Sophia's Arguments; And to prove the Natural Right of the Men to Sovereign Authority over the Other Sex*, published with *Beauty's Triumph* in 1751. Compare with the rabid sermon on the God-ordained inferiority of women preached by the Rev John Sprint at a wedding on 11 May 1699 (*The Bride-Woman's Councellor*). It caused a considerable stir at the time. Several women rushed into print to defend their sex.

32. In 1739 Joanna Stevens was awarded a grant of £5,000 from Parliament to pursue medical research. Her efforts proved fruitless, but it is interesting nonetheless that she received the money at all.

33. Other later 'feminist' writers, typically Mary Wollstonecraft and Lucy Aiken, also urged scientific studies on women.

PART II

The Media of Science

Introduction

The growth of scientific literacy in women was encouraged and supported by a parallel development in the 'media' of science. These included books and other forms of literature, lectures, personal tuition and schools, field work and membership of scientific societies. These media varied greatly in quality and sophistication, but they all contrived to hearten rather than deflect the interest that women were taking in science.

In the scientific literature that was generated from the middle of the seventeenth century onwards, there were some particular categories that were of especial interest to women. First of all, there were the standard works, written for a general readership but which in surprisingly many instances found many keen female readers as well. An assessment of the numbers of women who may have read these books can only be subjective. But from the evidence of the subscription lists alone, it is certain that a surprising number of women bought them. Some women, at least, are known to have read them. In addition there are some attested cases of women compiling their own scientific libraries, thereby signposting their preoccupations in a most interesting way.

More significant evidence of an unfolding female interest in science was the early acknowledgement of the existence of that interest by scientists and writers. Almost as soon as popular science books were available, works appeared that targeted women. They claimed to be designed especially to cope with the particular problems that women might experience beginning the study of a branch of science. To underline the writers' commitment to their female readership these books were often dedicated to some individual woman who had distinguished herself in her scientific studies. With the increase in the production of popular science in general, the numbers of science books written with women in mind gradually increased, becoming a steady trickle during the eighteenth century.

A unique testimony to the interest of women in science was the appearance in the early eighteenth century of a new publishing phenomenon, a diary for women. This extraordinary publication, and its few imitators, not only encouraged the scientific predelictions of women, but also sustained them by offering opportunities through correspondence for women to exercise their mathematical abilities and to make contact with each other. Since many of these ladies included their names and addresses with their letters, it is possible by this means to gain a little insight into the distribution of scientifically interested women throughout the country.

The appearance of books written by women themselves in the latter half of the eighteenth century marked a new stage in the story. Unlike the science writings of women in the seventeenth and early eighteenth centuries, these publications were mostly elementary textbooks for women and children in which the science was put across through the medium of female characters, thus effectively underlining the naturalness of women participating in science. During the following century many more women authors entered the field, producing not only introductions and school textbooks, but also books of considerable significance and influence. Some of the most celebrated science writers were ladies, and it is generally agreed that their contribution to the dissemination and progress of science at this time was an important one.

In addition to the volumes of straight science being published, there was another medium which both expected and reinforced a basic scientific literacy in women. This was the ephemeral literature which developed in quantity and importance in the first decade of the eighteenth century and was often aimed at women as its main readership. Science intruded in these publications as analogy or illustration for other topics, but often in its own right as a general interest item. A degree of scientific knowledge in readers was taken for granted. Somewhat later, when the papers designed for an exclusive female readership appeared, they too advocated the study of science among women.

The early recognition of ladies as important consumers of scientific paraphernalia is evident from the advertisements for such things that appeared in places likely to catch a woman's interested eye, such as women's magazines. Microscopes were a particular favourite. For a time they achieved the status of fashion accessory, while globes, other instruments and study aids were soon accepted without further comment.

There was also poetry. Poetry was a popular and particularly successful channel for conveying scientific information. It appealed to a wide audience. It had high status value, much greater than drama or fiction. In its traditional forms, it erected no barriers to understanding. It was an excellent medium for conveying the abstruse facts of science. During the eighteenth century the fashion for scientific poetry grew, eventually producing some of the best sellers of the time. It was on the foundation of this tradition that the Romantic poets also exploited science in their work.

The various forms of scientific literature were complemented by the public lecture. Very often, the two were inseparable, for successful lecturers published their lecture series or wrote scientific poems. The public lecture had its beginnings in the 1660s but developed its universal appeal in the following centuries. Finding out how many ladies attended these events is obviously difficult, but there is evidence, even from the seventeenth and eighteenth centuries, to suggest the presence of women. It derives from the lecturers themselves, from the women who left some form of testimony, most often letters to other interested women, or from the advertisements used to attract the public. During the period, too, the ladies of the royal family not infrequently displayed a particular interest in science. Conjecturally, this would have made the subject appealing to ladies further down the social hierarchy. Certainly by the end of the eighteenth century, ladies seemed to take for granted their appearance at scientific meetings.

CHAPTER 5
Scientific Literature

The seventeenth century

Fortified by the example and exhortation of formidable preceptresses like Bathsua Makin, Mary Astell and the Duchess of Newcastle, the 'enfranchiz'd Ladies' who decided to examine the mysteries of science had at their disposal the standard scientific books. They were fortunate in that even these books took into account the fact that potential students of science might very well come to the subject without any previous educational training. Poor Latin and little mathematics was no hindrance to the study of science.

Furthermore, in those early days of modern science, it was a deeply held conviction among the leading men in the field that lucid and comprehensible communication was essential to further the cause of scientific research. The preoccupation of the late seventeenth century with linguistic perfectibility and esoteric modes of speech was scorned by the scientists. Despite the prestige that such elevated language enjoyed, they refused to have anything to do with it. What they wanted was to be understood.[1]

It was not scholars but the men of business and their workers whom the scientists wished to reach. Works written in Latin or couched in the high rhetoric style of the period would have been incomprehensible to these groups of people. To compensate for their shortcomings and to facilitate the expansion of the scientific community as efficiently as possible, seminal works by Bacon, Gilbert, Galileo, Harvey and others, originally conceived in Latin, were speedily translated into English, and, with some notable exceptions, new works were usually written in the vernacular.[2]

The great Robert Boyle regarded it as an essential part of his pedagogic duty to tailor his publications to the needs and undoubted short-comings of his audience. When his editor, Robert Sharrock, prepared his works for publication, he explained to the 'Friendly Reader' that the reason that such a learned man as Boyle chose to use English, the language of the ignorant, was because the readership which he courted was not the university men, but plain men of action and commerce who were more interested in the mechanics of existence than the niceties of language (*New Experiments*, 1660, sig. b2v).

It was part of the aim of these educators to encourage the common man to understand his role in current developments and to participate, however humbly, in them. To this end the recently founded Royal Society sought to break the stranglehold of academic learning on the intellectual life of the country, at least in so far as scientific investigation was concerned. Their aim was to do away with the accumulation of groundless theory and hypothesis, the legacy of scholastic education, and to direct the attention of scientists to the pressing need for accurate observation and careful records, for which one needed nothing more than a discriminating eye and a methodical mind. Robert Hooke, first secretary of the Society, compared the old with the new method in *Micrographia*, an important early work on the microscope produced by the Royal Society in 1665:'The truth is, the Science of Nature has been already too long made only a work of the Brain and the Fancy: It is now high time that it should return to the plainness and soundness of Observations on material and obvious things' (sig. bir).[3]

The year before, Dr Henry Power's popular textbook, *Experimental Philosophy* (1664), had also recommended the accurate application of empirical observation as the best method of forwarding modern science. To his mind, all that was necessary to break the anachronistic hold on intellectual life of the now discredited classics, what he called 'the old Rubbish', was constant resort to experiment and close investigation. This was the only way in which to 'build a true and permanent Philosophy':

This is the Age wherein (methinks) Philosophy comes in with a Springtide; and the Peripateticks may as well hope to stop the Current of the tide, or (with Xerxes) to fetter the Ocean as hinder the overflowing of free Philosophy: Methinks I see how all the old Rubbish must be thrown away, and the rotten Buildings be overthrown, and carried away with so powerful an Innundation. These are the days that must lay a new Foundation of a more magnificent Philosophy, never to be overthrown: that will Empirically and Sensibly canvas the Phaenomena of Nature deducing the Causes of things from such Originals in Nature, as we observe are producible by Art and the infallible demonstrations of Mechanicks: and certainly, this is the way and no other, to build a true and permanent Philosophy. [p. 192]

The chief beneficiaries of this policy of universal accessibilty were indeed the surveyors and draughtsmen, the mariners and fishermen, the builders and traders and the many gentlemen of court and country who found the new study in accord with their natural and commercial inclinations. But women interested in science also benefited, if somewhat inadvertently, from this strategy of openness and accessibility. As books and pamphlets on all branches of science poured from the presses and were advertised for their simplicity and their comprehensibility to the 'unlearned', women were able to understand these as well as any artisan or farmer. If they so desired, they too could have read the popular works by the partnership of William Leybourn and Vincent Wing, which were among the earliest science books in English. Leybourn and Wing prided themselves on their efforts to democratize the field. As the authors of the first astronomical work to be published in English, *Urania Practica* (1649), they declared proudly that 'to our knowledge, there is not any one yet extant in the English tongue, that delivers any accurate Rules and Tables Astronomical to compute the true motions and passions of the two great Luminaries' (sig. A2v).

Leybourn and Wing were typical 'new men'. They recognized the benefits that the new science would offer industry and commerce, but they were also keenly aware of the profit potential of the new knowledge and were anxious to cash in on the market as far as was possible. In the years that followed, scientific books formed an important element in the yearly crop of published titles.[4] They were never as popular as works on religion or the law, which were always the best-sellers, but they were sufficiently sought after for it to be worth a publisher's while to produce greater numbers of scientific titles than books of poetry or drama. Introductions and guides to elementary science were particularly copious.

A typical example was the do-it-yourself textbook, brought out by Leybourn some years later, which was precisely the sort of handbook that the person trying to study at home needed. It was an *Introduction to Astronomy and Geography Being a Plaine and Easie Treatise of the Globes* (1675). It was designed for the complete novice and was part of a 'study package' consisting of a pair of globes on special offer from the publishers, Robert Morden and William Berry. For the price of £4 for the pair, the student, who need have no previous experience, could study 'all the Constellations, fixed Stars, Circles, Lines etc.' of the Heavens on one globe, and, on the other, the continents and major towns of the earth. In all of the literature on this level, the emphasis was on the usefulness of the work to the 'unlearned' student.

Other study aids, such as flash cards and games based on digests of geography, geometry and astronomy, all proved as popular then as they are today. Advertisements for these were often appended to the various textbooks, as, for example, in *Mechanick Dyalling* (1697), a handbook produced by Joseph Moxon who kept a well-known shop stocking scientific equipment.[5] Globes, other astronomical para-phernalia and microscopes were plentiful. Their makers and vendors frequently advertised their goods in publications favoured by women.[6] The cost of these items would have been an important consideration for women. One of the least expensive pieces of equipment was a pocket Quadrant and Nocturnal, which, together with its case, cost 6s. in 1676 and was accompanied by an explanatory leaflet costing 6d. which detailed how to 'learne to know the Starrs'. Another typical title that could have been useful to women was Thomas Street's *The Description and Use of the Planetary System for the easie and ready finding of the places of the Fixt Stars, Planets, Eclipses etc.* published in 1674.

At a higher level, similar efforts were made to keep the public abreast of the latest developments. From 1665 the Royal Society produced its readable *Philosophical Transactions*, which were read by supporters and detractors alike.[7] Another of the publications that endeavoured to inform was a weekly digest of what was being published in England and Europe. Dedicated to Robert Boyle, it was called *Weekly Memorials for the Ingenious or An Account of Books lately set forth in several Languages with some other serious Novelties relating to Arts and Sciences* and was available in 1682. Its editors, Henry Faithorne and John Kersey, covered a wide variety of scientific works. Long articles and books, including those published in other languages, were reduced to a couple of pages of very legible type and readable English prose, with the occasional diagram included for greater lucidity. A particularly interesting aspect was the frequent coverage of articles written in learned European journals as well. English readers could dip into the contents of the *Acta Eruditorum* from Leipzig, or the *Journal des Scavans* from Paris.

These and similar guides were available to all. Their authors do not mention the possibility that women might be among their customers. But it did not take very long for the idea to strike that the interest that the 'fair sex' was evincing in science should be catered for in a special way. Before long, women were regarded as prize customers, and books, journals, instruments and lectures, all designed to help them overcome the special difficulties, appeared in profusion.

Science books for women

The first significant scientific work to be written expressly to satisfy the curiosity of the growing numbers of scientifically minded women was *Entretiens sur la pluralité des Mondes* (1686) by the French author, Bernard le Bovier, Sieur de Fontenelle, scientist and man of letters. Although its theories were already a little out of date on publication, it was a resounding success, underwent repeated translation, was read by everyone, men and women, and certainly guided many an early female student in her first hesitating steps.

Fontenelle aimed to provide women with an intelligent, yet humane, introduction to scientific subjects, principally astronomy, physics and microscopy. To this end, he adopted and perfected the old literary model of the conversation. In so doing, he not only made the subject more accessible, but also, and perhaps not unimportantly, furnished women with a refreshing literary type over which to ponder, that of the female who was infinitely more interested in her scientific discoveries than in mundane matters of love and marriage in which, it was always supposed, her sex was chiefly absorbed.

In his book there are two participants, the young scientist, learned and courteous but poised for the excitement of a little flirtation, and 'Madam the Marquise', beautiful, of course, but astute and witty and more involved in the adventure of science than in frolics of love. In this respect, as in many others, she stands as a telling contrast to the female figures of literary fiction who, all too often, opted for the tutor rather than for what he taught. Fontenelle's heroine had a pithy way of dismissing her teacher's attempts to woo her, always bringing him firmly back to the subject under discussion. As she says on one occasion, 'Pray Sir, … let Adorers alone, and let us speak of the Sun' (p. 19).[8]

More significant perhaps was Fontenelle's appreciation of the potential of a woman's mind to undertake any form of academic activity. He shared the topical opinion that a woman, untrammelled as she was by the remote and irrelevant subtleties of a classical education, was particularly receptive to an understanding of the newest scientific theories. He agreed with the other half of the equation that suggested that men had removed themselves from any true study of nature by their devotion to the book learning of the past. In Fontenelle's opinion, that brand of learning formed a great barrier to true knowledge: 'But what signifies the Reading of so many vast Volumes over, since there are a great many Men who have made that the Business of their whole lives, to whom, if I durst, I would scarse allow the knowledge of anything?' (sig. a8v).

Equally instructive was the careful way in which Fontenelle depicted Madam the Marquise as a woman who had elected to study science even though she had no formal education or previous scientific knowledge. A woman's natural quickness of wit coupled with her sharp deductive powers was all that was needed for scientific endeavour, declared Fontenelle, together with a willingness to devote a reasonable amount of time and an acceptable degree of application, just about as much as a woman might employ in the reading of romantic fiction. Thus equipped, any woman would be capable of understanding the complexity of the scientific theory he was about to explicate.

In his book, this explication is organized into five parts, each set during a moonlit summer night when the astronomical subject of the discussions is fully visible. The first lesson covers the heliocentric structure of the universe as interpreted by Copernicus. Some twenty years earlier, Robert Hooke, then Secretary to the Royal Society, maintained before a scientific audience that only 'the more knowing and judicious' were able to understand Copernican theory. Among 'the generality of others, either out of ignorance or prejudice', it was still considered 'a most extravagant opinion' compared to the apparent common sense of the older Ptolemaic theory.[9] In the intervening generation, some women at least had joined the 'knowing and judicious', and the Marquise now displayed not only an understanding of Copernicus, but also an appreciation of the more recent theories of Descartes. It is no surprise that she very quickly mastered the names and positions of the more conspicuous planets.

On the second night, the revolutions and rotations of the moon form the subject of the Marquise's inquiry. Part of the lecture dealt with the possibility of life on the moon, a topic hotly debated in the seventeenth century. The alluring possibility of space travel was also discussed. Both were themes that fascinated many eminent people at the time. The Marquise and the scientist were entranced by what appeared to be the very imminent possibility of journeying into outer space. Contemporary enthusiasm and support for global exploration, which could still be stirred by the glorious feats of Columbus and Drake, embraced such possibilities with fervour. There was a strong feeling that a breakthrough was close. The scientist spoke for many when he told the delighted Marquise, 'The Art of Flying is but in its infancy. Time must bring it to Maturity, and one Day Men will be able to flie to the Moon' (p. 48).

The problems that space travellers would have to overcome occupied part of the third night's discourse. However, the difficulties of discussing, let alone defining, the nature of the vital mystery element that would compensate for the moon's lack of atmosphere, whose rumoured discovery teased generations of scientists, persuaded the two conversationalists to relinquish the subject in favour of the sublunary, but equally fascinating, world of the microscope.[10]

The microscope was a particular favourite with ladies in the late seventeenth and early eighteenth centuries. It was cheaper, and therefore more accessible, than larger instruments. The models that women liked best were those that were easily portable. Often confined to their gardens or immediate neighbourhoods, ladies were able to derive much pleasure and interest from these small instruments. Fontenelle was reflecting, as well as inspiring, an interest in microscopy among women that would continue for generations when he had the Marquise marvel at the revelations for which the instrument had been responsible. The young scientist comments:

> The Late Invention of Glasses, call'd Microscopes have discovered thousands of small living Creatures in certain Liquors, which we cou'd never have imagin'd to have been there ... Several Bodies, which appear to be solid, are nothing else but Collections of little Heaps of these imperceptible Animals, who find there as much room, as is requisite for them to move in. [p. 65]

Like so many others of the time, notably the Duchess of Newcastle, Fontenelle was fascinated by the thought of miniature worlds invisible to the naked eye, but visible, or nearly so, through the magnification of the microscope. In the *Entretiens* he invoked the alluring possibility of whole kingdoms, even worlds, existing comfortably in a piece of rock or clod of earth. To some tiny creature a leaf might well appear to contain all the contours of the earth, while its edges would seem to be the distant horizons. Equally a small piece of stone could house for the whole of its secret existence some minute animal as yet unknown to science. Set aside the carefully executed prose poetry in which Fontenelle dressed these speculations and here are the rudimentary beginnings of microbiology. The Marquise was as excited by this branch of science as by those discussed in the previous lectures.

Fontenelle's strength lay not only in the intrinsic interest of his subject, but in the direct and immediate manner in which he presented it. The conversations between the Marquise and her tutor never flag and the reader is carried along enthralled. Part of this enchantment was due to Fontenelle's tactful linking of scientific theory with an irresistible appeal to the imagination. His introduction to matter and the universe set an example in accessibility for later writers. Whether dwelling on the rudiments of the Copernican system, the revelations of the microscope, the description of Venus, Mercury, Saturn and the other planets of the fourth night's discussion or the attempt to describe the Cartesian theory of vortices on the fifth night (which were, of course, to be rejected in the following year by the publication of Newton's *Principia*), he sought to convey a sense of a vastly expanding universe of knowledge whose foothills only had yet been explored. And at the same time he made it plain that women, too, could join in this new and exciting investigation.

Fontenelle imparted to his subject an almost unrivalled poetry and emotion. By setting his discussions during the moonlit hours of night, he was able to exploit the nascent interest in the 'Sublime' qualities of that time of day, its obscurity and silence, the diversity of the stars and the compelling and colourless gloom of the landscape. When the Marquise extolled these beauties, she was anticipating the 'correct' aesthetic attitude to the 'powerful attraction' of night, afterwards the stock in trade of the 'Sublime' poets of the eighteenth century and the Romantic poetry of the early nineteenth century. As they would later, she had already found the charms of bright day insipid, that time too full of petty distractions after profounder nocturnal thoughts, and the whole landscape made unpleasingly uniform by the brash and unsubtle light of the ubiquitous sun.

Another notable characteristic of the *Entretiens* was its decidedly secular tone. Fontenelle's well-known and carefully nurtured bias against religion permeated the scientific discussion. It is to be remembered that the Duchess of Newcastle was already of the secular party in scientific matters. In later years it was an attitude that became increasingly and alarmingly conspicuous among scientists, and one which many women amateurs accepted without question (see Part III). Fontenelle's silence on the religious implications of science, 'Religion is not at all concerned in this System' (Preface, p. vii), may very well have fixed such notions in his female audience.

Despite its sometimes questionable scientific theories and its rather subversive undertones, Fontenelle's book was a staggering success. It was repeatedly recommended to women as suitable scientific reading, for it seemed to offer not only a readable introduction to some basic science, but an important image of a lively female intellect grappling with scientific problems. It was a favourite with many men as well. Joseph Addison, the co-author of the *Spectator*, frequently referred to it.[11] There were several early translations into English. The first of these was presented to the English public as *The Theory or System of Several New Inhabited Worlds* in 1688. (Others were *A Plurality of Worlds* (1695) and *Conversations on the Plurality of Worlds* (1715).)

This translation was undertaken by the woman playwright, Aphra Behn (1640–89). A successful writer who is well known as the first woman to earn her living with her pen, Aphra Behn also cultivated the pursuit of science. She claimed to have made an entomological collection during a putative journey to Surinam, a feat not beyond the capability of a determined woman at the time.[12] It had already been accomplished by Maria Sybilla Merien, naturalist, artist and explorer.

After a colourful career, it is said, as a spy for the government of Charles II, Aphra Behn's doubtful reputation as a woman who wrote for the theatre allowed her easy, if sometimes fraught, contact with London's raffish community of artists, writers and playboy aristocrats. Mrs Behn shared many of the progressive and daring opinions of these acquaintances, thereby consolidating her notoriety in God-fearing sections of the community. She, too, thought religion best kept strictly within churches. Allowed outside, it was nothing less than an incitement to civil disturbance. Human reason and scientific knowledge were the pillars on which society should establish its security. She formed a friendship with the Earl of Rochester, who combined the dubious reputation of rake and atheist with an abiding enthusiasm for the new science. It is known that he and Aphra discussed and possibly performed some of the new experiments. They were in agreement on many matters. Significantly, both dismissed the Genesis story of creation and sought a more scientific explanation of the age of the universe and the structure of existence.

In the last months of her life, now ageing, unwell and out of favour, Aphra Behn saw the translation of Fontenelle's best-seller as a means of avoiding the total poverty which threatened her fragile existence. She admitted that her primary motive in translating the work was a financial one. Yet, as she examined the book, she made a curious admission. Feeling that Fontenelle had not been entirely successful in what he had set out to do, certainly as regards the consistency of the character of the Marquise he had created, she confessed to an unfulfilled, and now never to be fulfilled, ambition to have made some personal contribution to science herself. In her preface to the reader, she wrote that she would have liked to have written an original work on astronomy herself in which the reader would have found 'the subject quite changed', a hint perhaps of a more topical explication of the state of the science. However, she was obliged to acknowledge that the exigencies of her situation prevented such an undertaking. Having little 'health or leisure' to spare, she had to reconcile herself to a strict and faithful translation, leaving readers to wonder what she might have written.

The eighteenth century

Fontenelle's introduction to science for ladies inspired many other books designed especially for women with scientific leanings. Although these works were usually consciously adapted with the limited education of women in mind, many adopted the more complimentary attitude that Fontenelle had assumed. Some, too, regarded the task as rather more than the neutral one of inducting women into the study of science. An evangelical note often crept in. Science could save women from their unfortunate inclination to fritter and trivialize their lives. This was the message in the work of the science lecturer and teacher, John Harris, DD. The book was entitled *Astronomical Dialogues between a Gentleman and a Lady: wherein the Doctrine of the Sphere, Uses of the Globes, and the Elements of Astronomy and Geography are explain'd: In a Pleasant, Easy and Familiar Way. With a Description of the famous Instrument called the Orrery* (1719). In a prefatory address to the woman to whom he dedicated the book, the Lady Cairnes, Dr Harris confessed that his aim in life was the noble one of 'the engaging of Persons of Birth and Fortune in a Warm Application to useful and real Learning: to induce them to detach some of their happy Leisure from being lost by Sports, Play, or worse Avocations, and to dedicate it to the Improvement of their Minds' (p. iv).[13]

Charles Leadbetter was more concerned with making the subject comprehensible to even 'the Meanest Capacity' among the fair sex. In an advertisement for his book *Astronomy* (1727), cleverly placed by the publishers in one of the scientific media most popular with the ladies, the *Ladies Diary* (1727), not only was the dedication to a Mrs Catherine Edwin noticed, but the book's suitability for the improvement of the most 'unlearned' of women was also stressed. It promised 'short and easie Rules and New Astronomical Tables', and claimed to be 'a Work entirely New, and in a Method hitherto unattempted'. A later example was Jasper Charlton's *The Ladies Astronomy* (1735), which also built on the enthusiasm that Fontenelle had fostered.

But the scientific book for women that was most nearly to rival the popularity of Fontenelle's work was the introduction to the Newtonian theory of optics written by the Italian, Francesco Algarotti. Algarotti fully acknowledged the pioneer work of Fontenelle in his dedication of the book to him:

> Your Plurality of Worlds first softened the savage Nature of Philosophy, and called it from the solitary Closets and Libraries of the Learned, to introduce it into the Circles and Toilets of Ladies. You first interpreted to the most amiable Part of the Universe those Hieroglyphics which were at first only for Initiates; and found a happy Method to embellish and intersperse with the most beautiful Flowers a Field, which once seemed incapable of producing any Thing but the most rugged Thorns and perplexing Difficulties. You may be said to have committed the Care of revolving the Heavens to Venus, and the Graces, instead of those Intelligences to whom Ignorance had anciently assigned those Offices. [*Il Newtonianismo per le dame*, 1737, p. ii]

Behind this popular emulation of Fontenelle lurked one of the best concealed scandals of the eighteenth century, which, since it involved one of the most famous women of the period, and one with a considerable intellectual reputation at that, is worth relating.[14]

It appears that the young Algarotti was superbly handsome and irresistibly attractive. When he arrived in England in March 1736, he carried with him the portrait of herself that the famous French scientist Emily, Marchioness of Châtelet had given him (she expected that he would dedicate his book to her) as well as letters of introduction from her friend, Voltaire. Algarotti was promptly nominated for membership of the Royal Society and soon had the ear of Queen Caroline, whose scientific inclinations added to the attraction of the subject for other women. He also had an introduction from Voltaire to Lord Hervey, and through Hervey made the acquaintance of the most fashionable women in society, the notorious author, political journalist and determined feminist – in fact the 'she-meteor' of the age, as she was called – Lady Mary Wortley Montagu. Both Hervey and Lady Mary fell madly in love with the dashing young Italian, and, for a time, both felt their passion to be reciprocated by the object of their desire. But Algarotti was no fool. An ambitious man, his only aim was to gain a foothold in the scientific world and to publish a version, in the style of the *Entretiens*, of Newton's *Opticks* which had first appeared in 1704.

He succeeded when *Il Newtonianismo per le dame* was published in Milan in December 1737. When he returned to Europe he was followed precipitously by the lovesick Lady Mary. Leaving her husband and family, Lady Mary sacrificed everything for a peripatetic existence in southern Europe and the hope that her lover would eventually join her. This was not to be, but Lady Mary found she preferred the casual manners of her life abroad and so chose to continue her unconventional lifestyle there almost until her death, even after Algarotti made his indifference plain.

While this unhappy sequel was being enacted far away from the stern gaze of English society, the book which was to parallel Fontenelle's work in importance for female amateurs of science was being translated into English just as Fontenelle's had been, by another English women. Her reputation, however, was never sullied by the taint of scandal. She was Elizabeth Carter (1717–1806), most famous of all that famous group of intellectual women in the mid-eighteenth century, the Blue-stockings. Algarotti's book was offered to English ladies under the explanatory title of *Sir Isaac Newton's Philosophy explained for the Use of the Ladies in Six Dialogues on Light and Colours* in 1739, and again in 1742 and 1765. This was one of Elizabeth Carter's first published works and was to mark the beginning of her long and distinguished career as a leading woman intellectual through to the end of the eighteenth century.[15]

Elizabeth did her countrywomen an important service. The *Opticks* was a helpful introduction and always had popular appeal. However, in the early decades of the eighteenth century, anyone wishing to acquire more than an elementary knowledge of current scientific thinking was obliged to come to grips with Newtonian physics. Highly theoretical and uncompromisingly presented in Latin, Newton's *Principia* was inaccessible to all but a small élite of highly trained mathematicians with an easy command of that language. That ruled most women out, and, it should be noted, most men as well. Even John Locke, the greatest philosopher of the time, found the *Principia* incomprehensible.[16] Those esoteric explications of Newtonian theory by, for example, W.J.'s Gravesande, whose works were translated into English in 1726 and 1735, were just as impossible to understand. What these frustrated hopefuls, both men and women, needed was a scholarly explication of the great scientist's works which would take into account their academic deficiencies and compensate for them.

With this end in mind and, as always, interested in women's studies in science, Voltaire produced a version of Newton's theories which attracted the attention of many women. Published in England in 1738 as *The Elements of Sir Isaac Newton's Philosophy*, it was prefaced with a dedicatory poem to Voltaire's lover and fellow scientist, the unconventional French aristocrat Emily, Marchioness of Châtelet, whose own pioneer scientific work was well known in England. The verses made it plain that the author expected other women to follow his mistress's example in undertaking scientific study, if in nothing else.

But probably the most acceptable of the books produced to supply the universal need for an explication of Newtonian theory was Henry Pemberton's *A View of Sir Isaac Newton's Philosophy* (1728). A keen reader, who gave it the attention it merited, would have finished this book with a fair idea of the whole of the Newtonian achievement in the realms of physics. The book, like many contemporary publishing projects, was published by subscription. The list of those who bought the volumes illustrates a lively female interest in Newtonian physics. It was already a well-established practice for women to pay in advance for books on scientific subjects. For example, Dr Plot's famous *History of Staffordshire* (1686) had had its female supporters. Jane Lady Gerard, Lady Margaret Hall, Miss Persehouse, Mrs Wedgewood and Miss Catherine Young were among the otherwise anonymous ladies pledging their money in advance.

The social rank of the ladies who pledged their money in advance to Pemberton demonstrated the fact that an interest in science was never solely the prerogative of the richest or grandest women in society. Ladies of higher social classes did figure more prominently than others. There were Right Honourables, such as the Countess of Pembroke who purchased ten copies, or Lady Paisley and the Countess of Lippe, whose names also appeared regularly on the subscription lists of many other scientific works. But there was an even greater number of untitled ladies, notably a Mrs Anne Newnham. She too subscribed to many other scientific books and, if she read them all, would seem to have been a very determined student indeed. At least one working woman bought a copy, a Mrs Yeo who owned a bookshop in Exeter. That book may have been destined for a customer, or perhaps Mrs Yeo liked to have the latest scientific works in stock.

One of the best known of Pemberton's lady readers was undoubtedly the Hon. Mrs Celia Fiennes (1662–1738), granddaughter of the first Viscount of Saye and Sele. She it was whose curiosity about her native land had prompted one of the earliest recorded solo expeditions by a woman on horseback. Her ride around England took place during the reign of William and Mary and provided an accurate account of the industry and commerce of the country, the first such comprehensive survey since the works of William Harrison in 1577 and William Camden in 1586 and 1605.[17] Unlike later, more romantic travellers, what inspired the interest of Mrs Fiennes was not the pursuit of beauty or solitude. The joys of the landscape, the lofty sublimity of mountain ridges or the softer emotions of the rural scene were not pleasures that attracted her attention. What she enjoyed and recorded in her *Journal* was all that struck her as evidence of industry and progress. She applauded the sight of a bustling market town, well-clad people and all incipient signs of civic spirit, and what especially delighted her was evidence of scientific endeavour. As she passed through the towns of England, if the chance arose she would seize the opportunity to get herself invited to what was a popular draw for over a century, the public dissection. (The local gallows usually supplied the necessary specimen.) One dissection she attended was in the Barber Surgeons Hall in Newcastle:

> I went to see the Barber Surgeons Hall which was within a pretty garden walled in, full of flowers and greenes in potts and in the borders; its a good neat building of brick, there I saw the roome with a round table in it, railed round with seates or benches for the conveniency in their dissecting and anatomiseing a body and reading leactures on all parts; there was two bodyes that had been anatomised, one the bones were fastned with wires the other had had the flesh boyled off and some of the ligaments remained and dryed with it, and so the parts were held together by its own muscles and sinews that were dryed with it; over this was another roome in which was the skin of a man that was taken off after he was dead and dressed and so was stuff'd the body and limbs, it look'd and felt like a sort of parchment; in this roome I could take a view of the whole town, it standing on high ground and a pretty lofty building. [pp. 211–12]

That this lady had no squeamish reservations about satisfying her curiosity on any matter, even Newtonianism, was no surprise.

Mrs Vesey's library

Another lady who owned a copy of Pemberton's interpretation of Newton and many other scientific works was Mrs Elizabeth Vesey (1715–91). The fortuitous survival intact of her library until quite recently (1926) provides some indication of the books an intelligent woman in the mid-eighteenth century thought interesting and what her scientific leanings were.[18]

Mrs Vesey was popularly credited as being the original Bluestocking. Only a few scant details have survived about her early personal life or her education. She was the second daughter of Sir Thomas Vesey, Bishop of Ossory in Ireland. She married a cousin, Agmondisham Vesey, a man who shared some of the scientific preoccupations of the time. In the late 1760s he supported the Dublin Society's efforts 'to enable Youth to Persue Geographical, Nautical, Mechanical, Commercial and Military Studies'. Gossip at the time implied that his wife's romantic interest in him had soon dwindled. Their country seat was a splendid mansion in Lucan, County Dublin, but of course most of the season was spent in London.

Mrs Vesey, it was agreed by all, was a woman of great charm and appeal. Her slender and graceful beauty won her the accolade of the 'Sylph', the name by which all her friends knew her. She was the greatest hostess of the third quarter of the eighteenth century. She knew everybody. Her invitation lists included all the leading intellectuals of the day – Sterne, Johnson, Burke, Boswell, Bennett Langton, Horace Walpole, Fanny Burney, Mrs Montagu, Elizabeth Carter and the young playwright, Hannah More.

According to legend it was Mrs Vesey who decided to alter the tone of London society by showing the world that many women were capable of rational conversation. In the early 1750s she introduced the idea of the evening *salon* and held her first reception. Her friends, especially Mrs Elizabeth Montagu, and other acquaintances, among them Mrs Hester Thrale, followed suit and the era of the Bluestockings began. The efforts of these ladies on behalf of the improvement of the intellectual and cultural life of London were said to be significant. The more usual pastimes of alcohol and card games were excluded in favour of brilliant after-dinner conversation in which men and women participated freely.[19] Such was Mrs Vesey's skill as a hostess that she maintained her grip on the cultural and intellectual life of the city for several decades. During that time, most people of any eminence would have been invited to her drawing room or to the drawing room of one of her friends.

The mid-eighteenth century and later was a time of great political upheaval. In the early 1760s the war with Spain excited women as much as men. During the heated parliamentary debates the galleries 'of the House of Commons were crowded with women.[20] Politics and history were Mrs Vesey's passion, but she also cultivated a number of lesser interests of which science and mathematics were the most important.

The contents of Mrs Vesey's library accurately reflect these preferences. Politics and history dominate, followed closely by letters, but respectable science, if a less consuming interest, is also represented. As will be evident later, this admixture sums up the attitude of the Bluestockings to science.[21]

The books divide up into three main subject groups and a number of smaller ones. The largest group, history and politics, numbered 82 volumes; classical poetry and history constituted the next largest group with 71 volumes; English prose and poetry consisted of approximately 51 volumes of poetry and 28 of prose and was represented by the usual eighteenth-century selection, except that the novels of Samuel Richardson were conspicuously absent. By and large the Bluestockings did not approve of novels, and the work of Richardson in particular was considered insufficiently important.[22] They were serious literary scholars and belonged to that school of thought that relegated the innovative but unprestigious genre of the novel to the more appropriate sphere of the 'unlearned' and lesser minds of servant girls and schoolroom pupils, as well as occasionally fulfilling the more useful purpose of lining hat boxes.[23] More curious, perhaps, is the absence of many books on medicine, divinity and law, the traditional top-selling categories. In this respect as well, Mrs Vesey's book-buying inclinations were at odds with the prevailing taste.

The scientific section of Mrs Vesey's library comprised approximately thirty volumes.[24] She had purchased or kept only a few books on astronomy and none at all on microscopy, again unlike most of the scientific book-buying public. If the books she owned can be regarded as evidence of her interest, it would seem that she, like other Bluestocking ladies, was overwhelmingly interested in mathematics.[25]

Euclid was an outright favourite. She had several editions and various other geometry books, such as J.L. Cowley's *Euclid* (1758) and his *Geometry made easy, or a New and Methodical Explanation of the Elements of Geometry* (c.1745), a translation of Le Clerc's *Practical Geometry or a New and Easy Method of Treating that Art* (1742), Issac Barrow's *Geometrical Lectures* (1735) and H. Boad's *Artium Principia; or the Knowledge of the First Principles of the Mathematics made easy* (1733). Among the simpler textbooks that had been published in her girlhood and which she had still kept were Kiel's popular *Elements of Plain and Spherical Geometry* (Dublin, 1726) and Edward Wells's standard work for students, *The*

Young Gentleman's Arithmetic, Geometry, Trigonometry, Mechanics, Opticks, Astronomy, Chronology and Dialling (1713). She also gave shelf space to books on algebra and logarithms.

Newtonian physics obviously interested her, for as well as the copy of Henry Pemberton's *A View of Sir Isaac Newton's Philosophy* (1728) mentioned above, she also owned Colin MacLaurin's *Account of Sir Isaac Newton's Philosophical Discoveries* (1750) as well as a much earlier French work, predating both of these, J. Rohault, *Physica in adnotationibus ex illustrissmi Isaac Newtoni* (1718).

Miscellaneous works included Patrick Gordon, *Geography Anatomised* (1730), Joseph Harris, *Description and Use of the Globes and the Orrery* (1738), Benjamin Martin, *A New Compleat, and Universal System or Body of Decimal Arithmetick* (1735), J. Robertson, *A Treatise of such Mathematical Instruments as are usually put into a Portable Case* (1747) and D. MacBride, *Experimental Essays on Medical and Philosophical Subjects* (1767). Mrs Vesey was, perhaps, more typical of her sex in her possession of Fontenelle works, *Oeuvres Diverses*.

In some of her books, perhaps those which she often used, or of which she was especially fond, she had written her name. A second edition (she also owned a copy of the first edition of 1713) of Edward Wells, *The Young Gentleman's Astronomy, Chronology and Dialling*, published in 1736 when she was twenty-one, is autographed. Her name was also inscribed in *The Use of Globes; or the General Doctrine of the Sphere* (1740), a work by the internationally famous and popular teacher, Thomas Wright. It may well be that she, like some of her Bluestocking friends, had employed his services as a private tutor or perhaps attended his public lectures.[26] The *Lectures on Select Subjects in Mechanics, Hydrostatics, Pneumatics, and Optics with the Use of the Globes and the Art of Dialling* (1764), the work of James Ferguson, another well-known lecturer, also bore the name of its owner. It is not impossible that Mrs Vesey had at some time listened to his well-attended lectures. She also wrote her name in Hugh Hamilton's comprehensive three-volume work entitled *Philosophical Essays; I, The Principles of mechanics; II, The Ascent of Vapours and formation of Clouds, Rain and Dew; III, Observations on the Aurora borealis and the Tails of Comets* (1766).

Natural history, and Buffon in particular, had a wide popularity among women. Mrs Vesey's library included all fourteen volumes of his *Histoire Naturelle*. Botany, on the other hand, was a field not yet appropriated by the ladies, although the Queen, her mother-in-law, the Dowager Princess of Wales and George III were keen botanists. So, it may be that it was local patriotism or the duty of patronage on

Mrs Vesey's part, as much as personal interest, that prompted the acquisition of Threkeld's work on the botany of Dublin, *Synopsis Stirpium Hibernicarum. Being a Short Treatise on Native Plants, especially such as grow spontaneously in the vicinity of Dublin* (1727). A subject of more general interest was electricity, and among Mrs Vesey's most up-to-date acquisitions was Benjamin Franklin's *Experiments and Observations on Electricity* (1774). He was one of the scientific lions lured by society ladies to their *salons*. One can speculate whether the book might have been a gift to his hostess.

The Ladies Diary

Not many women had sufficient disposable funds to compile as extensive a book collection as Mrs Vesey. For those with scientific interests, the appearance of *The Ladies Diary, or The Woman's Almanack ... Containing many Delightful and Entertaining Particulars peculiarly adapted for the Use and Diversion of the Fair-Sex* in 1704 and its continuation for well over a century must have been very gratifying. Useful and cheap, it attracted the attention of many women throughout the country, particularly in the first decades of its issue. For their money they got an almanac, the first of its kind, as well as a wealth of interesting scientific information with a general emphasis on mathematics.

A compact little volume of some twenty leaves, a convenient size to tuck away in a lady's reticule, it was the brainchild of John Tipper, one of the new breed of schoolmasters who taught science and mathematics. Almanacs were common enough at this time. By 1708 there were at least twenty-six on the market. But *The Ladies Diary* was the first diary expressly designed for the use of women whose contents were almost entirely mathematical and scientific. Even more interesting was the fact that it was the women themselves, the purchasers of the *Diary*, who had dictated that this was the format they wanted.[27]

In the earliest issues, Tipper had leavened the scientific content, introduced for the 'good' of his readership, with more typical women's subjects, homeopathy, cookery, hints on housekeeping and some romantic fiction. He soon decided on a new format. He recorded that he had been deluged with letters from all over the country (few of the senders remembering to pay the postage), congratulating him on his venture but insisting that the science need not be packaged with the trivial topics of housekeeping and homemaking. The ladies who wrote to Tipper, whether or not they paid the postage, declared that only mathematics and science would hold their interest. In the 1709 number, therefore, Tipper felt bound to explain that, in response to the 'multitude of letters ... received from all parts of the Kingdom' he had discovered that 'the Enigmas, and Arithmetical Questions, above all other Particulars, give the greatest Satisfaction and Delight to the obliging Fair'. In answer to this pressure, he could follow no other course than to 'defer the *Receipts of Cookery* etc. to a more favourable Opportunity' and to 'insist the longer' on the ladies' apparently favourite topic, mathematics and related subjects (sig. B3r). Subsequent issues remained true to the formula, thereby creating for the first time in publishing history a journal devoted exclusively to women's mathematical and scientific interests.

The *Diary* also proved a valuable medium for publishers and instrument makers who wanted to attract the attention of ladies to what they had to offer. It has been noted that Charles Leadbetter's *Astronomy* (1727), dedicated to Mrs Catherine Edwin, was advertised there. In answer to the enthusiasm of these women amateur scientists for 'optick glasses' designed for their use, one advertisement placed by John Marshal in 1709 described 'The True Spectacles' ground on brass tools and approved by the Royal Society that he had available, as well as double microscopes 'for viewing the Circulation of the Blood in Fishes', 'Tellescopes [*sic*], Microscopes, Reading, Burning, and all other Optick Glasses'. His shop was at the Archimedes and Two Golden Spectacles, an appropriate sign for a scientific instrument maker, in Ludgate Street, the then science park of London.

When Tipper died in 1713, he was succeeded by Mr Henry Beighton, FRS who was just as dedicated to the scientific and mathematical interests of women. His aims were in keeping with the goals of those reformers who were attempting to improve women's scientific education by raising mathematical standards among the sex: 'The Design is different from all our Annual Writers, being intended to promote some Parts of Mathematical Learning amongst the Female Sex.' In the 1718 issue he noted how skilfully the *Diary* was accomplishing this aim: 'I believe that the *Diary* has the good Fortune to fall into a Multitude of Hands, which Mathematical books seldom or never would ... and at a small Price' (pp. 1–2). Ever on the lookout for new subscribers, he now triumphantly proclaimed the success of the *Diary*'s mathematical evangelism. He prefaced that issue of the *Diary* with a fulsome address to his female readership in which he claimed not only that the English lady mathematician was a credit to her sisters and a glorious embellishment to England's reputation abroad, but that four or five hundred a year sent him answers to the questions set in the *Diary*:

And that the rest of the Fair Sex [i.e. those who have not yet contributed to the almanac] may be encourag'd to attempt Mathematicks and Philosophical Knowledge, they here See, that their Sex has as clear judgments, as sprightly quick wit, as penetrating Genius, and as discerning and sagacious Faculties as ours, and to my knowledge do, and can, carry them thro' the most difficult Problems. I have seen them solve, and am fully convinc'd, their Works in the Ladies *Diary* are their own Solutions and Compositions. This we may glory in as the *Amazons* of our Nation; and Foreigners would be amazed when I shew them no less than 4 or 5 hundred several Letters from so many several Women, with Solutions *Geometrical, Arithmetical, Algebraical, Astronomical and Philosophical.* [1718, pp. 1–2]

In addition to the hundreds who went to the trouble of dispatching their answers to the *Diary*'s offices in London, there must also have been many women who simply bought the *Diary*, or had it given to them, and studied the problems at home without ever sending in their efforts. According to the editor, even out-of-date almanacs were popular. In one year several thousand copies of the previous year's edition were sold off by New Year.

The *Diary*'s range of interests was indeed wide. In 1705 the ladies were entertained with an article on astronomy. This was followed in 1706 with instructions on how to make a model of the eclipse of the sun. Then there were the famous problems, set in one year's *Diary* and to be answered in the issue of the following year. Some knowledge of geometry, algebra and trigonometry was essential. This was a typical question from the 1709 number:

Walking through Cheapside, London, on the first day of May, 1709, the sun shining brightly, I was desirous to know the height of Bow steeple. I accordingly measured its shadow just as the clock was striking twelve, and found its length to be $253\frac{1}{8}$ feet; it is required from thence to find the steeple's height. [p. 35]

Mrs Mary Wright of Crewe in Cheshire provided the correct answer which was that the steeple was 384.31 feet tall. She won a new almanac for her pains. Both she and her sister, Anna, were keen mathematicians and appeared several times in the pages of the *Diary* with correct answers to the set questions. Mrs Jane Giles of Highworth and Mrs Ann Inman of Chewton, near Wells, were also up to the mathematical standard of the *Diary*.

There was to be a novel development in the sophistication of the ladies in the 1711 edition when a Mrs Barbara Sidway set a new trend, not only by answering a number of questions correctly, but by devising her own brainteaser as well:

> From what height must a heavy body fall so that the time of descent to the earth's surface may be equal to the time in which sound would move the same height; and with what velocity would the body strike the ground. [p. 42]

Mrs Mary Wright, she who had answered the question correctly in 1709, began to formulate her own questions too, demonstrating that she possessed some astronomical expertise as well:

> What star of the second magnitude was nearest to the north pole at the Creation, supposing it to have happened 5,716 years since; also what was the distance from the pole at that time? [p. 36]

Most of the ladies, like those mentioned above or those who appeared in the yearly editions of the almanac such as Mrs Susan Chorley or Mrs Mary Nelson of Newmarket, were happy to allow their names to appear in print in this, the first ever women's scientific journal. But there were also others with whom modesty and decorum weighed heavier than fame. Although they were keen to exercise their scientific knowledge, they preferred to do so under the decent disguise of anonymity. There were Silvia, Anna Philomathes, Adrastes and many more. One veteran contributor adopted the unlikely sobriquet 'Blowsabella'. She had more on her mind than mathematics. She was suffering from a shortage of suitors. Her keen mathematical interests may well have been the reason for her continued spinsterhood. Or, perhaps, it was she who could not accept a union in which she would be obliged to lay aside her scientific preoccupations. Whatever the case, she appealed to the Editor, in a good-humoured if somewhat desperate way, to extend the scope of the *Diary* to include a matchmaking service. She described the partner she sought. He resembled closely that popular stereotype of the Dutch merchant, well known for his wealth and for his appreciation of a wife with a head for figures.

As the years went by, the changing editors began to take their female readership for granted. By then the intellectual tenor of the almanac had also attracted a sizeable male readership that was eventually to commandeer the entire publication. But before that happened there was still room for the lady philomaths. Towards the end of the century, the star of several issues was Miss Nancy Mason of Clapham in Yorkshire. She answered almost every question set in the journal during the 1790s. Occasionally she set her own. This was one example:

A plumb or weight of 20 pounds, hung at 30 inches distance from the fulcrum of a steel-yard, will counterpoise a cask of red wine, suspended at two inches from the fulcrum on the other side; req. how many gallons of wine the cask contains, supposing the weight of wood in it to be 40 pounds? [*A Supplement to the Ladies Diary* (1794), p. 47]

Miss Mason's contributions were so frequent that the then editor, Charles Hutton (1737–1823), one time Professor of Mathematics at the Royal Military Academy at Woolwich and editor of the *Ladies Diary* from 1773 to 1818, eventually dropped the polite appellation of 'Miss' and she became simply 'N. Mason' and merged with the male contributors. Other women who were frequent guests in the pages of the *Diary* were treated similarly, and the editor took to addressing his audience simply as 'gentlemen', thus obscuring for all but the most persistent researcher the fact that ladies still contributed to the journal they had long called their own.

Occasionally small scraps of personal detail filtered through with the theorems and the trigonometry. On 1 January 1795, Miss Nancy Mason was 21 years, 11 months and 7 days old and her popularity with other readers was made apparent through their enthusiastic compliments on this rather eccentric anniversary. One, the Rev Mr Ewbank of Thornton-Stewart, who took a particular pleasure in complimenting lady philomaths, resorted to a verse eulogy in honour of Miss Mason which the *Diary* published.

Miss Mason's contributions ceased abruptly three years later in 1798. Did she marry and have Mr Ewbank officiate at her wedding as he had suggested he would do in his poem; did she lose interest and choose another hobby; or, perhaps more likely, did she die young as did so many of her contemporaries?

Other ladies filled her place. There were the Misses Nancy Dent, Betty Boys and Sarah Cowen, Miss Elizabeth Wright of Flaxton, Miss Betsy Ruddock and Miss Maria Middleton, of Eden, near Durham, and the Misses Harriott and Sally Pitts, who were lucky enough to have a personal mathematical teacher, a Mr John Cavill, himself a contributor on many occasions. It may have been his idea to encourage his pupils to tackle the problems as part of his teaching.

It is evident that a certain camaraderie developed among some of the ladies. Sometimes they communicated with each other through the pages of the *Diary*, offering mutual encouragement and support in their unusual choice of interest. On one occasion, one lady exhorted another to stick to the pleasures of mathematics and not be tempted to more fanciful recreations, such as poetry or novels, 'the flights of *Fancy* and its wild extremes/The heights of fiction, and its airy dreams'. This was Miss Eliza Wright to Miss Maria Middleton in the *Diary* for 1800.

While the *Diary* retained its predominantly female readership, its editors were keenly aware of their unusual clientele. One editor dared an execrable rhapsody in celebration of the 'happy ladies of the British Isles' who had so wisely developed their mathematical abilities. He saw them as pioneers of new developments in science, as the mathematical leaders of the future:

> Hail Sacred Nymphs; whose Merits are divine,
> Who like bright Stars illustriously do shine.
> The times approach, (if right the Muse divine)
> When *Female Honour* in its Turn shall reign;
> Then *Aristotle* shall grow out of date
> And *Euclid's* Fame share poor *Megara's* Fate
> *Stella* shall her *Archimede* forget
> And *Plato's* Praise will Athens' Honour set;
> *Ptolemy's* Name in Egypt shall expire,
> While all the world, the *British Dames* admire.[28]

The *Diary* spawned at least some imitations, one of which was the *Ladies Complete Pocket Book*, printed by John Newbery. The 1760 issue was partly a diary and partly an account book. Included among the household hints, the tips on social etiquette, the songs and dances was more pertinent information on the state of the stock market, particularly those shares that would be of interest to women, as well as an essay on their legal position, together with articles on the 'Sun, its Nature and Progress', the moon and other related subjects, all of which assumed a basic knowledge of astronomy in the diarist. The example of this *Diary* that I have seen was used fitfully by a lady in 1789–90 to record her journeys around the regions of England and a more exciting trip to the Channel Islands and France.

By the mid-eighteenth century, the market in popular scientific textbooks for both male and female students was in the hands of entrepreneurial writers and publishers like Benjamin Martin and John Newbery. Their books held their place in the market for decades to come. John Newbery's *The Newtonian System of Philosophy explain'd by Familiar Objects in an Entertaining Manner for the use of young Persons* (or, with the catchier *nom de plume* of 'Tom Telescope', *The Newtonian System of Philosophy explained by familiar objects, in an entertaining manner, for the use of Young Ladies and Gentlemen*) was still standard reading at the end of the century in England and America.

Scientific books by women authors from the late 1700s

But for all their popularity these books were not without their faults, at least such was the opinion of many who ardently supported the general scientific instruction of the literate population. One girl who was studying science during the mid-eighteenth century recalled in old age her distaste for the 'masculine' books of the time. In her opinion, times had changed for the better; 'Books were then written only for men; now they are written so that women can participate in them.'[29] It was obviously not an entirely uncommon view. Somewhat later, Dr Erasmus Darwin, who was to draw up a scientific curriculum for a girls' school in 1797, also noted the pressing need to produce more books suitable for the scientific studies of girls.[30] He called on competent writers to try to bridge the gap between the esoteric and difficult and the popular and inaccurate.

There had, of course, been women science writers earlier. In one field alone, medicine, there had always been women who wrote for their own sex and who were accepted, albeit grudgingly, by society. The professional antecedents of these women were, for the most part, rooted in the humble and despised occupation of midwife, but they were not all from the lower social orders. In the seventeenth century, as John Evelyn noted disapprovingly, even 'Discreet Ladies' were joining the 'huge swarm of petticoat physitions [*sic*] and chyurgians' who were profiting from the ill-health of society.[31] Some individuals emerge from these anonymous ranks. Sir Theodore Turquet de Mayerne, physician to Charles I and an active scientist himself, recorded a consultation with a medical chemist in a letter to Lord Conway on 19 September 1648. She diagnosed his complaint and provided an efficacious ointment for his treatment. Despite entreaties, she refused to disclose the secrets of her prescription.[32] The work of Anne, Lady Halkett (1622–99) among the wounded after the Battle of Dunfermline was well known.[33] John Evelyn, too, mentioned in his diary a dinner party at a great house in London where he met 'a Gentlewoman cald *Everard*, that was great Chymist'.[34]

In the early eighteenth century, 'she-doctors' began to take space in the newspapers to advertise their practices. Margaret Ridout was one of the first to appeal directly to the public in this way through the pages of the *Weekly Journal* for Saturday, 9 August 1718. Her surgery was at the sign of the Dove and Golden Ball in Salisbury Court, Fleet Street. There she offered gynaecological and beauty consultations. Presumably she directed her healing skills at a predominantly female clientele.

Not all of these women doctors restricted themselves to female patients. Susannah Kirleus, who may have been trained by her father, a Collegiate Physican of London and a sworn Physican in Ordinary to Charles II, aimed at as broad a practice as possible. She advertised her surgery at the Glass Lantern in Plough-Court, Greys Inn Lane, where she claimed to treat 'all Ulcers, Sores, Scurfs, Scurvies, Leprosies, and all Scorbutick humours, and the Venereal Disease, be it never so bad, at all times in the Year, without confinement, or the dangerous use of Mercury, which destroys many by raising the Malignity in the Head'. She also dispensed drugs 'to cleanse the Body and Blood of all Impurities which cause Dropsies, Gouts, Scurvies, Stone and Gravel, Giddiness and Pains in the Head, and other Parts'. She announced herself available to patients at all times and would also enter into correspondence with any that could not come to her rooms.[35]

It was not always easy for these lady practitioners. Judith Drake, who doctored 'my own sex and Little children', was censured by the College of Physicians for demanding money from patients. She defended herself vigorously in a letter to Sir Hans Sloane by pouring scorn on 'the Gentleman who now raises the clamour'. He had accepted her costs in advance, she claimed, and simply refused to pay for the medicines even after they had effected a complete cure in the lady for whom he had acquired them. She professed herself deeply respectful toward the College, but nevertheless refused to appear before them at the hearing: 'I beg that my not appearing may not be interpreted as a neglect to the Learned Body, for whom I have the greatest value.'[36]

Mrs Elizabeth Bury (1644–1720), on the other hand, won nothing but the respect of the community whom she served. She had studied medicine, anatomy, mathematics, astronomy and the sciences as well as the traditional classical curriculum. She was frequently called in by other doctors as a consultant. However, she was always conscious of the sexual discrimination of the time and was angered by the arrogance of men who refused to believe that women were capable of learning:

> She would often regret, that so many *Learned* Men should be so uncharitable to her *Sex*, as to speak so little in their *Mother-Tongue*, and be so loath to assist their *feebler* Faculties when they were any wise *disposed* to an accurate Search into Things curious or profitable, as well as others; especially ... since they would all so readily own,

That Souls were not distinguished by Sexes. And therefore she thought it would have been an *Honourable Pity* in them to have offered something in Condescension to their Capacities, rather than have propagated a Despair of their Information to future Ages.[37]

Not all lady doctors felt so isolated. Some were positively encouraged by the men in the profession. Constantia Grierson (1706–33) was a young Irish girl from Kilkenny. Her interesting career in medicine and her scholarly reputation was still a topic of discussion as late as 1829.[38] Mrs Elizabeth Walker, who died about 1690, was another medical woman who left an impressive legacy. She worked in the parish of Fyfield in Essex where her husband was Rector. Despite a large family and the usual philanthropic and charitable work that falls to the lot of a clergyman's wife, she took a decision to qualify herself as a doctor in order to be able to offer competent medical aid to those who needed it. She studied '*Physick* and *Chyrurgery*' both in theory and in practice. Her mentor was her brother-in-law, a member of the College of Physicians, but other medical men were just as helpful. She also collected an extensive and useful medical library in English, which was of considerable help to her in the rural isolation of Essex.[39] Even as late as 1788, there were still medical women with famous reputations. Catherine Hutton spoke of one Ellen Haythornthwaite who was a resident of the Forest of Bowland. She advertised herself as a 'noted surgeon' and was indeed reputed to be one of the best surgeons in the country.[40]

There were a great number of medical books in English to cater for the interests of these women. Mrs Jane Sharp's *The Midwives Book*, published in 1671, competed with Culpepper and went through several editions. A copy cost 2s. 6d. The book most often recommended to women was the famous manual written by Elizabeth Grey, Countess of Kent. Entitled *A Choice Manual of Rare and Select Secrets in Physic and Chirurgery* (1653), it reached its twenty-first edition in 1707 and was still selling well in 1710 and 1711 when the *Spectator* recommended it to readers. It was an example of those useful encyclopaedic books for women that rolled medicine, cookery and housekeeping into one. The books of Hannah Wooley were also popular and dealt with gynaecological matters. These included *The Accomplish'd Ladies Delight* (1675), which also cost half-a-crown.

One woman who made an interesting contribution to the literature of medicine was Elizabeth Blackwell (1712–70), who was partly responsible for *A Curious Herbal, containing 500 Cuts of the most useful Plants which are most used in the practice of Physic* (1737). She was a protégée of Sir

Hans Sloane and was much encouraged by Dr Mead, Philip Miller and others on the staff of the Chelsea Botanical Garden.

Other women authors, such as the Duchess of Newcastle and Maria Sybilla Merien, had written on a selection of different scientific topics. But the women authors in the last twenty years or so of the eighteenth century were of a different order. They saw their task as that of supplying this growing demand for scientific literature of general interest. Initially, most of them confined themselves to audiences of children and young girls, but quite soon writers appeared who were sufficiently competent to undertake more advanced books.

Of the former category was Mrs Sarah Trimmer (1741–1810). She was one of the earliest of these women authors and a very successful one. A competent journalist and author, she had many publications to her name. As the mother of twelve children, six daughters and six sons, and a deeply philanthropic woman, she was interested both in the education and in the well-being of the young. Most of her output was concerned with their moral training, and she thought it important to devise a medium that would be within their grasp. One of the techniques of explication that she used was the old catechism method of questions and answers. It provided the format for her best-known natural history textbook, the *Easy Introduction to the Knowledge of Nature* (1782), whose popularity ensured an eleventh edition by 1802. A later Trimmer lady, Mary, produced another similar book frequently used by the young. Based on the work of Gilbert White and the French naturalist Buffon, it was entitled *A Natural History of the Most Remarkable Quadrupeds, Birds, Fishes, Serpents, Reptiles and Insects* and came out in two volumes in 1826. It was also a frequently used textbook, although in the changing educational climate of the mid-nineteenth century it was books of this unimaginative stamp that Charles Dickens had in mind when he attacked the Gradgrind method of education in *Hard Times*.

There was another formula much favoured by these exponents of elementary science. It was the dialogue, often between a mother or tutor and children or young people. Usually ascribed Platonic origins, the formula was infused with new life by Maria Edgeworth in her Harry and Lucy stories (1780). The model was adopted by Mrs Anna Laetitia Barbauld (1743–1825) and her brother John Aiken for their immensely successful *Evenings at Home* (1792–5), described by Maria Edgeworth as 'the best book for children of 7 to 10 that had appeared'.[41] Mary Wollstonecraft also used it very successfully in her early pedagogical stories.[42]

Mrs Priscilla Wakefield's use of the technique was particularly effective. A committed campaigner for the improvement of the conditions of women of all classes, she had great expectations of the role that science could play in those changes (see below). Above all, she saw it as a tool that could not only contribute to developing the understanding of women, but also open up new possibilities of employment for them. Like Dr Darwin, she was aware of the great need to provide simple and cheap handbooks on the different branches of the subject. One of her first publications was a presentation of the outlines of botany to her female audience. At this time botany had not yet acquired hobby status among women. Geology, entomology and chemistry were much more popular. Priscilla Wakefield thought that women should investigate all branches of science, even those that had hitherto seemed too esoteric for them. Botany was one science still in the hands of the learned Latinists. In fact, the standard work on botany, James Lee's *Introduction to Botany* (1760), which was used in at least one girls' school, had been suggested by Lady Anne Monson, a working botanist who had surveyed the plant life of the Cape with C.P. Thunberg and F. Masson in 1774 and who had subsequently botanized in India while there with her husband.[43] Mrs Wakefield, however, decided that it was up to her to open up the subject in a way comprehensible to women. Her book, *An Introduction to Botany* (1796), reached its eleventh edition in 1841 and was well reviewed in women's magazines, such as the *Lady's Monthly Museum* in November 1798. But it was still to be many years before botany displaced entomology or geology in the affections of the ladies. In the meantime Mrs Wakefield offered, in the character of Felicia writing of her botanical researches to her sister, what was to become a stereotype of the nineteenth century, the demure young lady botanist.

Another popular work of Mrs Wakefield, *Domestic Recreations; or Dialogues Illustrative of Natural and Scientific Subjects* (1805), undertook the more general aim of cultivating 'a love for the works of nature, and a habit of reflection' among young ladies of the time. It was not only educative and vocational potential that Mrs Wakefield saw in science; she also regarded it as the perfect recreation for women:

> The curious phenomena that nature presents, is one of the most rational entertainments we can enjoy: it is easy to be procured: always at hand; and, to a certain degree, lies within the reach of every creature who had the perfect use of his senses, and is capable of attention. [pp. 77–8]

Unlike her earlier work on botany, this book concentrated on subjects that were guaranteed simply to give her readers pleasure. The ample table of contents of *Domestic Recreations* listed the topics chosen to amuse the ladies. Top of the list was entomology, followed by 'Instinct, Gradation of Being, Aphis and Ichneumon, Solar Microscopes, Animalcules, Sea Anemonies, Meteors, Light and Colours, The Human Eye compared with those of Animals, the Gnat, Singing of Birds, Natural History of the Cuckoo, Progress of Civilization ...'. In 1816 she supplied a complete guide to entomology in *An Introduction to the Natural History and Classification of Insects in a series of Letters*, which was no doubt very acceptable to her readership.

Mrs Wakefield was convinced that the study of science was of special value in the education of women. It inculcated good mental habits. In strong contrast to the learning-by-rote methods of Mrs Trimmer, she encouraged observation and experimentation in all her lessons. In *Domestic Recreations* she has the mother/tutor figure in her book insist that her daughters develop their own powers of discernment: 'That is the sure way to acquire knowledge. Without attentive observation, books and instruction are of little avail to enrich the mind; though with it, they are admirable assistants' (p. 14). She reinforced the intellectual independence of her pupils by urging them to rely on their own developing skills. These early nineteenth-century young ladies were told to work things out for themselves:

> Those who desire to become acquainted with the beauties and wonders of creation, must acquire a habit of patient and attentive observation, for experience is the surest guide to knowledge: and the idle, who rely wholly upon the information of others, are always liable to receive as truth, the misrepresentations of errors and falsehood. [p. 14]

Works like Mrs Wakefield's led to a rash of handbooks for ladies, providing introductions to the various branches of science which they could then pursue as hobbies. A typical later example was *The Young Lady's Book: A Manual of Elegant Recreations, Exercises, and Pursuits* (1839), which offered chapters on mineralogy, conchology, entomology, ornithology and botany, in conjunction with essays on writing, archery, riding, embroidery and the like. It is interesting to observe that, even at this late date, botany had still not acquired general appeal for the ladies. The author of this manual recommends the study of entomology to readers on the traditional grounds, that 'there is no branch of natural history more within the reach of our readers, than the study and investigation of these "little wonders"' (p. 115). Botany was a different matter. Young ladies, the author noted, still thought it 'insipid and useless – a sort of grave and dreary idling' (p. 33). On the contrary, readers should be aware that in cultivating it they will benefit from what could become an engrossing occupation, leading to an improvement of moral tone and a development of fine taste (pp. 34–7).

Of all the ladies who wrote scientific books in the first decades of the nineteenth century, two achieved lasting eminence. They were Mrs Jane Marcet and Mrs Mary Somerville. Mrs Jane Marcet (1769–1858) was a typical science student turned author.[44] She was a Swiss lady whose husband Alexander, a wealthy doctor, had retired to London to indulge his passion for chemistry. They moved in the best scientific circles in Britain and Europe. Encouraged by her husband, Mrs Marcet had begun attending the recently established lectures at the Royal Institution in London, among the first to be given there by Humphrey Davy. She had no academic or scientific background and, like most ladies, had to work up her subject from scratch. As she overcame her own difficulties, she hastened to smooth the way for others, particularly the many women whom she knew would have to undergo the same struggles as herself. To this end, she produced several of the most popular and influential scientific textbooks in the early nineteenth century. Her modesty was touching:

> In venturing to offer to the public, and more particularly to the female sex, an Introduction to Chemistry, the author, herself a woman, conceives that some explanation may be required; and she feels it the more necessary to apologize for the present undertaking, as her knowledge of the subject is but recent, and as she can have no real claims to the title of chemist.[45]

For all her modesty, Mrs Marcet had put her finger on a profound need. Her book, *Conversation on Chemistry, intended more especially for the Female Sex*, which appeared anonymously as a two-volume work in 1805, achieved enormous popularity. The identity of its author, which was not made public until the thirteenth edition in 1837, puzzled the readers, but the book's shelf life was long and profitable, reaching a sixteenth edition in 1853. There were to be three other *Conversations*; on vegetable physiology; on natural philosophy, written earlier than *Chemistry*; and on political economy, another new subject of interest to women at the time. In addition Mrs Marcet spawned a host of successful imitations and near plagiarisms with her highly successful use of the dialogue formula.[46]

In Mrs Marcet's books, the science is elegantly explained by 'Mrs B.', a lady of exquisite charm and refinement. Mrs B.'s extensive scientific expertise, far from unsexing her, only adds to her attractions.

Her pupils are Emily and Caroline. They are intelligent, inquisitive and keen to come to grips with the subject. Undoubtedly all these characters are fictionally limp, but, in their own context, they presented women with roles with which they could identify. There is no doubt that Mrs Marcet's books stimulated scientific curiosity among women.

If Mrs Marcet's women readers owed her a debt of gratitude, science owed her a greater. It was through the accidental discovery and reading of her works that one of the foremost scientists of the century found his true vocation. He was the young apprentice bookbinder, Michael Faraday. Sometime in the spring of 1810, he accidentally came on Mrs Marcet's *Conversations*. It changed the course of his life. It was not only her theory of electrochemistry, but the cosmic framework, derived from her knowledge of Humphrey Davy's theory, in which she located the subject, that inspired the young man to become a student of chemistry. Together with a friend he began to study the subject, and soon joined other like-minded men and women in the City Philosophical Society, one of the many societies devoted to amateur scientific research that were springing up among the lower social classes.[47]

Mrs Marcet was a personal friend of Mary Somerville (1780–1872), whose position and reputation as a professional scientist was indisputable.[48] Mary Somerville's books were of a different order to what had gone before, but she too expected women to read them. Before looking at her publications, it is interesting to review her life, which was, in many respects, much more difficult than what many young women who shared similar interests in the last years of the eighteenth century had to undergo. Born in Jedburgh in Scotland in 1780, she was still illiterate at nine years old, and the subsequent education that her parents approved for her concentrated on the two major fields of study, 'deportment and grace', inculcated by means of stiff stays, steel bands and rigid rods. Certainly none of the books discussed above, nor the ideas they dispensed, would have been permitted. It was only when she herself happened on a mathematical essay, appropriately positioned in the pages of a woman's illustrated monthly magazine of fashion, that her eyes were opened to new ideas.

In her *Personal Recollections* (1873), Mary Somerville described her fascination and frustration as she pored over the unfamiliar hieroglyphs of the algebraic equation. (pp. 46–7). Her mystification was unbearable. For months she wrestled with her ignorance. The simple expedient of seeking out a teacher, as some women were able to do, was apparently out of the question. Perhaps the reason for her secrecy was to be found in her father's reaction when later, through the willing assistance of her brother's tutor, a Mr Craw, she did get hold of Euclid's *Elements* and Bonnycastle's *Algebra*. He was convinced that these tomes would precipitate excessive study which would only result in mental strain and ill health, a belief later shared by Mrs Somerville herself when she became a parent.

Not all Scottish fathers were so opposed to the thought of properly educating their daughters. A generation later, Jane Welsh (1801–66), future wife of the great Thomas Carlyle, enjoyed an extensive mathematical education carefully supervised by a very concerned parent. Mr Welsh even hired the master of the local 'Mathematical School' in Haddington, East Lothian, to tutor the little girl. She was also, for a time, a pupil at the school, and was remembered as a 'dux' at algebra.[49]

Mary Somerville, however, was discouraged, and for a time she surrendered her interest. She continued to be denied any further opportunity for serious scientific study until 1804, when she went to London as the young bride of Samuel Greig.

At last it seemed she could take up her education by availing herself of the exciting opportunities for scientific study on offer in the capital. But once again fate was less than co-operative. Her husband, as depicted in her memoirs, was a cold and unsympathetic figure. His young wife's inclinations elicited no support from him, for, as she put it, he had 'a very low opinion of the capacity of my sex, and ... neither knowledge of nor interest in science of any kind' (*Recollections*, p. 75). Despite this setback, she did manage to lay the foundations of her interest by cultivating a wide scientific acquaintance and by making the most of lectures and discussion.

Three years later, recently widowed and with two little sons, she returned to Scotland. Now her intellectual ambitions were more clearly defined, and her widowhood had endowed her with a new freedom and leisure in which to pursue her avocation. Although ever a devoted and attentive mother, she now employed her leisure hours in serious intellectual study. Her first success came when she won a silver medal for her solution to a Diophantine equation in William Wallace's *Mathematical Repository*. She became something of a celebrity and was welcomed in scientific circles in Scotland.

A second marriage, to her cousin William Somerville, was a much happier union. Somerville was a kind, unambitious and sociable man. Although a medical doctor and veteran explorer, he appeared quite content to allow his wife to be the active scientist. It seemed to suit him to act as her secretary, agent and public relations officer and to make his own scientific contacts as a Fellow of the Royal Society available to her. Throughout their long life together, he edited and recopied her manuscripts, compiled her bibliographies and handled her correspondence. He also shared in and encouraged her scientific studies.

Their early common interest was the fashionable pursuit of geology, and together they collected a fine cabinet of minerals. With her husband's approval, Mary took up Greek and botany, and later she added meteorology, astronomy, physics and higher mathematics to her study programme. When the family returned to London in 1816, Mrs Somerville took her place among leading scientists of the day. William Wollaston added to her mineral collection and, within hours of his discovery of the solar spectrum, presented her with the prism that he had used in the experiment. Thomas Young explained to her how he used astronomical data to date Egyptian papyruses. Sir James South taught her how to observe binary systems. Sir Edward Parry brought her seeds and minerals from the Arctic, where he had named an island after her. She took lessons in mineralogy from Mrs Lowry, wife of the engraver and inventor, who had a large collection of specimens. Charles Babbage and Humphrey Davy were part of the Somerville circle. Lady Bunbury taught her the classification of seashells, and she had the company of working scientists' wives like Charlotte Murchison (1789–1869), Mary Buckland (1797–1857) and Mary Lyall (1808–73).

It seemed to be without much difficulty, despite pressing maternal and domestic matters, that Mrs Somerville took up her place in this community. In later years she did permit herself a wry comment on the conditions under which women had to work: 'A man can always command his time under the pleas of business; a woman is not allowed any such excuse' (pp. 163–4). She began doing her own experiments, with the most primitive apparatus imaginable, and writing up her research. Etiquette demanded that her husband be the one to convey her results to the Royal Society, but her acquiescence to convention did not diminish her reputation. She was accepted in the first circles as a scientist in her own right, and it was she whom Lord Henry Brougham chose to undertake the translation of Laplace's *Mechanique Celeste* for his Society for Diffusing Useful Knowledge, his philanthropic effort to bring science to the lower classes.[50]

Laplace's *Mechanique Celeste* was considered as second only in importance to Newton's *Principia*. It was a long and extremely complex work, based on the more modern mathematics in use in France. It drew together available astronomical information to show that the solar system was a stable and perfectly self-regulating mechanism. Mrs

Somerville's unusual scientific background had had the useful advantage that she had avoided the out-of-date mathematics still cherished in Newtonian England. Her education had benefited from the close Scottish connection with France to which progressive young mathematicians like Alex d'Arbley, the novelist Fanny Burney's son, Charles Babbage and John Herschel looked. It was this that now stood her in good stead.[51]

She introduced her subject by a lengthy 'Preliminary Dissertation' which reviewed the mathematical principles necessary for understanding Laplace's ideas, including a history of the subject and an explanation of Laplace's work with her own drawings, diagrams, mathematical derivations and proofs. The result was much too dense for the sort of audience Henry Brougham had in mind and he refused the work. Mrs Somerville turned to other outlets, and eventually the publisher John Murray was persuaded, somewhat against his better judgement, to handle it. In view of what he expected would be its extremely limited appeal, he agreed to a print run of some 750 copies (*Recollections*, p. 173).

The outcome was to amaze and exhilarate both publisher and author. The book that appeared in 1831 had taken four years to produce, and a deal of patience, application and concentration amid the demands of normal family life and the needs of small babies. But all effort was justified by the result. It was a sell out. It received enthusiastic reviews and it was to remain the standard text in higher mathematics and astronomy for the rest of the century. It consolidated Mary Somerville's reputation. She was showered with honours. Although not many lay men and women could read the book with true understanding, everyone knew that its author was a woman of genius, and it made money!

Mary Somerville's next book, *On the Connexion of the Physical Sciences* (1834), grew naturally out of the wide scope of her first success. It had become obvious to her that all branches of scientific activity were linked, but to attempt such a synthesis meant that she had to work up many subjects in which she had no formal training or qualification. In its final form, the bulk of the book was devoted to physical astronomy, the subject with which she was most familiar, but it also dealt with mechanics, magnetism, electricity, heat, sound optics, meteorology and climatology, in most cases incorporating the most advanced views of the age.

It is gratifying that Mary Somerville, despite her own advanced understanding of science, did not forget that other, lesser women also experienced scientific curiosity. Always an ardent supporter of efforts to improve the intellectual and social opportunities of women, she wrote, in her dedication of the book to Queen Adelaide, wife of William IV, that she had tried 'to make the laws by which the material world is governed more familiar to my country women'. At least one reviewer, in a journal by no means always sensitive to the intellectual aspirations of women, hailed this aspect of the work with enthusiasm as

> a most delightful volume ... the most valuable and most pleasing work of science that has been published within the century ... Her book is at the same time a fit companion for the philosopher in his study, and for the literary lady in her boudoir; both may read it with pleasure, both consult it with profit.[52]

This book was even more successful than the previous one. It went through ten editions during the next forty years, was translated into several European tongues and was, apparently, pirated in America. Each edition was carefully updated and expanded by the author to discard earlier unproven theory and to include new discoveries and material.

Once again Mary Somerville received general public acclaim, and many honours from learned societies.[53] She was the 'Queen of Nineteenth-Century Science'. However, the family's financial position, although somewhat relieved by the grant in 1835 of an annual pension of £200 (which was later increased to £300), was rapidly deteriorating. Eventually the need to live cheaply forced them into European exile, where they remained until her death in 1872. Other books had followed her early work; these included *Physical Geography* (1848), the first book of its kind in English, and *Molecular and Microscopic Science* (1869).

It was always part of her ambition to channel science to other women. Even in old age this concern remained alive for her: 'Age had not abated my zeal for the emancipation of my sex from the unreasonable prejudice too prevalent in Great Britain against a literary and scientific education for women' (*Recollections*, p. 345).

There were three other gifted scientists working at the same time as Mary Somerville, although she appears not to have known them. Their work took them into different fields, both interesting and demanding, and not infrequently shot through with adventure and romance. Maria Emma Smith (1787–1876) devoted herself to algology and conchology, a popular subject with women, many of whom made famous collections.[54] After she married John Edward Grey, her second husband, in 1826 she worked with him in his botanical and zoological research. Like many other assistant wives, she provided the drawings that formed the necessary illustrations. Between 1842 and 1874 she published privately five volumes of etchings entitled *Figures of Molluscan Animals for the use of Students* and also arranged and mounted the Cumming collections of shells in the British Museum.

An interesting aspect of her pedagogical zeal were the study packs of algae which she constructed and presented to schools in order to encourage the subject. Her own collection was bequeathed to Cambridge University Museum.

Sarah Wallis (1791–1856) was the only daughter of John E. Wallis of Winchester. After her marriage to Thomas Edward Bowdich, the naturalist, she remained for a time in England while he mounted an expedition to Ashantee in 1814. When she decided to follow him, she travelled alone to the Cape coast only to discover that her husband had already wound up the expedition and left. In the following year they both returned on an expedition to Africa. This was succeeded by four years of studying with Cuvier in Paris. In 1823 Bowdich died on the Gambia river. Sarah wrote an account of that journey, *Excursions in Madeira and Porto Santo* (1825), which was highly praised both for its zoology and for the artistic skill of the illustrations. She then went back to Paris, where Cuvier treated her very well. On his death in 1832 she published a memoir of him. In 1829 she was married a second time, to Robert Lee and then devoted the rest of her life to popularizing natural science. One of her more interesting ventures was to be a comprehensive survey of 'The Freshwater Fishes of Great Britain', of which only twelve parts appeared. Her reputation justified the award of a civil list pension of £50 in 1850.[55]

In 1843 the last of the three also received a pension from the civil list, of £100. She was Jane Webb (1807–58). Although her early training was in horticulture, one of the avenues a girl could choose at that time, she had to resort to writing to earn her living.[56] She produced a work of science fiction which not only brought her good reviews, but the reviewer as well. John Claudius Loudon, another horticulturist, was so impressed with the book that he sought out the anonymous author, assuming it would be a man. They met in February 1830 and married a few months later.

Their finances were never very secure, and when they fell into debt Jane saved the situation by writing popular botanical books. The most successful was *The Ladies Companion to the Flower Garden*, which was published in 1841, sold 20,000 copies and had a ninth edition in 1879. She also initiated several magazines for women, such as the *Ladies Magazine of Gardening* (1842) and the *Ladies Companion* (1850–1). By that time the woman's scientific-interest paper was a well-established genre.[57]

Science in ephemeral literature

There was another course of scientific education welcomed by women. In the ephemeral literature, the journals and magazines devoted primarily to manners and morals, gossip and fashion, that grew in bulk during the eighteenth century, much of it directed to female readers, a basic scientific knowledge was either assumed or encouraged. Mary Somerville always maintained that her interest in mathematics had been aroused by meeting algebra in the pages of a fashion magazine, by no means an uncommon union at the time.

The *Spectator* was an early and excellent example of a journal avowedly devoted to improving the moral and intellectual tone of society and instinctively classical in inclination, which nevertheless made enormous use of scientific matter and language. The targeted readership was a wide one, but the chief editor, Joseph Addison, made the education of 'the female world' his chief aim, hoping to wean the ladies from their fondness for 'dancing Monkies, Puppet Shows, opera, [and] exhibitions of lions'. It was his intention to persuade them, through his essays on life and literature, to discard their infantile amusements and allow themselves to be classed as reasonable human beings (*Spectator*, nos. 10 and 31).

Addison's use of science in his paper is interesting, for he himself was by no means a scientist. By and large, he had a layman's curiosity and was sufficiently knowledgeable to pepper his thoughts with scientific references and terminology. There are references to the air pump, the barometer, the quadrant, the microscope and the thermometer, to the atmosphere and atoms, and to glasses, globes and optics. The names of scientific men from Fontenelle (Addison owned a copy of the *Plurality of Worlds*) and Robert Plot to Sir Issac Newton, Francis Bacon and Robert Boyle crop up regularly, either in discussions on their achievements or with reference to other matters. Furthermore, Addison relied on his readers understanding the casual use of scientific jargon for both descriptive and metaphoric purposes.

In addition, the *Spectator* treated scientific topics that were expected to inspire special interest to a detailed and explanatory coverage. Such coverage included a review by Richard Steele, Addison's co-author, of recent astronomical discoveries (*Spectator*, no. 472); a study by Addison of the design and function of the human frame with reference to the circulation of the blood (*Spectator*, no. 543); an enthusiastic introduction to natural history, underlining the need for a comprehensive work on the taxonomy of animals (*Spectator*, no. 121); and an essay on bird behaviour, displaying somewhat defective ornithology (*Spectator*, no. 128), which since the publications of Ray and Willoughby in the late seventeenth century had become a popular subject.

Sometimes, too, other aspects of science were discussed. Echoing Bishop Thomas Sprat, Addison on several occasions celebrated the poetic aspects of science. He thought the advances being made in the use of the telescope and microscope were particularly useful to poets and imaginative authors (*Spectator*, nos. 472, 565, 574).

So many were the references to science in the *Spectator* and so great was its prestige, just 'next to the Bible', that a great number of women readers would certainly have absorbed some science from their contact with it.[58]

Later, the ladies acquired in the *Female Spectator* (1744–6) their own successor to the prestigious eponymous journal. Under the editorship of Eliza Haywood, it too included scientific subjects among its contents. On one occasion the author recommended to the ladies interested in science that they follow the old principles of Francis Bacon. Instead of expending their energies in sterile lucubrations over the works of Malebranche, Newton and others, the ladies were told they would be better off examining specimens at close quarters. Entomology is what was recommended. Acquire a suitable microscope, one of those 'that are as portable as a snuff-box', the lady readers were instructed, and explore the countryside, examine worms, insects, butterflies and caterpillars, investigate the wonders of nature at close quarters. She included her own observations as encouragement:

> Even the common fly, black as it is, is not without its beauties, whether you consider the structure of its frame, the curious glazing of its transparent wings, or the workmanship round the edges of them: – but above all, the eyes deserve attention; – they are like two half moons encompassing the head, both which are full of an infinite number of small eyes, which at once penetrate above, below, or each side, and behind, thereby freely gratifying the curiosity of the creature, if that term may be allowed to insects, and enabling it to defend itself from any threatening danger. [27 April 1745][59]

Mrs Haywood did not intend that ladies should simply pursue their entomological studies as a hobby. She was not without some hopes that their discoveries might push out the boundaries of the science. Were

women to apply themselves to their research with appropriate seriousness, 'they would doubtless perceive animals which are not to be found
in the most accurate volumes of natural philosophy; and the *Royal
Society* might be indebted to every fair *Columbus* for a new world of
beings to employ their speculations' (p. 138).[60]

*The Ladies Magazine; or Entertaining Companion for the Fair Sex, appro-
priated solely to their use and Amusement* was published during the 1770s
initially by Mrs Stanhope. It was a very serious journal which took up
important issues. Women's education was frequently aired, and full
biographies of famous women intellectuals of the period and the
immediate past filled many an issue. Hyspasia (*sic*) was the subject
of March 1779. There were more exotic subjects too: an all-female
administration of the country was proposed in 1778; similarly an all-
female regiment was mooted in November 1778.[61] There were also
articles on ornithology and on exploration.

Even more intellectual was the *Lady's Monthly Museum*, which made
its appearance in the last years of the century. Despite being greatly
opposed to the radical feminism of Mary Wollstonecraft (September
1798), it tended to highlight women, past and present, who had been
energetically active on behalf of their sex. It also reviewed a number
of serious books, especially scientific works, that would be of interest to
women: for example, Maria Edgeworth, *Practical Education* (September
1798), Mrs Sarah Trimmer, noting the numerous editions of her works,
and Mrs Priscilla Wakefield's *Introduction to Botany*, which got an enthusiastic review (November 1798). Other books on geography and astronomy were reviewed, including William Wright, *An Introduction to Plain
Trigonometry* (October 1799). The approbation of science as a study for
women in the *Lady's Monthly Museum* was intimately connected with its
wish to promote a higher moral tone among women.

Scientific poetry

That poetry can act as a medium for science is not a familiar idea in
the late twentieth century. It was otherwise in earlier times. Rooted in
the last decades of the seventeenth century, it was in the 1700s in
particular that the exploitation of poetic diction and rhythm as the
prefect channel for scientific explication gained momentum. All readers
responded to this poetry. The long scientific poem of the eighteenth
century was a popular genre. It provided Joseph Trapp, the Professor
of Poetry at Oxford, with a useful lecture topic in 1715. He informed
his audience that 'philosophical speculations' made a fit subject for

poetry: 'nothing shines more in Verse, than Disquisitions of natural History. We then see the strictest Reasoning join'd to the politest Expression. Poetry and Philosophy are happily united.'[62]

Cowley, John Reynolds, Blackmore, James Ralph and, in particular, William Diaper's *Dryades*, Edward Young's *Night Thoughts*, James Thomson's *The Seasons* and Mark Akenside's *The Pleasures of the Imagination* and others inspired generations of dedicated readers.[63] The 'scientific' poets of the Romantic Age, Coleridge and Shelley, had a long tradition behind them on which to build.

These poet-scientists were conscious that women were among their readers and they were prepared to make concessions for them. Moses Browne addressed his 'Essay on the Universe' (*The Works and Rest of Creation*, 1752) to the fair sex in general and suggested that science poetry made an excellent study aid for many ladies. The verse made the theories more palatable:

> But chief, ye Fair, whose tempted Hand invites
> The Rose of Science, while it's Thorn affrights;
> Who, by the Poet's Effort, may be won
> To read deep Systems, that in Prose ye shun. [pp. 4–5]

Another popular theme with scientific poets was to praise the efforts of ladies in the various scientific fields. When, in *The Wanderer* (1729), Richard Savage wished to compliment Mrs Oldfield, the actress, he referred to her scientific knowledge:

> *Bacon* and *Newton* in her Thought conspire;
> Not sweeter than her voice is *Hendel's* Lyre. [p. 103]

Dedications of scientific poems to ladies were commonplace. One typical example was the Reverend Tipping Silvester's *The Microscope. A poem* (1733), in which the anonymous Mrs L.—— is addressed. Ladies who engaged in scientific pursuits were also likely to be poetically complimented. Bearing in mind that women were known to be fascinated by insects, and used their microscopes to peer at all creeping and flying things, the fashionable poet Stephen Duck's 'On Mites, to a Lady' (*Poems on Several Occasions*, 1736) was unexceptional both in subject matter and dedication. Henry Jones, the Irish bricklayer and popular poet, honoured the scientific ladies of Dublin in *Philosophy, a Poem, addressed to the Ladies who attended Mr Booth's Lectures in Dublin* (1749), and John Dalton congratulated two ladies who had gone off to explore some mines in Cumbria, a novel form of tourism in the mid-eighteenth century, in *A descriptive Poem addressed to Two Ladies, At their*

Return from Viewing the Mines near Whitehaven (1755).

Some women poets were just as enthusiastic. Lady Mary Chudleigh, a keen scientist, found that astronomy could offer welcome imagery and new thoughts, as indeed Bishop Sprat had suggested. In her preface to *The Song of the Three Children Paraphrased*, she explained:

> I have made use of the Cartesian Hypothesis, that the Fixt Stars are Suns, and each the Center of a Vortes, in order to heighten the sublimity of the Subject, because it gives me a noble and sublime Idea of the Universe, and makes it appear infinitely larger, fuller, more magnificent, and every way worthier of its great Artificier. [*Poems on Several Occasions*, 1703, sig. K3r]

Jane Brereton wrote several scientific poems which were published in a collected edition in 1744. Like many other ladies, she directed her compliments to Queen Caroline, the wife of George II, whom she addressed as 'Patroness of Science' ('On the Bustoes in the Royal Hermitage', 1735). The Queen and her family were keen amateur scientists and often enjoyed the personal tuition of some of the most famous teachers of the day.[64]

Two other poetesses who deserve mention are Elizabeth Tollett (1694–1754) and Mary Leapor (fl. 1748). Both these women appear to have been diligent scientific students and produced poetry that acquired a certain popularity. Elizabeth Tollett was the daughter of George Tollett, a Commissioner in the Navy during the reigns of William and Anne. Tollett had noted his daughter's academic inclinations and ensured that she received an excellent education in Latin, Italian, French, history, astronomy and mathematics. These last two became her favourite subjects. The poem for which she was best known was one entitled 'On the Death of Sir Isaac Newton' (published in *Poems on Several Occasions*, 1755), in which she defended women's right to consider 'the mysteries of nature'.

In contrast Mary Leapor turned to poetry having only studied a little science. She admitted ruefully to having none of the qualifications normally deemed essential in that neo-classical age. According to her own account, she had attempted to improve her mind and dissipate some of the ignorance thought to be her proper lot as a woman by studying science, in particular the theories of Tycho Brache and Copernicus ('An Epistle to a Lady' in *Poems on Several Occasions*, 1748).

The public lecture

The ladies were well served with scientific literature. In addition to the general works, they had the books written for and by them as well as the reinforcement of their scientific literacy that poetry and light reading provided. But merely reading about science was not sufficient. Women who wanted to study science needed the assistance and inspiration that only a competent teacher could offer. And they did not want in vain. From the very beginnings of modern science and the incipient interest of women in that branch of learning there were always some possibilities for women to benefit from public scientific teaching. In the early days these opportunities were few, but as time went by they increased in number and popularity throughout the country.

The phenomenon of the public lecture in science appeared, together with many other new fashions, in the aftermath of the Civil War in England. Out of that war-torn society emerged a conviction that lecturing was one of the best means of bringing science to the people, and as always, almost incidentally, the women benefited.

Among the first lectures to be advertised for the good of the general public were those sponsored by Sir Balthazar Gerbier in 1650. He proposed a series of talks on the languages, arts and sciences. His aim was to involve women in the educational process, for like other promoters of the welfare of society he acknowledged the crucial role that women could play in reinforcing social structures within the home. As he said, he wanted to attract 'not only the Fathers of Families, but also the Mothers (mutually interested in the good education of their sonnes)'.

Sir John Cutler, a wealthy but notoriously mean London merchant, confounded his critics when he established a series of lectures in 1665 to be delivered at the public meetings of the Royal Society at both Gresham College and Arundel House. The lectures, or *Lectiones Cutlerianae*, began in 1670 and were delivered by Robert Hooke. It was in his first lecture, 'An Attempt to prove the Motion of the Earth by Observations' in which he described Helioscopes and other instruments, that he commented on the limited acceptance of Copernican theories (*Lectiones Cutlerianae*, 1679, pp. 1 ff.). It is unlikely that many women attended these demonstrations.

But another lecturer, the Honourable Robert Boyle, had no reservations about inviting a female audience to his lectures. As we have seen, Boyle was concerned with the democratization of science. It was part of this concern to seek to stimulate an interest in science among women. His sister, Lady Ranelagh, in whose house he spent the greater part of his life and established a full laboratory, was sympathetic. One of his nieces, Lady Thanet, acquired a considerable reputation as an amateur scientist. She always credited her interest in the field to the early scientific training she had received from her uncle.[65] It was his earnest hope that the importance of scientific research would come to be recognized by society at large. But he knew that the public would attend to science only if it could be persuaded of its intrinsic value and if its interest could be sustained. Being something of a showman, he gave value for money. The tricks that he had demonstrated to the Duchess of Newcastle on her visit to the Royal Society were part of his armoury.

He appears to have always been willing to include women, as well as other interested persons, among the audiences gathered to observe his experiments. His famous trials with the air pump were witnessed by 'Persons of differing Qualities, Professions, and Sexes, (as not only Ladies and Lords, but Doctors and Mathematicians)'. On the occasion of one such demonstration, he recorded affectionately that the natural outcome of these experiments, the sacrifice of the laboratory animal, was prevented 'by the pitty of some Fair Lady's ... who made me hastily let in some Air at the Stop-cock, the gasping Animal was presently recover'd, and in a condition to enjoy the benefit of the Lady's Compassion' (*New Experiments*, 1660, pp. 360–1).

Scattered throughout his works are repeated remarks which make it clear that Boyle regarded tapping into the interest of women in scientific matters an important part of awakening society in general to the need for greater knowledge of these subjects. It was to this end that he devoted his time to research into colour, a subject he knew would interest many women. In his *Experiments and Consideration touching Colours* (1664), he describes, with considerable modesty, how successful this research has been with the ladies. In fact, he claimed it was the enthusiastic reception he met with from delighted audiences of 'so many persons of differing Conditions and ev'n Sexes' that confirmed his resolution to publish his results (Preface, sig. a3v). The ladies who came to watch his experiments with colours and to hear his explanation were clearly as delighted as the Duchess of Newcastle when she witnessed a similar performance in the Royal Society.

Boyle was also aware that he laid himself open to criticism by encouraging women to view scientific study as entertainment or recreation. His defence was that very often what might begin as simple pleasure seeking often ended up as serious study:

if Aristotle, after his Master Plato, have [*sic*] rightly observ'd Admiration to be the Parent of Philosophy, the wonder some of these Trifles have been wont to produce in all sorts of Beholders, and the access they have sometimes gain'd ev'n to the Closets of Ladies, seems to promise, that since the subject is so pleasing, that the speculation appears as Delightful as Difficult, such easie and recreative Experiments, which require but little time, or charge, or trouble in the making, and when made are sensible and surprizing enough, may contribute more than others ... to recommend those parts of Learning (Chymistry [*sic*] and Corpuscular Philosophy) by which they have been produc'd, and to which they give Testimony ev'n to such kind of persons, as value a pretty Trick more than a true Notion, and would scarce admit Philosophy if it approached them in another Dress: without the strangeness or endearments of pleasantness to recommend it. [Preface, sig. A3v–A4r]

Part of Robert Boyle's legacy to the nation was his wish that the tradition of lectures to which he had made such an important contribution should be continued. He left a bequest that a series of lectures bearing his name was to be delivered annually. From the beginning it was taken for granted that women would be welcome at these events. In fact, they were frequently exhorted to be present. It was typical that the *Spectator* was among the pundits that encouraged the ladies to attend in order to improve their minds. In 1711 female readers were urged to turn up to the Robert Boyle lectures being delivered that year in St Mary le Bow Church, by the Revd William Derham, Rector of Upminster in Essex and Fellow of the Royal Society. 'Mr Spectator' based his enthusiasm for a wide attendance at these and other scientific lectures on the fact that they would tend to inculcate religion and learning. Derham echoed this in his prefatory remarks 'that nothing tended more to cultivate true Religion and Poetry in a Man's Mind than a thorough Skill in Philosophy'.[66]

William Derham's lectures were very popular. When they were published shortly after their delivery, they found a ready market. They maintained their reputation for many years. By 1754 the book had reached its twelfth edition. Those ladies and gentlemen who flocked to St Mary le Bow were instructed in current scientific theory and were also able to observe certain experiments. Derham dwelt at length on the properties of the element which later generations called oxygen. He demonstrated the complexities of the air pump and the diving bell. The audience was also told some of the scientific rumours then in circulation.

One popular one was the 'submarine' or underwater vessel, equipped with a 'Liquor ... that would supply the want of fresh Air', reputedly invented during the reign of James I by one Cornel Drebell. Its potential as a military weapon was supposed to have been put to the test in the murky water of the Thames (p. 5). Derham told his audience that he had had the story from Richard Boyle himself!

But side by side with such outlandish ideas the audience learnt somewhat more orthodox explanations of wind, clouds and rain, the nature of light, gravity and the structure of the earth. The Revd Derham, being a devout churchman, was not willing to become involved in the growing speculation on the apparent conflict between new geological discoveries and the received wisdom of the Bible and the Church fathers. He accepted without question the commonly held belief that the earth was approximately six thousand years old and that the Divine Architect had himself carefully designed its structure and ecology as a complex interlocking jigsaw in which the infinite variety of nature snugly fitted. It followed from this belief, increasingly challenged by others, scientists and laymen alike, that the whole of creation was designed for the pleasure and benefit of Man alone:

> it is sufficient to say, that this great Variety [of creation] is a most wise Provision for all the Uses of the World in all Ages, and all Places. Some for Food, some for Physick, some for Habitation, some for Utensils, some for Tools and Instruments of Work, and some for Recreation and Pleasure. [p. 57]

Thus, in Derham's scheme of things, the good Lord had created head lice, merely as a tactful reminder and motivation to human beings to maintain adequate standards of personal hygiene.

The Revd Derham's lectures were not the only means to an understanding of science open to the residents of the capital. In the early years of the eighteenth century, interested Londoners could pick and choose among a dozen or so science courses. It occurred to Sir Richard Steele, co-author of the *Spectator* and other similar journals, that what the city needed was a well-appointed lecture hall with facilities for both sexes to come and enjoy talks on 'all Works of Invention, all the Sciences, as well as mechanick Arts'. So probably sometime between 1712 and 1715, he equipped a large room in the York buildings in Villars Street, 'conveniently fitted for Ladies as well as Gentlemen', as reported in the *Daily Courant* (16 March 1716), and it was to this place that many newspaper advertisements during these decades summoned enthusiastic audiences. On 17 November 1719, the *Daily Post* announced that

> At Sir Richard Steele's great Room in Villars-Street, York-Buildings, on Tuesday, the 1st of December will begin two courses of Experimental Philosophy, (the same Lecture of each Course being performed the same Day) the one at 12 at Noon in French by Dr Desaguliers and Mr Watts, the other at 6 in the Evening by Mr Worster and Mr Watts, and at both Courses the Experiments will be made into the curious Apparatus belonging to Mr Worster and Mr Watts from Little-tower Street, with several new Machines contriv'd by Dr Desaguliers. Catalogues may be had gratis, and Subscriptions are taken in at Mr Innis' near St Pauls' Church.[67]

It is not clear what the subscription was that was levied on the ladies and gentlemen who attended these lectures, but the advertisements run by Benjamin Worster for the courses he offered independently give some indication of the amount involved. At this time he ran an academy in Little Tower Street which could best be described as an early example of a city business school. In contrast to the education that gentlemen's sons at public school were receiving, the courses offered in Worster's academy included accounts and other business studies, as well as mathematics, experimental philosophy, a little French for business purposes, and drawing. The glaring absence of the Latin grammar and the concentration on vocational studies indicated that this was a school not for gentlemen, but for the sons of wise City merchants. It also, of course, bore a strong resemblance to the school advocated for girls by Mrs Bathsua Makin.

In addition to teaching the children of the City, Worster also offered a public course on 'the Principles of Natural Philosophy' which covered physics, mechanics, the laws of motion, hydrostatics, pneumatics and optics. The cost of this course was $2\frac{1}{2}$ guineas. It is reasonable to suppose that, in view of the possibly more fashionable audience that would have crowded in Villars Street, the lectures held there would have been somewhat more expensive. Some years later, a practice developed in some towns for ladies to be admitted to lectures at half-price.[68]

Probably the most popular and single most successful lecturer at the time was Dr John Theophilius Desaguliers (1683–1744) of the newspaper advertisement. The son of an emigrant French Protestant teacher, he had been a student at Christ Church in Oxford and from there had pursued a career in science by the path followed by many likeminded men, that of holy orders. His religious calling never inhibited his scientific zeal, which appeared to be his true vocation in life. His prolific literary output included but one pamphlet on divinity. All the rest dealt with scientific matters.

After an academic career at Oxford as successor to Dr John Keill who was Lecturer in Experimental Philosophy in Hart Hall and who had initiated a series of public lectures on natural philosophy in 1704, Desaguliers was elected a Fellow of the Royal Society in 1714 and was invited to become their demonstrator and curator. In the meantime, however, he had been asked to give a number of lectures to the royal household. This experience had taught him how effective he could be in teaching science to an unscientific audience. He was convinced that he would be better employed meeting the public demand for scientific enlightenment. To disseminate to ordinary people the mysteries of Newtonian physics in as comprehensible a manner as possible was, he felt, his duty, if not indeed his vocation. His life in London thereafter was spent in lecturing year after year to the groups of men and women who thronged to hear him and to witness his experiments. After Boyle, it was Desaguliers who had the greatest influence on the growth of interest in popular science among ordinary people. When, towards the end of his life, he came to publish the lecture series that he had been wont to deliver, he described the transformation of the scientific scene in London during his time as a lecturer there. Among his proudest boasts was the fact that women had been enticed to take an interest in his talks:

> About the year 1713 I came to settle at London where I have with Great Pleasure seen the Newtonian Philosophy so generally received among Persons of all Ranks and Professions and even the Ladies, by the Help of experiments: that tho' several ingenious Men have since that Time with great success taught (and do still teach) Experimental Philosophy in my (or rather Dr. Keill's) manner, I have had as many Courses as I could possibly attend; the present Course which I am now engaged in being the 121st since I began at Hart Hall in Oxford, in the year 1710. [*A Course of Experimental Philosophy*, 2 vols, 1734 and 1744, I, sig. C1v]

It was also a matter of some pride with him that, of the eleven or twelve other people lecturing in London in 1734, eight had been trained by him.

Desaguliers' lectures differed from Derham's in his avoidance of theological matters in favour of purely scientific fact. He also kept in mind the limitations that the mathematical shortcomings of his audience would impose on his treatment of the different topics. He carefully tailored his talks, claiming that all that he required of his audience was 'attention and common sense, with a very little Arithmetic'. On that basis, he declared, he had always been able to make his listeners comprehend whatever proposition he discussed. Like all successful lecturers, he believed too in leavening the purely scientific fare with a little light entertainment. An amusement quota to enliven the interest of a wearied or flagging audience was always part of his talks.

In his lectures, Desaguliers gave most time to 'the Causes and Motions of the heavenly Bodies, and the Phaenomena of our system'. He stressed the practical aspects of physics and devoted a significant part of each lecture to experiments. In this manner, he examined motion, velocity, weight and balance, 'on which depends the whole Doctrine of Mechanics ... for from hence are easily deduced the Form of Machines, which are compounded of Pulleys, Leavers [*sic*], cords and Weights ascending directly or obliquely, and other mechanical Powers, as also the Form of the Tendons to move the Bones of Animals' (p. 126).

In other lectures Desaguliers explained the nature of gravity and friction, which included theories of carriage building, a matter of great interest to eighteenth-century passengers, the laws governing the motion of the battering ram, hammer, pendulum, sling and spring, and hydrostatics (pp. 284.ff). He was well pleased when he reviewed the results of his many years of effort to enlarge general scientific knowledge. Improvements in experimental techniques meant that abstract mathematical theories could now be demonstrated. Consequently, many more people, especially the 'unlearned', had received an early introduction to practical science, and had been so enthralled by their discoveries that they had advanced to more demanding levels of achievement:

> since Machines have been contriv'd to explain and prove experimentally what Sir Isaac Newton has demonstrated mathematically and several of his own experiments are shown in publick Courses; a great many Persons get a considerable knowledge of Natural Philosophy by way of Amusement; and some are so well pleased with what they learn that way, as to be induc'd to study Mathematicks by which they at last become eminent Philosophers. [sig. B2v-C1v]

The popularity of the public lecture created a new profession, that of itinerant teacher. As more and more of the major towns of England, Scotland and Ireland began to make their own arrangements for introducing their citizens to the marvels of modern science, the demand for peripatetic teachers grew. Men of humble origins and little wealth could make a reasonable living as travelling lecturers. In not a few cases their very real scientific knowledge made them welcome in the highest professional circles. But many more simply did what they could with their little knowledge and supplemented their income as lecturers by publishing their courses in popular formats.

One of the most hard working and prolific was Benjamin Martin. He had tried schoolmastering in Guildford and Chichester before taking to the road. Although obviously motivated by economic pressures, he too seemed devoted to the improvement of scientific knowledge among the leisured classes, women as well as men. It was his contention that anything of any significance in life, from poetry to mechanics, depended on science. Obviously women could not be excluded from life's most important aspects. To assist their instruction he produced a course of lectures which, when published in 1743, bore the title *A Course of Lectures in Natural and Experimental Philosophy, Geography and Astronomy; in which the Properties, Affections and Phaenomena of Natural Bodies, hitherto discover'd, Are exhibited and explain'd on the Principles of the Newtonian Philosophy.* It covered physics, mechanics, hydrostatics, hydraulics, pneumatics, phonics, light and colours, optics, astronomy and geography.

From these lectures it is apparent that he had worked hard to ensure that the ladies in the audience derived full benefit from his teaching. He seems to have been quite successful. At any rate he made the claim that, even in the provincial towns, the study of science had become a popular fashion among the ladies, a claim which was made repeatedly by many other interested parties:

> why should not the Ladies understand and study the Sciences of Humanity, of which Philosophy holds the First Place? *Knowledge is now become a fashionable Thing, and Philosophy is the Science a La Mode.* Hence, to cultivate this study, is only to *be in Taste*, and Politeness *is an inseparable Consequence.* Wherefore *nothing can be more consistent and rational, than that the Ladies should study* Philosophy; or more monstrous and stupid, than that objection, *which is* sometimes made against it, viz That the Gentlemen will not like them so well for it. *This is a gross Reflection on the good Sense of Gentlemen, and tends to deprive the Ladies of those Qualities which would principally recommend them to their valuable Esteem and Choice.* [Preface]

Another of Martin's best-selling self-help books was *The Young Gentleman's and Lady's Philosophy.* In it Martin described an idealized vision of co-educational scientific study in which male and female pupils work together on equal terms. Two youngsters, brother and sister, sit by the globes discussing the hopes and difficulties of the young woman who applies herself to science. The girl is tentative, obviously looking to a time when feminine interest in science might be more generally acknowledged. She admits to considerable embarrassment because of her interest in scientific matters: 'I often wish it did not look quite so masculine for a Woman to talk of Philosophy in Company; I have often sat silent, and wanted Resolution to ask a Question for fear of being thought assuming or impertinent' (p. 2). The boy is more sanguine. In his opinion, science has become a truly womanly accomplishment, almost more so than needlework or music. In some quarters it is regarded as a peculiarly feminine fashion. Thus encouraged, the girl agrees that there is no branch of science that she should ignore, and she looks forward hopefully to a future time when 'the Ladies may modestly pretend to knowledge, and appear learned without Singularity and Affectation' (p. 3).

It is interesting to view this debilitating modesty in the light of the efforts made by lecturers to attract women into their audience. As well as guaranteeing that the subject matter would be comprehensible to their possibly less well-prepared intellects and occasionally offering them special concessionary fees there were other ways too in which to encourage the ladies. When Dublin was being treated to one of its many science courses in 1749, the poet Henry Jones, who sought the patronage of upper-class ladies, dedicated a poem of encouragement to all those Dublin ladies who thronged to the city's well-attended scientific lectures. Entitled *Philosophy, a Poem, address'd to the Ladies who attended Mr Booth's Lectures in Dublin*, it began:

> To Science sacred Muse, exalt thy Lays;
> Science of Nature, and to Nature's Praise;
> Attend, ye Virtuous, and rejoice to Know
> Her mystick Labours, and her Laws below;
> [*Poems on Several Occasions*, 1749, p. 22]

Although there were many cases where women seemed to take appearing at these lectures in their stride, to do so could still be a demanding experience in some, more conventional, provincial towns. Personal accounts of women who took the plunge are therefore especially interesting.

One newly married lady was determined to set a trend in her husband's birthplace. She was Mrs Elizabeth Coltman, née Cartwright, who, in about 1766, moved to St Nicholas Street, Leicester, then a small town of some fourteen thousand inhabitants. Mrs Coltman was an outgoing and well-educated young person. As a girl she had shared her intellectual interests with her closest friend, later the historian and traveller, Catherine Hutton of Birmingham. Not surprisingly, the young Elizabeth had some literary pretensions herself. Only one poem was ever published, and that rather graciously by Richard Dodsley, the famous publisher who was also a distant relative. The poem, dealing with the intellectual and career aspirations of women, 'Would you obtain my honest heart/Address my nobler, better part,/Pay homage to my mind', and the pressing necessity to improve the unequal lot of the sex, appeared in the *Lady's Magazine* in 1760.[69]

With such notions, it was not to be wondered at that, when Mrs Coltman arrived in Leicester, she took her place with ease among the leading lights of the town. This was a lively coterie of serious-minded people (one of whom was Mrs Arnold, sister of Mrs Catherine Macaulay-Graham and married to Dr Arnold (1742–1816), the famous doctor and expert on madness). They were united equally by their religious Dissent, their manufacturing interests and their thirst for scientific knowledge. A vigorous literary and philosophical society already flourished in the area, and Mrs Coltman was soon canvassing the support of like-minded ladies to open up what academic pursuits there were to women. When her husband invited one Mr Waltyre to give a series of science lectures in the town, she decided to make sure that women were welcome from the beginning. Consequently, when the day of the first discourse arrived, she and a friend, Mrs Reid, took their seats in the philosophical lecture room, acutely conscious of being the first ladies to attend a public science lecture in Leicester.[70]

It was not always only middle-class girls who seized any opportunity to be present at science lectures. Working girls were occasionally just as interested in intellectual pursuits. Two such girls were Ann Taylor, later a popular author, and her sister. Their father, a Colchester engraver, was an enlightened and practical man. He saw to it that his elder daughters were educated and competently trained as professional engravers, thus opening up in the mid-eighteenth century yet another new profession for women. Mrs Gilbert, as she then was, looked back with pride on their pioneering efforts as career women: 'We had, I might almost say, the honour of stepping first on a line now regarded as nearly the one thing to be accomplished, the respectable, renumerative, appropriate employment of young women' (*Autobiography of Mrs Gilbert*, 4th edn, 1879, p. 74).

Mrs Gilbert's father had other unusual ideas as well. He thought his girls would profit from classes in science. Towards the end of 1798, he heard that 'an astronomical lecturer of repute' was to deliver a course of science lectures at the Old Moat Hall in Colchester. To ensure that his daughters would benefit fully from this opportunity, he decided to institute some introductory science study for them, and such of their friends as wished to join in, in his own home.

The resulting interest and enthusiasm shown by Ann and her friends was so gratifying that what had been conceived as a single event became a free monthly lecture over a period of three to four years. It was attended faithfully by some sixty to seventy local youngsters and covered such subjects as astronomy, geography, geometry, mechanics, general history and anatomy (*Autobiography*, pp. 89–90).

There are interesting parallels between this interest in science among the daughters of tradesmen and the daughters of the upper classes. Caroline Girle (1738/9–1817) was conscientiously educated in the best progressive manner of the mid-eighteenth century. In fact, her parents (her father was a wealthy doctor in Lincoln's Inn Fields) seem to have put into practice all the most forward-looking principles of girls' education. In addition to her schoolroom exercises, Miss Girle was permitted to enjoy the ancillary activities then considered necessary to the scientific education of the female. In 1757 she participated in the vogue of visiting coal mines. Later she was one of the earliest visitors to the newly opened British Museum (1759) and, as an inveterate diarist, gave a detailed and accurate account of what in Sir Hans Sloane's museum had interested her. Again, like other young ladies of the period, she was a dedicated entomologist and so it was the work of Maria Sibella Merian that enchanted her.

Her liberal education made something of a feminist of her, and her diary is full of remarks on the injustices meted out to women because of the seemingly permanent imbalance between the two halves of the human race. She was clearly very familiar with the usual arguments used to justify a women's inferior role and had concluded that they were illogical:

> 'tis my opinion that women might be made acquainted with serious subjects they are now ignorant of, more for want of instruction than capacity, and what at first may appear intricate, after a quarter of an hour's converse, might give entertainment. But is it anything surprising the sex should amuse themselves with trifles when these lords of creation will not give themselves the trouble (in my conscience, I believe for fear of being outshone) to enlarge our minds

by making them capable to retain those of more importance?[71]

She herself maintained her scientific interests even after marriage and parenthood, and ensured that her own daughter, another Caroline, acquired similar tastes. Mrs Powys, as she then was, and Caroline became keen palaeontologists, carefully building up their own collections. Their interest in zoology took them to see the Duchess of Portland's collection and the exhibitions in the British Museum. Mrs Powys also shared another feminine interest at the time: a curiosity about developments in industry and the insides of factories of all kinds. On 26 May 1788 she attended a demonstration of the latest in electrical and mechanical technology given by one Mr Dillon: 'Mr Dillon [lit] up an aerestatic [*sic*] branch suspended from the cupola of the saloon, in which light is produced in an instant of time, which Mr Dillon carries at will, and extinguished in an instant, wonderfully pretty' (p. 232). They also enjoyed the public lectures on astronomy given by the popular lecturer Mr Walker, in Henley in December 1791. The whole neighbourhood braved the winter weather to be there.

The great age of the science lecture for women was about to dawn, but already the fair sex were making the most of their opportunities.

Notes

1. Sprat, 'Their Manner of Discourse', see above, pp. 28–9.

2. E.g. Newton's *Philosophiae Naturalis Principia Mathematica* (1686–7).

3. *Micrographia: or some Physiological Description of Minute bodies made by Magnifying Glasses with Observations and Inquiries thereupon* (1665).

4. David M. Knight, *Natural Science Books in English 1600–1900* (1972) is a source of useful information.

5. Joseph Moxon's was one of the shops that supplied the wants of all the enthusiastic science students. See below, p. 142.

6. E.g. the *Ladies Diary*. See above, p. 99.

7. M.H Nicolson with N.H. Mohler has shown how much of Swift's *Voyage to Laputa* was based on his reading of the *Transactions*. See *Science and Imagination* (Ithaca, N Y, 1956), pp. 110–54.

8. Compare with the similar sentiments of the heroine of Susannah Centlivre's *The Bassett-Table* (1706).

9. *An Attempt to prove the Motion of the Earth By Observations* (1674), published in *Lectures and Collections* (1678), pp. 1–2.

10. See below, p. 125.

11. E.g. in *Spectator*, nos. 294, 346, 373, 487, 571, 576.

12. In *Oroonoko: or, The Royal Slave, A True History* (1688), p. 148.

13. See below, p. 117.

14. R. Halsband, *The Life of Lady Mary Wortley Montagu* (1961), pp. 153–78.

15. See below, pp. 150–4.

16. Preface to Desaguliers, *A Course of Experimental Philosophy*, 2 vols (1734, 1744), I, sig. b2v.

17. *The Journeys of Celia Fiennes*, ed. by Christopher Morris (1947), p. xxxix.

18. William H. Robinson, *The Library of Mrs Elizabeth Vesey 1715–1791* (1926).

19. There are many descriptions of the Bluestocking drawing rooms. Among those I like best is D. E. Allan's in *The Naturalist in Britain* (1978).

20. *Mrs Montagu, 'Queen of the Blues'*, ed. by Reginald Blunt, 2 vols (1923), I, p. 13.

21. See below, pp. 150–9.

22. In later life, of course, Elizabeth Carter mellowed somewhat, in particular towards the novels of contemporary women writers. See *Memoirs* (1807) p. 299.

23. Although not relevant to the present topic, a significant section of Mrs Vesey's library consisted of books by women writers both English and European. She also owned the type of books that every estate owner required – in architecture and agriculture. Her husband had subscribed to R. Barton's *Lectures in Natural Philosophy upon the Petrification, Gems, Crystals etc of Lough Neagh in Ireland and a Natural History of the County of Armagh* (1751).

24. Compared with 55 books of poetry or 71 volumes of the classics.

25. See below, pp. 150–9.

26. See Elizabeth Carter, *Memoirs*, p. 16, and below, p. 153.

27. Earlier women's almnacs were those produced by Sarah Ginnar (1659), Mary Holden (1688, 1689) and Dorothy Partridge (1694). Their main interest was astrology and "women's subjects" and they were shortlived. Dr. Sara Mendelson directed me to these almanacs.

28. *The Ladies Diary*, (1724), titlepage.

29. *Life of Mary Anne Schimmelpennick* (1858), p. 125. Much earlier, in 1711, Addison had been critical of the fact that 'most Books' were 'Calculated for Male readers'. See *Spectator*, no. 92.

30. See below, p. 167.

31. *Mundus Muliebris, or, The Ladies Dressing–Room unlock'd And her toilette spread* (1690), sig. A4r.

32. *Conway Letters. The Correspondence of Anne, Viscountess Conway, Henry More, and their Friends, 1642–1684*, ed. M.H. Nicolson (New Haven, 1930), p. 20.

33. Anne Lady Halkett, *Autobiography* (written 1677–8), ed. by J.G. Nichols (1875).

34. *Diary*, July 1650, III, p. 13.

35. See *Spectator*, ed. by D.F. Bond, IV, p. 61, and nos. 331, 341.

36. Judith Drake to Sir Hans Sloane, 1 September 1723, Sloane Ms. 4047. I am indebted to Dr Sara Mendelson for this reference.

37. Revd William Tong, *An Account of the Life and Death of Mrs Elizabeth Bury ... Chiefly collected out of her own Diary*, (2nd edn 1721), p. 7.

38. *Ladies Pocket Magazine* (1829), pp. 206–8.

39. [Anthony Walker], *The Holy Life of Mrs Elizabeth Walker Late Wife of A.W. D.D. Rector of Fyfield in Essex* (1690).

40. Catherine Hutton, *Reminiscences of a Gentlewomen of the Last Century: Letters of Catherine Hutton*, ed. by Mrs C. Hutton Beale (Birmingham, 1891), p. 60. There had long been many women who had practised or written medical matters. See Audrey Eccles, 'The Reading Public, the Medical Profession, and the Use of English for Medical Books in the 16th and 17th Centuries' in *Neuphilologische Mitteilungen*, no. 75 (1974), pp. 143–56; Audrey Eccles, 'The Early Use of English for Midwiferies 1500–1700', *Neuphilologische Mitteilungen*, no. 78 (1977), pp. 377–85; Margaret Pelling and Charles Webster, ch. 'Medical Practitioners', pp. 223 ff. in *Health, Medicine and Mortality in the Sixteenth Century*, ed. by Charles Webster (Cambridge, 1979); Margaret Pelling, 'Occupational Diversity: Barbersurgeons and the Trades of Norwich, 1550–1640', *Bulletin of the History of Medicine*, no. 56, pp. 508–9; Margaret Alic, *Hypatia's Heritage*, pp. 100, 200–2.

41. Preface to *Practical Education*.

42. See below, p. 224.

43. *Dictionary of National Biography*, vol. 38, p. 196.

44. 'Miss Martineau in her *Biographical Sketches* says, Mrs Barbauld's *Early Lessons* were good; Miss Edgeworth's were better, but Mrs Marcet's are transcendent as far as they go': Jerome Murch, *Mrs Barbauld and her Contemporaries* (1876), p. 9.

45. *Conversations on Chemistry, intended more especially for the Female Sex* (1805), p. v.

46. E.g. the *Conversations* written by the sisters Elizabeth and Sarah Mary Fitton, on botany (1817) and on geology (1840). Because the tutor character in *Conversations on Chemistry* was named 'Mrs Bryan' or 'Mrs B.' the work was sometimes ascribed to Mrs Margaret Bryan, in *Bibliographia Britannia* and in the *Biographical Dictionary of Living Authors*. For the work of Mrs Margaret Bryan see below, pp. 179–80.

47. L. Pearce Williams, *Michael Faraday* (New York, 1965), pp. 18–20.

48. For further information on Mrs Somerville's scientific activities see below, pp. 208–9.

49. Virginia Surtees, *Jane Welsh Carlyle* (1986), pp. 8–12.

50. For the middle and upper classes who wished to pursue the study of science he had founded London University in 1828.

51. E.C. Patterson, *Mary Somerville and the Cultivation of Science 1815–1840* (1984), p. 83.

52. *Athenaeum*, 15 March 1834, quoted in Elizabeth Patterson, *Mary Somerville and the Cultivation of Science 1815–1840* (1983), p. 136.

53. Alic, p. 188.

54. The most famous collector of all was Lady Margaret Cavendish Bentinck (1714–1764), wife of the second Duke of Portland (1714–1824), who maintained the largest natural history collection in Europe at her great mansion at Bulstrode in Buckinghamshire. George III and Queen Charlotte, not to mention numerous naturalists and lady amateurs (see below, pp. 180–82), all visited it. See D.E. Allen, *The Naturalist in Britain*, p. 29.

55. *Dictionary of National Biography*, vol. 11, p. 820.

56. Mary Wollstonecraft thought farming a suitable way of life for an independent women. See *The Rights of Woman* (1792; Everyman edn, 1977), p. 163; Priscilla Wakefield, *Reflections on the Present Condition of the Female Sex* (1799), suggested gardening and horticulture as appropriate careers for women. See below, p. 227.

57. As the nineteenth century matured, numerous women began to follow Priscilla Wakefield's example and write botanical books. Among the most interesting were Anne Pratt (1806–93), Catherine Gage (1816–92), Catherine Mary McNab (1809–57) and Isabella Gifford (1823–91), who wrote a notable book entitled *The Marine Botanist* (1840).

58. *Private Letter Books of Joseph Collet*, ed. by H. Dodwell (1933), p. 100, quoted in *Spectator*, ed. by D.F. Bond, I, p. xcv. Other journals that encouraged a female interest in science included the *Free-Thinker* (1718), the *Weekly Medley or Gentleman's Recreation* (1718) and the *Ladies Magazine: or, the Universal Entertainer* (1749).

59. 5th edn (1755), III, p. 133.

60. See also III, p. 264 for a description of a hilltop laboratory.

61. Demands for all-female bodies were not new. As early as 1709 Sir Richard Steele was suggesting that the jury at rape trials should consist only of women, although he disapproved of the high attendance of females at such trials: *Tatler*, no. 84.

62. *Praelectiones Poeticae* (1711–15), trans. as *Lectures on Poetry* (1742), p. 189. Lecture 15 was entitled 'Of Didactic or Praeceptive Poetry'.

63. P. Phillips, *The Adventurous Muse*, pp. 43–57.

64. See below, pp. 126–8.

65. Flora Masson, *Robert Boyle* (1914), p. 303.

66. *Physico-theology or a Demonstration of the Being and Attributes of God from His Works of Creation* (1711–12, 3rd edn 1714), Preface, sig. A4v.

67. Quoted in John Loftis, 'Richard Steele's Censorium', *Huntingdon Language Quarterly* no. XIV (1950–1), p. 62.

68. Nicholas Hans, *New Trends in Education in the 18th Century* (1951), p. 148.

69. *Catherine Hutton and Her Friends*, ed. by Mrs Catherine Hutton Beale (Birmingham, 1895), p. 6.

70. *Catherine Hutton and Her Friends*, pp. 64–5.

71. *Passages from the Diaries of Mrs Philip Lybbe Powys, 1756–1808* (1899), p. 75.

CHAPTER 6
Science Education: formal and informal

Scientific literature and the public lecture were complemented by various types of formal or informal education – in school or at home. Most women and girls during the eighteenth and early nineteenth centuries were educated at home. While this education was usually in the hands of a governess, in the case of girls and women who wished to study science it was most often the man of the house, in his capacity as husband or father (or, as in the case of the Duchess of Newcastle, brother-in-law), who took on the role of science tutor to his female dependants. In so doing he was, of course, participating in the venerable tradition approved of by fifteenth-century humanists, that the man should undertake the enlightenment of the woman. The history of women's scientific curiosity is rich in conscientious men who encouraged the study of science within the domestic circle. If a male relative who understood science was not available, some ladies, notably many of the queens of England as well as ladies of the upper ranks wealthy enough to do so, employed a tutor to assist their studies.

The scientific interests of particular groups of women or individuals contributed greatly to the popularity of science among women in general. The curiosity of the royal ladies was always influential. The Bluestocking ladies of the second half of the eighteenth century displayed a limited concern for scientific matters which, because of their intellectual prestige, cannot be ignored. The reputation of Caroline Herschel, the astronomer, was important. She renewed the pleasure that women had always taken in astronomy, particularly in fashionable centres like Bath and London where surveying the heavens could constitute the nexus of a social evening.

The ladies of the industrial heartlands of the Black Country, however, were more wholeheartedly committed to the pursuit of science. There industrialists and scientists were welcome in the drawing rooms and it was from there that some of the most influential voices in favour of women studying science emanated.

On occasion, women themselves took on the role of tutor. There were some women who not only taught themselves, but acted as tutors within their own families, to brothers and sisters, children or friends. Some others were able to carry on the tradition of Bathsua Makin and establish schools for girls in which science played a major part in the curriculum.

Not content with remaining passive consumers of science literature and lectures, ladies were soon taking a more active part in their studies. The resources of science supplied these leisured ladies with enjoyments ranging from recreation to research. For some women this took the form of early scientific tourism; others, however, performed serious field work and made modest contributions to science. Indeed, some women of humbler birth found that science could offer them a living.

The adventurousness of women interested in science was often striking. They participated in a variety of field trips, although usually on a more domestic scale than the dangerous trips to Surinam of the seventeenth-century Dutch explorer Maria Sybilla Merien, or the unescorted trips to Africa in the early nineteenth century of intrepid English ladies like Sarah Lee Bowdich. Simple nature rambles were popular. In view of cumbersome clothes and the difficulties and discomforts of travel, the energy with which these ladies scaled cliffs, climbed down into caves or traversed the countryside in search of curious landscapes and geological or palaeontological specimens was admirable. Industrial geography was another weakness. Ladies of this era were fascinated by the manifestation of science in industry. A favourite holiday recreation with them, although anticipated by at least one stalwart seventeenth-century woman, was the fact-finding outing to the Black Country and other centres of industrial progress.

In the lives of many individual women, a scientific preoccupation often constituted a significant share of their intellectual and social life. Many of them devoted considerable time and leisure to their studies. Textbooks, lighter literature and the public lecture were important, but even more necessary was some form of tuition. In very many cases, often corroborated by personal testimony, the ladies pursued their studies at home. These home students included individuals from the royal family and the nobility, from the professional and industrial classes, from the families of clergymen and Dissenters and from among the intellectual women who were part of Dr Johnson's circle of acquaintances.

Parallel with the continuity of scientific interests in the home were developments in the scientific curricula in girls' schools. The importance of science in women's education, as foreshadowed by seventeenth-century educationalists, evolved further during the eighteenth century and was given greater respectability by the theory and practice of some well-known figures of the time.

Some royal exemplars

Many of the queens of England, from the Restoration in 1660 onwards, evinced some curiosity about scientific matters. Undoubtedly, this royal patronage encouraged similar interests among lesser ladies. It must be said that not all of these royal ladies were disinterestedly motivated. In the early days of her marriage to Charles II, the pretty Portuguese, Catherine of Braganza, frequently joined her husband in his nocturnal astronomical observations. It is unlikely that the hours she spent in the observatory developed a passion for astronomy. But viewing the glories of the night sky was one way to pursue the beguiling post-nuptial courtship that was necessary in arranged marriages. Regrettably, Catherine's infertility and poor health soon wearied Charles's vigorous sensuality and frustrated his longing for an heir. Her vacant place in these night-time vigils at the telescope may well have been taken by the fecund and fatally attractive Lady Castlemaine, whose robust constitution even permitted her to hunt with the King on the day following the birth of one of her children by him.[1]

Charles's cousin, Mary Stuart, led a more decorous life as wife to William of Orange. She developed her interest in science during her early married life in Holland, where she had the benefit of tuition from some of the most eminent men of the time. She was fortunate, for there had been little in her education to encourage such interests. Her father, James II, although a very amiable parent, had strong ideas on the evils of women's education. As a result, she and her sister, Anne, had been carefully trained in nothing but the 'accomplishments'. In Holland, however, Christian Huygens, the famous Dutch scientist, became her tutor and friend. He was on hand when Halley's comet appeared in 1682, and so appreciative was he of his royal pupil's interest that, when an eclipse of the sun was about to occur in mid-July 1684, he presented her with a little oculaire of smoked glass he had made himself.[2] The princess and her ladies-in-waiting could then observe the phenomenon in safety.

Scientific subjects appeared to suit Queen Mary's temperament and her domestic inclinations. Even after her accession to the throne of England (on her father's hasty departure) she continued her studious recreations. She seems to have derived great benefit despite her late development as a student and even acquired some reputation for cleverness in the sciences. She certainly gained the respect of some of the great men of the day on the basis of her mental acumen. Many years later, Sir Christopher Wren's son wrote of his father's regard for her knowledge not only of the principles involved in architecture and building, in which she was keenly interested, but also of 'other branches of mathematics and useful learning'.[3]

It is not known whether Queen Mary's sister and successor, Anne, ever cultivated scientific pursuits to any great degree. In any case her seventeen pregnancies and almost permanent ill-health, coupled with the wearisome misery of watching child after child die, presumably left little time for purely intellectual speculation.

It was different for the women of the House of Hanover. Blessed with an admirable strength of character, many of them seemed able to develop some scientific interests regardless of their domestic problems. Dr Desaguliers had given his earliest scientific lectures in London to George I and his wife. On the accession of George II (1727–60), scientific talks became part of palace routine. The new queen, Caroline of Anspach, was an intelligent woman and Desaguliers honoured her interest in science by dedicating to her a poem celebrating the accession. It was a 'scientific' poem in which he fittingly drew attention to her knowledge: 'I was resolv'd to endeavour at something that might at once shew my Zeal and Loyalty, and at the same Time divert her most Gracious Majesty with my first Poetical Experiment, as I have had the great Honour of entertaining Her with my Philosophical ones.' He made it clear to his other readers that the Queen would have no need of the annotations with which he had carefully bolstered the science in the poem. The intriguing way in which poetry and science were seen to have a natural relationship is evident in the poem's very title: *The Newtonian System of the World, the Best Model of Government: An Allegorical Poem With a plain and intelligible Account of the System of the World, by Way of Annotations* (1728).

The next generation of the royal family, Frederick, Prince of Wales and his wife, Princess Augusta, also cultivated their scientific enthusiasm. Even after Frederick's death in 1751, the Princess and her friend and adviser Lord Bute continued their studies. They were able to call on the tutorial skills of Stephen Hales, one of the most celebrated scientists of the eighteenth century.[4] The branch of science favoured by the Princess was botany, and she and her children devoted many pleasant hours away from the political intrigues of the day to their study of plants and flowers. Her hobby eventually laid the foundations of what are now the Royal Botanic Gardens.[5]

When her son became George III in 1760 and married the German princess Charlotte Sophia, the royal tradition of science studies continued. Once again the influence of their position secured the very best tuition available. As the rising star of astronomy, William Herschel, began to make his reputation in Bath, the Queen and the princesses were able to follow his progress at close quarters. During the 1780s Herschel was developing his ever more powerful telescopes and was frequently invited to the palace to demonstrate their increased range. After his move from Bath to Datchet near Slough, very close to the royal palace at Windsor, the royal ladies and their companions were regular visitors at his new observatory. When Caroline Herschel, his sister, achieved personal eminence as a professional scholar, she too was patronized by the ladies at court. Undoubtedly the fact that the Herschels were also German made their influence as teachers even greater.[6]

Home tuition of upper- and middle-class ladies before 1700

If queens were always in an excellent position to avail themselves of the teaching of the greatest scientists of the day, the same was not necessarily true for other women. Lacking the power of the regal summons, they were more usually obliged to make do with whatever chances for study happened to come their way. However, ladies who were interested in science often displayed an impressive opportunism in exploiting even the slightest opening when it came to furthering their studies. Perhaps the most unusual case involved Sir Walter Raleigh, imprisoned in the Tower of London awaiting execution. He and his companion, Mr Ruthen, decided to continue with their scientific investigations while awaiting the grim end of their confinement. At that time the Lieutenant of the Tower was Sir Allen Apsley. His wife, motivated by compassion certainly, but not uninfluenced by her own intellectual curiosity, financed their 'rare experiments' and received an excellent training in chemistry in exchange. She put her knowledge to good use and her medical skills became renowned among the poor. She also saw to it that her daughter, Lucy, was as well educated as her brothers.[7]

The circumstances in which another young woman was introduced to scientific study were more mundane but more typical. When young Samuel Pepys agreed to his wife Elizabeth's suggestion that she undertake the study of science, he was, though unaware of it, following in a long and venerable tradition dating back to the days of the great humanist teachers. Their notions of the education of women included the belief that the man, as head of the family, ought to be in a position to undertake the instruction of his wife, who, in her turn, would teach her children.

Elizabeth and Samuel's discovery of a mutual interest in astronomy began in February 1663, and by the late summer of that year Samuel was investing in some expensive equipment to further Elizabeth's studies. For all his penny-pinching meanness towards his wife (he invariably spent considerably more on his own clothes than on hers), he betook himself 'to Moxon's and there bought a payre of globes, [which] cost me £3.10 with which I am well pleased, I buying them principally for my wife, who hath a mind to understand them – and I shall take pleasure to teach her' (*Diary*, IV, p. 302).[8]

The reasons for Elizabeth's initiative are not known. The education that she received as a young girl in France was unlikely to have laid deep intellectual foundations. Her marriage had taken place in 1655, when she was fifteen and Samuel was twenty-two. (Pepys's *Diary* was begun some five years later on 1 January 1660.) It is impossible to know whether her interest may have been due to intellectual curiosity, whether she was aping the current fashion, or whether she was making a desperate attempt to please her difficult husband. If the latter, she was certainly successful, at least temporarily. For months on end her enthusiasm delighted him and stimulated his own. For a time he appeared to forget his growing discontent with his marriage and was less likely to seek his own pleasures in the town while leaving her to the petty drudgery of her boring and empty days.

Neglecting for once his favourite haunts of the theatre and concert hall, Samuel stayed at home to start his wife on the programme of mathematical study which was necessary before any work on astronomy could begin. Elizabeth was ignorant of even the rudiments of arithmetic so Samuel began at the beginning. On 21 October 1663 she had her first induction into that subject, as Samuel recorded: 'This evening after I came home, I began to enter my wife in Arithmetique, in order to her studying the globes and she takes it very well – and I hope with great pleasure I shall bring her to understand many fine things' (Vol. IV, p. 343).

Samuel approached the mathematical training of his wife with all the evangelizing energy of the newly converted. His own understanding of the 'many fine things' that mathematics could offer was of very recent date. When he had been appointed to the Navy Board, a well-educated young man, late of St Paul's and Trinity College, Cambridge (which he had entered in 1650), his innumeracy was so complete that, like Elizabeth, even the simple rules of arithmetic were unknown to him. The tutor, hastily hired in July 1662 to compensate for the omissions of the best the English educational system could do, set him to learn his multiplication tables (*Diary*, 4 July 1662). Needless to say, his classical education, on the other hand, had been so thorough that all his life he sought relaxation in the reading of Latin prose.

As the days went by, Mrs Pepys, basking once more in Samuel's uncritical favour, applied herself to her studies with a creditable diligence and concentration. She seemed to have found in science and mathematics some relief from the disappointment and loneliness of her married life. Often she had one, and sometimes two lessons a day from her husband, at lunchtime and again when he returned home after the customary late evening at the office. The effect on their childless marriage was certainly beneficial: 'December 1. 1663. At noon I home to dinner with my poor wife, with whom nowadays, I enjoy great pleasure in her company and learning of arithmetique' (vol. IV, p. 403).

Eventually Elizabeth's skills in 'Addition, Subtraction and Multiplication' were so accomplished that Samuel decided the moment was ripe to begin their work on the globes. Elizabeth continued a devoted student. In January 1664 she took a lecture from him in geography, 'very prettily and with great pleasure'. Very soon, geography and astronomy were put on the nightly timetable. 'January 8. 1664. So having done [at the office], I home and to teach my wife a new lesson in the globes and to supper and to bed' (vol. V, p. 8).

Two years later the *Diary* was still affirming their enjoyment of their shared study. They had, by then, taken to viewing the heavens from the top of the house with 'a twelve-foot glass' delivered by 'Mr Reeve', who had supplied Samuel with other optical paraphernalia. On the night of 7 August 1666 they attempted to observe the moon, Saturn and Jupiter, but ominously 'the heavens proved cloudy, and so we lost our labour'. At the same time their mutual affection had once again begun to wear thin.

In the meantime, however, they had taken up the study of the microscope. Although he did not become a member at Gresham College, the new home of the recently established Royal Society until 15 February 1665, Samuel was, nevertheless, excellently placed with his connections about town to know which microscope to buy and which introductory books to read. On 13 August 1664 he bought his first microscope for £5 10s., horrified at the huge price but hopeful that it would be as effective as the manufacturer claimed. That very night he sat down to master the work of Dr Henry Power, whose *Experimental Philosophy* (1664) was a natural companion for a novice at the microscope.[9] It has to be assumed that Mrs Pepys was, at the very least, a willing listener to his interpretations of Power's work, for the next day, the book finished, they both applied themselves at the microscope to put what they had learned into practice. But they were disappointed. After the inspiring and exciting introduction of Power, they were chastened to discover that the unforgiving nature of their rudimentary microscope prevented their seeing what they had hoped they would see. The glass that Samuel had acquired at such huge expense was a clumsy tool, as most of these optical glasses were. But the experiment was an enjoyable experience for all that. Samuel's endearing optimism shone through his disappointment: 'then my wife and I with great pleasure, but with great difficulty before we could come to find the manner of seeing anything by my microscope – at last did, with good content, though not so much as I expect when I come to understand it better' (*Diary*, vol. V, p. 241).

But not even science could solve the problems of the Pepyses' relationship. Samuel's shortcomings as a husband, his persistent tightfistedness, his inveterate egocentricity and his unwillingness to oblige his wife in the little comforts she wanted were sharpened by the strain he was under through being called to account before a parliamentary investigation into the conduct of the recent war with Holland. Elizabeth suffered too and showed little understanding of or sympathy for her husband. She was also fatally tiring of Samuel's incontinent philandering, the destructive nature of which he knew only too well. He admitted that he was powerless to cope with the effect of attractive women had on him. He described it as 'a strange slavery that I stand in to beauty, that I value nothing near it' (6 September 1664).

There was a showdown in October 1668 when she discovered his latest and what was to be his most serious love affair, with her companion Deb Willett. Elizabeth was not prepared to endure such a direct insult. She resorted to what weapons she had, an hysterical outburst and even violence. One night she attempted to brand her husband with red-hot fire tongs. Within a few months, however, the deadlock was resolved with finality. Elizabeth died suddenly on 10 November 1669, of a fever contracted during a holiday in Holland.

Elizabeth Pepys's interest in science was typical of that of many women during the 1660s and later. She came to the subject without any previous training, stimulated only by some sort of curiosity and enthusiasm. She then evinced a propensity for the study which, in her case as with many other women, her husband encouraged. Even for an amateur such as herself, science offered all the pleasures of an absorbing recreation.

In her inadequate education and early marriage, Elizabeth Pepys resembled many women of her time, but by no means all women were quite as illiterate or as innumerate as she. There were some ladies who developed their scientific interests on top of an admirably comprehensive education. Of this privileged minority two women were especially interesting. One was a noblewoman, Ann Finch, Countess of Conway (1631–79); the other, Ann Baynard (1672–97), belonged to the next generation and was a daughter of the professional middle classes.

Ann Finch was one of that rare breed, the female philomath, who gained the respect and admiration of many eminent men of her day. She was also unusual in that she was one of very few women to have benefited from a university education of a sort, for she enjoyed the privilege of unofficial tuition from Henry More, an eminent Cambridge tutor.

Little is known of her childhood. She was an aristocrat, the only daughter of Sir Henry Finch, recorder of London and speaker of the House of Commons. Her own pedigree and her marriage in 1651 to Edward Conway, a man ten years her senior, made her one of the first ladies in the land. More information exists on how she was educated. Her brother followed the usual pattern of public school followed by Cambridge, while Ann, according to the practice of her class, remained at home. Although she suffered from very poor health, the symptoms of which were severe and debilitating headaches, she was nevertheless encouraged by her parents to undertake an education exceptional in her time. She became an excellent classical scholar, but it emerged that her natural inclination was towards mathematics and science. While still a young girl, she applied herself to the works of contemporary philosophers, theologians and scientists. She went further and taught herself arithmetic and the *Elements* of Euclid. As she progressed, she engaged a tutor to guide her through more advanced work.

The man she married when she was twenty was just as interested as she was in the new science. He too belonged to the scholarly group that had founded the Royal Society, and he would certainly have known Charles Cavendish and John Pell. Like her, he had also developed his mathematical interests when he reached adulthood. With such a receptive husband, it is not surprising that the Countess's married life began happily enough. As time went by, however, this happiness was diminished. The Countess's own ill-health, which resulted in appalling physical sufferings, was not helped by the death of her one child, a little boy who bore the family name of Heneage Edward. As her husband's career demanded more of his time, she retreated from the world, eventually becoming involved with the Quakers, then a highly eccentric and suspect sect. Old friends, like Henry More, watched powerlessly as she evaded their affection.

Within a year of her death, her husband married again and her name and reputation soon slipped from memory in England. In Europe, however, her fame endured rather longer. The people spoke of her as the 'English Countess, a woman learned beyond her Sex', and it was known that both More and Leibnitz credited her with the inspiration for some of their most original work.

While still comparatively healthy, the young Countess had been keenly interested and well read in many of the major issues in science and philosophy which preoccupied the great men of the time. Henry More was originally her brother's tutor, but he happily gave her as much of his time as she needed and was frequently her guest during the long vacations. He repeatedly praised her 'speculative' and 'penetrant' intelligence. His own biographer testified that More found her so inspiring that many of his learned treatises were 'expressly owing to her own Desire or Instigation'.[10] Her letters to her father-in-law also display her acute interest in intellectual and mathematical matters.

Her lasting reputation rested on her only published work, *The Principles of the Most Ancient and Modern Philosophy*, which was considered so important by her literary executors that in 1690 it was published posthumously in Latin in Amsterdam, and then, for the benefit of 'unlearned' readers, was translated back into English and published in 1692. This was a work that the Countess had written for her own use after some years' intensive study of the philosophical systems of Descartes, Hobbes and Spinoza.

Although primarily an exercise in metaphysics, the critique demonstrated a ready understanding and application of the most progressive
scientific thought in the field of astronomy, microscopy and mathematics. Henry More summed up the Countess's scientific credentials
when he attested that she

> understood perfectly, not only the true System of the World, call it
> Copernican or Pythagorick as you will, with all the Demonstrative
> Arguments thereof; ... To say nothing of her perusing (by the Benefit
> of the Latin Tongue, which she acquir'd the Skill of ...) of both Plato
> and Plotines, and of her searching into and judiciously sifting the
> abstrusest Writers of Theosophy [p. 241].

She was also able to understand his own philosophical work and that
of his great rival, Descartes

Of lesser rank but cursed by similar ill-health, Ann Baynard acquired
at least some degree of recognition in her time. What we known of
her intellectual life and achievements derives from a funeral oration
delivered over her grave by her friend and spiritual adviser, Dr John
Prude (*A Sermon at the Funeral of the Learned and Ingenious Mrs Ann Baynard*,
16 June 1697). In this amazing document, the priest concentrated his
entire eulogy on Ann's intellectual merits and scientific accomplishments. He appears to have held the unusual opinion that an excellent
education and a sophisticated grasp of science constituted all the virtues
required in a young girl. In his praise of the character of Ann Baynard,
he made no reference to any of the virtues traditionally associated with
young maidenhood.

Her father was Edward Baynard, himself a scientist and a Fellow of
the College of Physicians of London. It may well have been he who
undertook the education of his clever daughter. He certainly encouraged her intellectual ambitions, for she educated herself to a degree
that did him, and her, credit. The point of the funeral oration was to
stress that, during her short life, Anne devoted herself to study and
derived so much pleasure from it that she made an earnest attempt on
her death bed to persuade other young women to give more serious
attention to their own education.

She appears to have been a very serious-minded girl, given to
thoughtful contemplation. It was said of her that much of the last two
years of her life was spent meditating in the churchyard at Barnes in
Surrey. For her science was intimately linked to devotional zeal. She
applied herself to many different branches of science, but especially to
those with a classical pedigree, astronomy, mathematics and medicine,

all the while in the grips of the wasting disease that killed her in her twenty-fifth year.

Dr Prude assessed her reputation, as a student of science, as equal to that 'of a bearded Philosopher'. Everyone, apparently, had admired the diligence with which she studied in her determination to 'understand natural Causes and Events; ... know the Courses of the Sun, Moon and Stars, the Qualities of Herbs and Plants; ... be acquainted with the demonstrable Verities of the Mathematicks'.

While giving his dead friend full credit for her academic achievement, Dr Prude also chose to stress that, in her scientific interests, she should not be regarded as separate or different from all other, lesser women. On the contrary, he made it clear that her successful studies were due to nothing more than her industriousness and application, and that other women would be able to do as much: 'she was a clear and lively instance, that neither the Crabbedness of Languages, nor the Abstruseness of Arts and Sciences can be too hard for Diligence and Application' (p. 26).

Listening to Dr Prude's funeral sermon, members of the congregation heard that Ann herself had been of the opinion that science offered one of the best ways through which a woman could charge her life with energy and significance. On her death bed, he reported, she had pleaded with him to make her hopes and wishes known:

> That women ... are capable of such Improvements, which will better their Judgments and Understandings, is past all doubt; would they but set to't in earnest, and spend but half of that time in study and thinking, which they do in Visits, Vanity and Toys. 'Twould introduce a composure of Mind, lay a sound Basis and Ground-work for Wisdom and Knowledge; by which they would be better enabled to serve God and help their Neighbours. [pp. 30–1][11]

Like other women, she too believed that the road to virtue could pass through the science laboratory. Her message to her sex was that by learning to 'read the great Book of Nature', to understand 'the Order of the Universe' and 'the Production and Preservation of things', they might combine their own intellectual curiosity with the acquisition of a knowledge that would enable them to appreciate and understand 'the Wisdom and Power of the Great Creator' (p. 30).

Not all women expected such profound results from their study of science. There seem to have been many ladies who indulged their curiosity and left it at that. It gave them a pleasant hobby and their friends the opportunity to buy them appropriate presents. At one time the ladies' microscope, neatly packaged in an exquisitely crafted case such as the example purchased by queen Mary, was a highly desirable fashion accessory. When Jonathan Swift was paying one of his visits to London, it was a microscope that took his fancy as a present for his friend Esther Johnson, or 'Stella' as he fondly called her, back home in Dublin. Swift's account of the matter of the purchase of the instrument throws light on the acceptability of microscopy as a ladies' subject at the time and the types of microscope deemed suitable for a lady's use. It also reveals something of the methods that the manufacturers used to inform the public about their products. Swift described his visit to Ludgate Street, where most vendors of scientific instruments kept their shops, in pursuit of the microscope:

> I called at Ludgate and I doubt it will cost me thirty shillings for a microscope, but not without Stella's permission; for I remember she is a *virtuoso*. Shall I buy it or no? 'Tis not the great bulky ones, nor the common little ones, to impale a louse (saving your presence) upon a needle's point; but of a more exact sort, and clearer to the sight, with all its equipage in a little trunk that you may carry in your pocket. [Letter IX, p. 97][12]

The sequel was embarrassing for Swift. When he returned to the shop to pick up the microscope, the owner wanted him to accept it free of charge in return for recommending his instruments to his circle of friends and acquaintances. Clearly Swift's political and social standing was not unknown to him. Swift extricated himself by refusing the bribe but promising him 'all service I could do him', and he subsequently appeared to regret that he was now 'obliged in honour to recommend him to everybody' (I, p. 135). How many ladies might have bought microscopes similar to the one that Swift planned to give Stella because of this form of indirect advertising is not known.

In due course, shops stocking microscopes and other scientific instruments were common enough in other parts of the kingdom. Eventually, similar retail outlets were to be found even in Dublin itself, at least one of which was run by a woman. The widow and daughter of Alexandre Tournant, the instrument maker who worked for the Academy of Sciences in Berlin and then for the Duke of Richmond, were set up by his friends and employers with an instrument business in Dublin in 1789.[13] How much these instruments cost, bearing in mind currency fluctuations, is evident from the advertisements for the Chichester shop run by Benjamin Martin in the late 1730s. There a pocket reflecting microscope with a micrometer cost one guinea. Without the micrometer, the microscope cost 12s. 6d. Martin's other wares included 'the best Double Reflecting Microscopes with a Micrometer at £2. 12s 6d; without, at £2. 2s. Also Telescopes, with or without Micrometers; Scioptric Balls for Dark-Chambers, and other optical Instruments at the lowest prices.' This advertisement was included in his handbook of the microscope, *The Description and Use of a New Invented Pocket Reflecting Microscope with a Micrometer* (*c.*1738; larger edition, 1742).

Bluestockings and science

The Bluestocking ladies of the second half of the eighteenth century were not the most obvious students of science. Their allegiance was to the classics, and their pride was to be able to undertake at least some part of classical studies on an equal footing with their male friends. So they never recognized science as a wholly respectable academic discipline and, apart from the classically approved subjects of astronomy and mathematics, tended to ignore the typical female interests of microcopy, entomology, chemistry and natural history. Sharing the cultural arrogance of their intellectual class, they were instinctively conscious of the relative prestige attached to an appreciation of Homer or Juvenal as compared with an understanding of the properties of air or the mechanism of the eye of a fly.

But in what appeared to be their calculated campaign to reform and improve the cultural and intellectual life of the capital city, by instituting social gatherings in which alcohol and comestibles were replaced by scintillating conversation and the exchange of ideas, they were obliged to take note of the growing interest in science among men of letters.[14]

Among the Bluestockings who, in addition to Mrs Vesey, took an active interest in science were the famous Elizabeth Carter and her friend Catherine Talbot. Elizabeth Carter (1717–1806) combined classical pursuits and scientific studies with her usual determination, and it was through her interest in the subject that she met Catherine Talbot (1721–70). They were brought together by the tutor they shared, who thought their interest in science ensured a mutual sympathy. Even more devoted to her scientific interests was Mrs Hester Thrale. Although a popular London hostess, she never quite acquired the reputation in which the ladies of the first rank of Bluestockings were held. There may have been more than a little element of jealousy in this exclusion because Mrs Hester Thrale and later her daughters were warmly appreciated and encouraged in their scientific interests by no less a man than Dr Samuel Johnson himself.

Although Elizabeth Carter was to devote considerable time and effort to the study of science, it has to be said that she never truly regarded it as on the same level of importance as the classics. Like other devoted classicists, she was convinced that the ancients had revealed all there was to know of the truths of existence. Anything the moderns might claim as novelty would be of superficial interest. As a young woman she had put the case against science on behalf of the 'learned' Bluestockings when she explained that what were hailed as great advances in science simply aroused her scepticism. Too often the supposed progress was the result of nothing more than haphazard good fortune without the intercession of any intellectual method, and appeared to be, for the most part, irrelevant to the true business of life.

It was soon after J.T. Desaguliers had produced *A Dissertation concerning Electricity* in 1742, the first English work entirely on electricity (except for a short tract by Boyle), that Elizabeth had gone to one of the travelling roadshows which exploited the still mysterious power of electricity to pull in the audiences. She was shocked and more than a little contemptuous at the ease with which the showman had managed to tease and terrify his willing audience.[15]

While these less critical witnesses gasped in astonishment at the sparks, shocks and flickering lights, Elizabeth Carter could only echo Gulliver and shake her head over man's childish and thoughtless delight in frivolous novelty. In a letter to Catherine Talbot, she mused, 'Perhaps not only in this but in most other instances, all the discoveries of the Moderns tend only to convince one of the good sense and true philosophy of the Ancients, and to prove what they have asserted'.[16]

By that time, Elizabeth Carter had spent nearly twenty years arduously acquiring that depth of classical knowledge for which she was to become famous. It is hardly surprising that she chose to regard what appeared to be specious tricks of nature with disdainful suspicion. As a young girl she had unhesitatingly chosen to adopt the traditional educational model. It was a task in which many failed. Elizabeth was doubly courageous, for she betrayed none of that early intellectual promise that often identified women who were to become famous for their intellectual feats. Her father, a kindly clergyman with advanced notions on the equality of women, had taken it for granted that his sons and daughters would be educated alike, but when he observed the straits into which such a plan plunged Elizabeth, he begged her to desist and to reconcile herself to her evident intellectual limitations.

The story of her refusal to accept that her intellect was limited is well known. Eventually her self-imposed regime of long hours of study at night, during which she kept herself awake by chewing snuff or green tea and applying cold compresses to head and stomach, produced the result she desired.[16] She became an internationally renowned classical scholar and linguist. Her most famous work was a translation of Epictetus (1758) which was universally praised and appreciated, not least by other English women who felt their own intellectual ambitions to be vindicated by her work.[17] She made a respectable £1,000 for her efforts, more than enough for financial independence, and won the hard-earned accolade of 'the best Greek Scholar' he knew from Dr Samuel Johnson. Indeed, her reputation reached such heights that there was even a rumour that she was going to stand for Parliament.[13]

Yet, for all her classical scepticism at the trickery of electricity, not to mention the debatable value of science, she devoted a substantial amount of time to acquiring a certain mastery in different scientific fields. As had already been noted, among her earliest published works was the translation of Algarotti's book on Newton. Her work on this book displayed clear understanding of and thorough research into the subject. Despite its measured prose and comprehensive notes, which included many references to continental and European women who studied science, it is nevertheless a fact that, as her reputation as a classical scholar became firmly established, she held this little book to be of negligible importance and it was allowed to slip into comparative oblivion.

Elizabeth Carter was nothing if not thorough. Part of her classical studies included the noble sciences of astronomy and mathematics, two integral parts of the classical quadrivium. She made good progress in both subjects and in fact, like so many other ladies and gentlemen of the period, resorted to the recreation of solving 'problems, diagrams and projections', leaving many notes to that effect among her papers after her death. Although she always claimed that it was 'far from being her forte or from giving her that pleasure which she received from classic and historic learning', she was sufficiently captivated by the subject to employ a private tutor to direct her studies (*Memoirs*, p. 11). This was not unusual except in so far as she managed to employ the services of a man of some scientific eminence.

He was the well-known astronomer and antiquary Thomas Wright (1711–86). He came from Durham where he had earned his living as a scientific instrument maker. Like many such men in that walk of life, he was obliged to supplement his limited income by giving private lessons in mathematics and science to young men and women.[19] He was a very good teacher and his fame spread, even reaching the ears of the scientifically minded Catherine the Great of Russia. As part of her long-term plan to revitalize the intellectual life of Russia, she tried to entice him to St Petersburg to teach mathematics at the Imperial Academy there. Much to the relief of his friends and pupils, he declined the offer and remained in England to continue his role as dedicated teacher of many students.

It was, of course, through Thomas Wright that Elizabeth Carter met Miss Catherine Talbot. She and Catherine wrote frequent, long and gossipy letters to each other which detailed their reading and other serious intellectual pursuits. The two girls shared many interests, one of which was their scientific studies, but they had very different personalities. Elizabeth was the more vivacious of the two. In pleasant contrast to the many feminine valetudinarians, she enjoyed robust good health and an almost boisterous vivacity. She once described herself as 'restless and corky', and when at home in Deal in Kent she coped with this excess of energy by wildly indecorous and physically demanding hikes and scrambles over the hills and along the coast, preferably just as day was breaking.

Her love of the countryside was evident in her commitment to the conservation of natural beauty , a commitment that manifested itself, for example, in her opposition to clear felling. In this preoccupation with the claims of nature, she was sharing in a growing trend both to appreciate and to value the conservation of animals and habitats that was typical of the early decades of the eighteenth century.[20]

Everything Elizabeth Carter did was tempered with good humour and wit. Even her scientific pastimes were a source of amusement. After a very brief flirtation, for she was a confirmed spinster, she wrote to Catherine about the usefulness of mathematics as an antidote to such temptations:

> My heart, which I thought so secure and so uninvadable, was yesterday in one half-hour entirely given up to a ------; would you believe it? To a *Dutchman*. To be sure the reason of my being thus taken by surprise, was because I had not provided myself with my usual guard, as I never suspected there could be the least danger from the amphibious inhabitant of the bogs of Holland. But, I this morning took a dose of algebra, fasting, which has entirely cured me. [*Letters*, pp. 24–5]

Catherine Talbot had a more circumspect, if equally lively, intelligence. Her modest circumstances as the only child of a widowed mother and under the guardianship of the Bishop of Oxford may well have engendered a restraint that became second nature as the years passed. She had a serious disposition and she would probably have regarded the moral essays she wrote as her most important intellectual effort. In keeping with her modest assessment of herself, they were not published until after her death, when Elizabeth Carter saw them through publication under the title of *Reflections of the Seven Days of the Week*. Their success was immediate. A first edition in 1770 of a staggering twenty-five thousand copies was followed by three other editions in that year alone.

Of the two friends, Catherine appeared to have the truer scientific bent, a fact compatible with her natural inclination to intellectual humility. She had no classical ambitions. She was content to read within the limitations of English and French literatures and modern translations of the great works of antiquity. But she admired her friend's impressive learning and saw how it could advantage women like herself. It was she who suggested the translation of Epictetus to Elizabeth.

In her quiet, well-ordered and studious life, spent for the most part in the village of Cuddesdon on the east side of Oxford, Miss Talbot enjoyed riding around the peaceful countryside and paying calls on friends and neighbours. This calm routine was enlivened by the careful and dedicated study of astronomy and mathematics, aided by the teaching of Wright and occasionally the assistance of a helpful neighbour. One friend close by owned the latest model of the telescope invented by Huygens. Apparently Catherine derived great pleasure from time spent observing the heavens by this means. Her progress in astronomy and the discoveries she made, such as her first sighting of Jupiter, were excitedly communicated to the enthusiastic Elizabeth, at her home in Deal.

While it might appear that these young women were very well situated to devote their time to study and self-improvement, it should be noted that their leisure was more apparent than real. One of the greatest drawbacks endured by women has been the demand that they be communal. To withdraw from the family circle during the day would have been an unacceptable flouting of convention. It was necessary not only that they occupied themselves, but that they were seen to do so and always in a 'useful' manner. Although no domestic work was required of them or other women in their position, it was always necessary for a woman, particularly an unmarried one, to justify her existence, usually in the execution of a thousand household and chari-

ADVICE

To the *WOMEN* and *MAIDENS*

O F

LONDON.

Shewing, that inftead of their ufual Pa-
ftime; and education in Needle-work, Lace, and
Point-making, it were far more Neceffary and Profitable to apply themfelves to the right Underftand-
ing and Practice of the method of keeping books of
account: whereby, either fingle, or married, they
may know their Eftates, carry on their Trades, and
avoid the Danger of a helplefs and forlorn Condition, incident to Widows.

With fome Effays, or rudiments for young beginners;
in twelve Articles.

By one of that Sex.

L O N D O N,
Printed for *Benjamin Billingfley* at the Printing prefs
in *Cornhill*, 1678.

Douce A. 601.

The LADIES *Diary:*
OR, THE
Woman's ALMANACK,
For the Year of our LORD, 1716.
Being Biffextile, or LEAP-YEAR.
Containing many Delightful and Entertaining Particulars,
peculiarly adapted for the Ufe and Diverfion of the
FAIR-SEX.

Being the Thirteenth ALMANACK ever Publifh'd of that kind.

Hail Sacred Peace! Hail long expected Days
Which *Britain's* Glory to the Stars fhall raife!
Oh ftretch thy Reign, fair Peace! from Shore to Shore,
'Till Conquefts ceafe, and Slav'ry be no more.

Printed by *J. Wilde*, for the Company of *Stationers*, 1716.

*Advice to the Women and Maidens of
London* (1678). An early pamphlet
exhorting women to reject their traditional
domestic pursuits in favour of mathematics
and business studies. The writer argued that
proficiency in such subjects would ensure
the independence of women.

The Ladies Diary (1716) was the first
publication for women to concentrate on
science and mathematics. It prided itself on
its success in stimulating female interest in
these subjects.

Sir Isaac Newton's PHILOSOPHY

Explain'd

For the Use of the LADIES.

In Six Dialogues

ON

LIGHT and COLOURS.

From the *Italian* of Sig. *Algarotti.*

VOLUME I.

Quæ legat ipfa Lycoris. VIRG. EC. x.

LONDON:

Printed for E. CAVE, at St. *John's-Gate,*
MDCCXXXIX.

CONVERSATIONS

ON

CHEMISTRY.

IN WHICH

THE ELEMENTS OF THAT SCIENCE

ARE

FAMILIARLY EXPLAINED

AND

ILLUSTRATED BY EXPERIMENTS.

IN TWO VOLUMES.

VOL. I.
ON SIMPLE BODIES.

LONDON:
PRINTED FOR LONGMAN, HURST, REES, AND ORME,
PATERNOSTER ROW,

1806.

A COMPENDIOUS SYSTEM

OF

ASTRONOMY,

IN A

COURSE OF FAMILIAR LECTURES;

IN WHICH THE PRINCIPLES OF THAT SCIENCE ARE CLEARLY
ELUCIDATED, SO AS TO BE INTELLIGIBLE TO THOSE
WHO HAVE NOT STUDIED THE MATHEMATICS.

ALSO

TRIGONOMETRICAL and CELESTIAL PROBLEMS,

WITH

A KEY to the EPHEMERIS,

AND

A VOCABULARY OF THE TERMS OF SCIENCE
USED IN THE LECTURES;

WHICH LATTER ARE EXPLAINED AGREEABLY TO THEIR APPLICATION IN THEM.

By MARGARET BRYAN.

These are thy glorious Works, PARENT of GOOD,
ALMIGHTY! thine this universal frame,
Thus wond'rous fair; THYSELF how wond'rous then!
Unspeakable! who sit'st above these Heav'ns,
To us invisible, or dimly seen
In these thy lowest works; yet these declare
Thy Goodness beyond thought, and Pow'r Divine. MILTON.

LONDON.
PRINTED FOR THE AUTHOR,
And fold by LEIGH and SOTHEBY, York Street, Covent Garden;
And G. KEARSLEY, No. 46, Fleet Street.
1797.
[Entered at Stationers' Hall.]

(*Above left*) Francesco Algarotti's work (1739) was aimed at the ladies who required a simple introduction to Newtonian theory. Written in Italian, it was translated into English by Elizabeth Carter.

(*Above*) Mrs Jane Marcet designed her book on chemistry (1806) for women who, like herself, had no previous knowledge of the subject. It was this book that stimulated the interest and enthusiasm of the young Michael Faraday.

(*Left*) Margaret Bryan was a well-known science teacher and writer. Her books were based on the extensive science classes which constituted a large part of the curriculum of her school.

Two young science students in the mid-eighteenth century. Frontispiece of Benjamin Martin's *The Young Gentleman and Lady's Philosophy* (1744).

Plate XI from Margaret Bryan's *Lecture on Natural Philosophy* (1806). She illustrated all her works herself. These diagrams illustrate experiments with sound.

(*Above left*) Bathsua Makin (?1610–?1675) was an ardent supporter of the equality of the sexes. She wanted women to improve their own position by applying themselves to higher education. She advocated science and mathematics as subjects more appropriate to women than either the traditional feminine accomplishments or the traditional masculine preserve of the classics.

(*Above*) Caroline of Anspach, wife of George II, was keenly interested in science and set an example to ladies in the highest ranks of society.

Augusta, Princess of Wales, mother of George III, was particularly fond of botany, an interest she shared with her friend and advisor, Lord Bute. Their collections, which were made with the assistance of the royal children, eventually formed the nucleus of Kew Gardens.

Maria Edgeworth, the novelist, was encouraged by her father to develop scientific interests. Astronomy was her favourite subject. She knew many of the leading scientists of her time. With her father, she devised an educational curriculum which placed great emphasis on the study of science by girls.

George Eliot (Mary Ann Evans) devoted a considerable amount of time to science before turning to writing. While living in Geneva she attended weekly lectures at the academy.

Cartoon by Du Maurier in *Punch*, 1874: 'Miss Hypatia Jones, Spinster of Arts, informs Professor Parallax, F.R.S., that "Young men do very well to look at, or to dance with, or even to marry, and all that kind of thing!" but that "as to enjoying any rational conversation with any man under fifty, *that* is *completely* out of the question!"'

Sketches of the meeting of the British Association for the Advancement of Science in Bath, 1888.

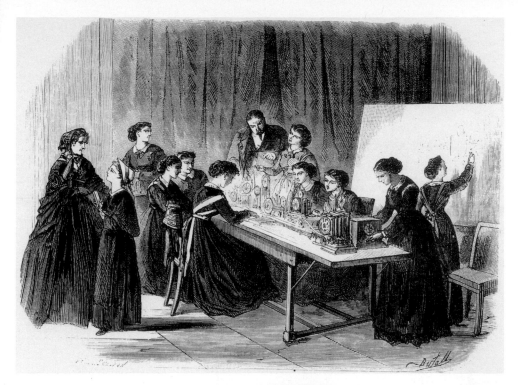

BY THE 1860s WOMEN HAD
BEGUN TO ENTER PROFESSIONS
PREVIOUSLY CLOSED TO THEM
AND WERE ALSO FORGING
AHEAD IN NEW CAREERS MADE
POSSIBLE BY DEVELOPMENTS IN
TECHNOLOGY.

Women were accepted as
telegraph operators in Western
Europe and the USA from the
beginning.

Women students dissecting a
body in Paris, *circa* 1900.
Medicine offered women a
profession in many European
countries years before the
English medical establishment
was ready to welcome them.

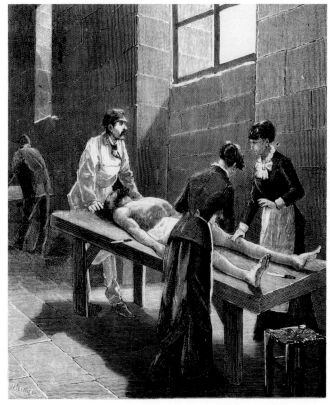

The female science student was a familiar sight in the late nineteenth century.

A lecture at the Society of Arts, London, 1900. The scientific lecture was a form of popular education particularly enjoyed by women from the mid-seventeenth century onwards.

table tasks, of which the most onerous would have been the supply of household linen. Elizabeth Carter sewed by hand all the shirts required by her father and brother, as well as her own clothes. A woman who wished to pursue a plan of study requiring concentration and commitment could only do so if she was willing to pore over her work during the unsociable hours of the late night or early morning, in a cold and poorly lit bedroom. To withdraw from the domestic circle at other times of the day was unthinkable.[21]

It sometimes happened that, if several of the ladies in a household were interested in serious subjects, one of them might assume the role of tutor by reading aloud some instructive tome while the others busied themselves with necessary household tasks. The practice was so well known that Joseph Addison could poke fun at it in the essay in which he invented Lady Lizard and her daughters reading serious scientific (Fontenelle?) books as they made jam.[22] The Bluestockings were not inclined to suggest that the jam need not be made. That a woman should be as useful as she was intellectual was an integral part of their attitude to the question of the female education. Their great argument was that a well-educated woman made the best wife and mother.

Another aspect of the character of women like Elizabeth Carter and Catherine Talbot, and one which coloured their attitudes to educational ambition, was a certain wry humour which seemed to strike when they contemplated their own efforts at self-improvement. This was particularly evident in one of Catherine Talbot's little exercises in self-parody. It was a memorandum she once wrote for an *alter ego*, like herself a mid-eighteenth-century miss who clearly aspired to a high degree of scientific erudition. With a refreshing and amusing self-ridicule from this most staid of bluestockings, the memo detailed a curriculum for self-improvement which the young lady proposed to undertake during the summer months. It was elaborate and was to include geography and mathematics, especially decimal fractions, as well as a close scrutiny of the scientific works of Newton and Voltaire. For all her good intentions, the project was doomed from the start, for the author had not taken into account the weakness of human nature. Who wants to pore over dusty theorems when the sun is shining? At the end of the summer the would-be philomath finds that she has whittled away a great deal of precious time with nothing to show for it but the humiliating revelation of a sad 'Abundance of Plays and Idle Books' (*Works*, 1780, pp. 212–13).

Hester Thrale belonged to the next generation of 'Blues'. Although just as well educated as Miss Carter, in her enthusiasm for science she was closer to Miss Talbot. A lively and affectionate mother and a fairly dutiful wife, Hester Thrale brought to all her projects an infectious enthusiasm which can still be felt in her writings today. Her ambition to shine in the highest ranks of London society was never to be completely realized, but she was blessed in many other ways. When it came to her scientific studies, these blessings included not only being the wife of a rich businessman but also having the 'Colossus of the Age' himself, Dr Samuel Johnson, as adviser and fellow student.[23]

Much loved by Johnson, at least in part for the comfort and rich dinners with which she pampered him as well as for the opportunity which she offered him to pursue his own scientific interests, Mrs Thrale was another of those well-educated women of the period for whom science afforded additional mental stimulation and the fulfilment of her considerable intellectual curiosity.

Her education had begun in earnest when she was about sixteen. She had studied modern languages and a respectable classical syllabus, and had had special tuition in astronomy. Through her long life, her scientific interests remained of real value to her, even after the total social disgrace that followed her husband's death when she outraged family and friends by marrying her daughters' music teacher. Gabriel Mario Piozzi was Italian and younger than she was. Society could not forgive such a blatant betrayal of convention. Mrs Thrale was never readmitted to her social circle.[24] As an old lady living in Bath, again widowed and still ostracized by society, she continued to attend lectures in chemistry, frequented scientific exhibitions and listened to talks on geographical and botanical exploration.[25]

She did cultivate other friends, however, notably Eleanor Butler and Sarah Ponsonby, the two extraordinary aristocratic Irish spinsters. They were famous for their joint flight from civilization to the wilds of Llangollen in 1780, there to put into practice the contemporary fad, inspired by Rousseau, for retreating to a rural idyll to cultivate the mind and the soul. They studied astronomy, botany and mineralogy, and when the then Mrs Piozzi visited them, she recommended that they read the work of the up-and-coming young scientist Thomas Beddowes on *Oxygen Air and Gas*[26]

Before this exclusion of Hester Thrale from polite society, and during her heyday as one of London's busiest hostesses, she and Dr Johnson pursued their scientific interests together in a room especially set up for the purpose in the Thrales' luxurious villa at Streatham. They had planned to build a laboratory in order to carry out more ambitious projects, but that idea had to be abandoned after one experiment went badly wrong, causing an explosion and a fire.[27]

Both Mrs Thrale and Dr Johnson were deeply interested in the education of the Thrale children, all daughters. The much-loved little boy had died of a burst appendix when he was ten years old. Like many another well-educated mother, Mrs Thrale was fascinated by the evidence of intelligence and mental agility in her first born, Hester Maria, fondly called 'Queeney' by her devoted parents and honorary uncle, Samuel Johnson. The educational programme that she devised for this child would have been formidable for a child, boy or girl, in any age. Mrs Thrale kept a close record of Queeney's educational achievements in the private diary she called 'The Children's Book'. She noted proudly the various stages that the toddler had successfully passed. On 17 December 1768, when Queeney was four and a quarter, she 'repeated her catechism quite thro', her Latin Grammar to the end of the five Declensions, a Fable in Phaedrus, an Epigram in Martial, the Revolutions, Diameters and Distance of the Planets'.[28]

By the age of ten, Queeney had further developed the scientific side of her studies, aided and encouraged by Johnson. When she began her collection of natural specimens, a popular hobby at this time, he saw to it that she had a special cabinet in which to display her best finds, and on every trip he made, he tried to find some new and interesting object to delight her and swell her collection. But it was her mathematical bent in particular that he sought to develop. Johnson himself was fascinated by mathematics, as were many of his contemporaries. He measured everything, from his fingernails and how long it took them to grow, to the proportions of whatever room he might be in. He regarded this awareness of 'number' as a useful mental discipline, and it was for this reason that he urged Queeney to develop her numeracy. He noted that she was taking tuition from a mathematics teacher and suggested that this teaching should be supplemented with additional work from other sources. The better taught she was, the greater would be the clarity and concision of her mind, qualities that would be of considerable benefit to her:

> You have done wisely in taking a master for arithmetick, a science of which I would not have you soon think that you have enough. It will seem at first difficult, but you will soon find its usefulness so great that you will disregard the difficulty; and the progress will be easier than the beginning. Do not be content with what a single master dictates, but procure books: different authors exhibit the same thing in different views, and what is obscure in one, may be clear in another.

When you can readily apply numbers on emergent occasions, you will find yourself to think with so much clearness and certainty that the pleasure of arithmetick will attract you almost as much as the use. [*Letters*, 26 April 1783, III, p. 21][29]

Letters to Queeney from Johnson were often preoccupied with her progress in mathematics. On different occasions he suggested that she read such standard authors as Cocker, Hodder and Wingate. And he encouraged her not to rest satisfied with just these. If other works were not readily obtainable, he recommended to her that she scour the bookshops in search of other helpful gems and, in that way, assemble her own little mathematical library.

Regrettably, Queeney Thrale did not repay the fond attention so generously lavished on her and her education. She grew up a cold fish, and her only apparent ambition, which she finally satisfied in her early middle age, was to marry a title. Her attitude to her impetuous and lively mother, who had been so lovingly devoted to her little prodigy, was one of embarrassment and contempt. As for her elderly and eminent mentor, regarded by so many as the greatest thinker of the period, he was soon forgotten.

But that was still in the future. While they were growing up, Johnson's interest in the intellectual attainments of Mrs Thrale's daughters continued. The second girl, Sophia, possessed an even greater mathematical aptitude than her sister. She appears to have chosen to study it in preference to literature. Johnson commented to her mother, 'her choice is certainly as laudable as it is uncommon, but I would have her like what is good in both' (*Letters*, 28 November 1783, III, p. 109). But he was as pleased with her as he had been with Queeney. To her he elaborated on how important mathematics could be to a woman. Any female giving the subject her attention would be rewarded in manifold ways: she would be amused and entertained; she would be capable of greater discernment and accuracy in matters of business and of science; and she would acquire an enviable reputation, a strange aim to suggest to a woman in that age.

Never think, my Sweet, that you have arithmetick enough; when you have exhausted your master, buy books. Nothing amuses more harmlessly than computation, and nothing is oftener applicable to real business or speculative enquiries. A thousand stories which the ignorant tell, and believe, die away at once, when the computist takes them in his gripe: I hope you will cultivate in yourself a disposition to numerical enquiries; they will give you entertainment in solitude by the practice, and reputation in publick by the effect. [*Letters*, 24 July 1783, III, p. 870]

The third sister, Susannah, likewise received the benefit of Johnson's advice. Her interests were somewhat more eclectic than those of her mathematical sisters. While in Bath for the season, like so many other ladies, she was attracted by the lectures in astronomy then being conducted for ladies by William Herschel. In writing to Susannah to encourage her interest, Johnson produced a defence of scientific curiosity which, had she ever heard it, might very well have influenced Miss Carter's scepticism during one of the London soirées they both attended:

With Mr Herschil [*sic*] it will certainly be very right to cultivate an acquaintance for he can show you in the night sky what no man before him has ever seen, by some wonderful improvements which he had made in the telescope. What he had to show is indeed a long way off, and perhaps concerns us but little, but all truth is valuable and all knowledge is pleasing in its first effects, and may be subsequently useful. [*Letters*, 25 March 1784, III, p. 144]

Caroline Herschel

Susannah Thrale was lucky to have made William Herschel's acquaintance. His pioneer work in astronomy was exciting great interest among the fashionable in the smart watering place. Many ladies found that their music lessons, for he had begun as one of Bath's most popular music teachers, were being transformed into study periods in astronomy. But Herschel's teaching abilities were to have greatest effect on his own sister, Caroline. Under her brother's tuition, she became an independent astronomer of international reputation. His concern was not entirely magnanimous: he needed a dedicated co-worker to assist him in forwarding his own newly found career.

Caroline Lucretia Herschel (1750–1848) was one of a numerous family born to a musician in the band of the Guards in Hanover. She received a basic education at the garrison school. Her abiding hope for many years was to become independent and self-supporting. To this end she assiduously practised the art of embroidery and applied herself to her music studies, for her ambition was to become a governess. When William, who was said to have deserted the Hanoverian Guards, set himself up in fashionable Bath as an organist and music teacher and asked her to come and be his housekeeper, Caroline accepted the offer and joined him in 1772.

She appears to have immigrated to England with the notion that this move would be a step on the road to achieving her own career ambitions. William assisted her music training and she began to appear in public as a singer. But at the same time, William was developing his great interest in astronomy. In the ten years following Caroline's arrival, the course of his career changed from musician to King's astronomer and celebrity. In 1773 he attended the lectures of James Ferguson, then on tour in Bath, and read his published work. Caroline was told all about it and he started giving her mathematical tuition when and how he could. These lessons usually took place at breakfast time, and she began to enter her work in a commonplace book which recorded her advances in taking altitudes, in how to convert sidereal time into mean time, and in geometry, logarithms and theorems for making tables of motion.[30]

On 4 March 1774 William succeeded with great difficulty in constructing a telescope with a focal length of $5\frac{1}{2}$ feet. With this he was able to observe the nebula in Orion and thereby mark the beginning of his career as an astronomer. It was then that he started giving lessons in astronomy to ladies, and in 1779 he contributed his first papers to the recently established Philosophical Society in Bath. His first printed work appeared in the *Ladies Diary* in 1780. It was an answer to a prize question on the vibration of strings. Caroline was not pleased. She found these changes to her daily life of housekeeping and singing immensely annoying. The elegance of their living arrangements was also threatened by the dilapidating effect of the accumulating litter from the mechanics of astronomy.

Her greatest irritation was caused by the growing realization that her dream of independence was being wrenched from her by these new considerations. Her brother no longer had the time to encourage her music. Years later her irritation was still palpable: 'In short ... I have been throughout annoyed and hindered in my endeavour at perfecting myself in any branch of knowledge by which I could hope to gain a creditable livelihood.'[31]

However, it seems that she continued to assist her brother willingly enough. When he set about constructing a larger and more accurate telescope with a 30-foot reflector, she worked without rest:

The mirror [for the reflector] was to be cast in a mould of loam prepared from horse dung, of which an immense quantity was to be pounded in a mortar and sifted through a fine sieve. It was an endless piece of work, and served me for many an hour's exercise; and Alex [another brother] frequently took his turn at it, for we were all eager to do something towards the great undertaking. [*Memoir*, p. 43]

The results, the first sighting of Uranus, were gratifying and Herschel won the approval of the King. This provoked their removal from Bath to Slough in 1786. It was here that their celebrity status was established. Caroline discovered an unknown comet which sent ripples of interest running through the circles of astronomical ladies at Windsor. Fanny Burney, then a lady-in-waiting, summed up the general feeling: 'The comet was very small, and had nothing grand or striking in its appearance; but it is the first lady's comet, and I was very desirous to see it.'[32]

Both William and Caroline hoped for great things from the royal patronage and for a time everything looked promising. William received £400 from the royal purse and an additional £200 annually to defray expenses. Caroline's work was also to be recognized. Her feelings at receiving her first pay packet were of undisguised delight:

A salary of £50 a year was also settled on me as an assistant to my brother, and in October I received twelve pounds ten, being the first quarterly payment of my salary, and the first money I ever in all my lifetime thought myself to be at liberty to spend to my own liking. A great uneasiness was by this means removed from my mind. [*Memoir*, pp. 75–6]

Regrettably, this was the only money that Caroline ever received. The promised annual pension was never paid. She always hated the dependent state into which astronomy had forced her brother and herself. In later life she put the blame on the 'shabby, mean-spirited advisors' to the King, whom she considered responsible for having prevented him spending as he wished the £80,000 granted to him by Parliament for patronage of the arts and sciences.

In May 1788, when William married a rich widow whose jointure secured his work, Caroline moved into a smaller establishment close to the couple. She plainly resented giving over the control of William's household to a strange woman, but the change did release her from the toils of housewifery and permitted her a fruitful period of astronomical research which established her as an astronomer in her own right. Between 1788 and 1798 she produced her most impressive work. Her *Index to Flamsteed's Observations of the Fixed Stars*, published by the Royal Society in 1798, attracted the welcome attention and congratulations of fellow astronomers. Never very self-effacing, Caroline was extremely pleased and gratified by their admiration. She could never rid herself of her overweening desire to somehow distinguish herself. In September 1798 she wrote to the Reverend Dr Maskelyne, the astronomer Royal:

> I thought the pains it had cost me were, and would be sufficiently rewarded in the use it had already been, and might be in future, to my brother. But your having thought it worthy of the press has flattered my vanity not a little. You see, sir, I do own myself to be vain, because I would not wish to be singular; and was there ever a woman without vanity? or a man either? only with this difference that among gentlemen the commodity is generally styled ambition. [*Memoir*, p. 96]

A later work, which she completed in her middle seventies, proved, although never published, to be the most valuable as well as the most demanding of all her research. This was 'The Reduction and Arrangement in the Form of a Catalogue in Zones of all the Star Clusters and Nebulae observed by Sir William Herschel' (1828). In due course she was to receive the greatest honour possible as a reward for her work. In 1828 the Gold Medal of the Royal Astronomical Society was voted to her, and this distinction was crowned with the even greater one of an honorary membership of the Society.

Caroline Herschel's work was known among the ladies of her own time. She was not an easy person to befriend, but many ladies among the intelligentsia, the authors Fanny Burney and Joanna Bailie as well as the German ladies at the court in Windsor, sought her out to make the acquaintance of the first lady astronomer on English soil.

The combined efforts of the Herschels, for William welcomed the correspondence of the scientific women of Europe and further afield (notably Princess Daschkoff, the Directress of the Petersburg Academy of Sciences, and the Empress Catherine herself), raised the science of astronomy to new heights of popularity among the fashionable. It was somewhat wryly that Caroline, the young girl who had wanted nothing more than to be a governess, acknowledged herself in old age as a professional scientist.

The Lunar Society and its ladies

The Lunar Society was a famous group of progressive and inventive men who lived in the various environs of Birmingham in the latter half of the eighteenth century. During the height of their creativity, they elected to meet every month on the Monday nearest the full moon. The reason for this choice of date was simple. Travelling on horseback or in carriages along bad and unlit roads was a trifle safer and a little more comfortable in the light of the moon. Because of this careful timing of meetings, they referred to themselves as the Lunar group, and Dr Erasmus Darwin, one of their number and an irrepressible wit, succumbed to the irresistible and coined the sobriquet 'Lunatic' for the individual members.

In its early days the Lunar Society was an informal body of men, closely knit by ties of blood, friendship and common interest. Originally the group comprised about fourteen men and included Erasmus Darwin, physician, poet and inventor, Josiah Wedgwood, potter and industrialist, James Watt, engineer and inventor, James Keir, industrial chemist, and Matthew Boulton, businessman and factory owner. Somewhat later, the Irish landowner and inventor Richard Lovell Edgeworth gained entry on the strength of his mechanical genius and his brilliant, if mercurial, personality. Jonathan Stokes, the physician and chemist, and William Withering, the botanist, were also admitted. Almost all the men involved were businessmen and their primary interest was the research and development of ideas that would promote the advance of industry. These included improvements in road surfacing, transport, steam engines and locomotion. The society, if it could be called that, for there were no formal rules or constitution and no records were kept, has been described as a 'pioneer industrial research establishment'.[33]

These ideas, and others of more general scientific appeal, natural history, botany, geology and politics, were the subjects discussed in the hospitable and well-lit drawing rooms of Matthew Boulton, Samuel Galton and the others who hosted Lunar evenings. 'Lunar ladies', certainly those of the hosting family, were present at these meetings. Mary Anne Schimmelpennick, the daughter of Samuel Galton, who was one of the later associates of the group, recalled evenings in which both she and her mother joined in the scientific exchanges, in one case with a very alert snake as a living specimen.[34]

Children of Lunar members tended to marry each other, indicating a degree of intimate social exchange. Thomas Beddoes, a former reader of chemistry at Oxford who opened his sanitorium, the Pneumatic Institute, at Clifton near Bristol in 1798, married Anne Edgeworth. Their scientific *salon* became famous in the south-west. Samuel Galton's son married Violette, daughter of Erasmus Darwin; Darwin's son

Robert married Josiah Wedgwood's daughter Susannah. Charles Darwin was their son.

The ladies of the Lunar circle were additionally fortunate in that many of the 'Lunatics' held progressive ideas on what constituted the education of daughters. Josiah Wedgwood believed in equality of opportunity in education, and his sons and daughters were taught together at home. Another progressive man, as regards the education of daughters, was Samuel Galton, Mary Anne Schimmelpennick's father. He was a devout Quaker. Unaware, apparently, of any contradiction between the tenets of his faith and the products of the family gun foundry, he had amassed a sizeable fortune from the profits. In 1785 he moved his wife and children from the family home in Steele House Lane, Birmingham, to the more dignified and salubrious rural retreat of a small estate at Barr in Staffordshire. Here Galton became a country gentleman, but also established a laboratory and pursued his many scientific interests, which included writing an introduction to ornithology for children, *The Natural History of Birds, containing a variety of facts selected from several writers and intended for the Amusement and Instruction of Children* (1786–91). This was to be his only published work, but it was well received and was a popular book in schools, and in one girls' school in particular.

Though he was acquainted with many of the leading scientists of the Birmingham–Staffordshire area, Galton never achieved any professional status as a scientist, but remained a devoted amateur. An account of the life of the Galton family, and of the education that the children received, was written by Galton's daughter Mary Anne. As a very old lady, writing after a life that had been fraught with family misunderstanding and the anguish that deeply held religious convictions can frequently cause, she loyally recalled:

> My father was a man of superior intellectual endowments; he had much taste for the exact sciences. He was often deeply occupied in courses of experiments on optics and colours and also on electricity and chemistry. He had long been a member of the Royal Society, and was one of the earliest members of the Linnaean Society. [p. 36]

Mary Anne also remembered her father as a devoted teacher. Part of his reason for retiring to Barr had been to undertake the instruction of his children in peace and seclusion. He and his wife, who emerges from Mary Anne's story as a stern, unbending woman, embarked on a systematic education of sons and daughters alike. It was a curious blend of the strictest religious principles, intensive and wide-ranging study and very carefully selected and restricted reading. Latin and French were part of the curriculum, and were entrusted to various governesses and masters, but most of Mary Anne's time was spent in the study of chemistry, botany, entomology and ornithology, all under the supervision of her father. Botany was a particular interest with her father. She recounted that 'during our walks we were constantly occupied in looking for new plants, which my French governess would afterwards draw under his direction. We were likewise employed in learning entomology' (p. 24).

If there were restrictions imposed on the amount and variety of imaginative literature that the children were permitted, the very opposite was true in their scientific studies. In these they were allowed to explore and experiment in a spirit of almost total freedom. It seems that the Galton parents assumed that some form of scientific hobby should occupy the children's recreation time. They were encouraged to make natural history collections and were liberally supplied with relevant books and microscopes. They were also invited to undertake their own chemical experiments in their father's laboratory. So, for example, Mary Anne wrote that she could recall many interesting and diverting hours playing with 'experiments with various acids and alkalines in solutions of metals'.

There was an amusing little footnote to this chemical expertise that the children were allowed to acquire. When dragooned, much against her will, into collecting specimens of fungi to assist William Withering in his botanical researches, Mary Anne set about a bit of quiet sabotage. Already irritated at having to include fungi in the search for botanical specimens that was an integral part of the daily schoolroom routine, she resented the unfair obligation continually to produce new and interesting specimens. So she and her brothers decided to assist nature in producing that apparently desirable result. After some stolen hours in the laboratory, 'painting over the fungi in sundry methods' with the various chemical preparations, they offered their collection to the botanist. They were happy with the result and certainly believed that Dr Withering had been hoodwinked by their efforts (p. 43).

The members of the Lunar group did not confine their educational ideas to the privacy of their families. Having experimented in the domestic environment, some of them were keen to disseminate their views on the value of science education to women to a wider audience. This resulted in some interesting publications that influenced the way in which many parents viewed their daughters' education.

One of these was the curriculum devised by Dr Erasmus Darwin during the 1790s for the boarding school established by the Misses Susan and Mary Parker (his two illegitimate daughters, born during the period of his widowhood). Published as *A Plan for the Conduct of Female Education in Boarding Schools* in 1798, it testified that the scientific activities of women during the previous decades were known, at least, to some interested observers.

What Darwin was suggesting was a systematic exploration of each subject up to the level of attainment appropriate to each student, with due allowance made for those who might wish to progress to more advanced levels. He certainly accepted that marriage and motherhood was the inescapable and preferred destiny of most women. He was strongly of the opinion, however, that it was not only in their interests, but in the interests of society in general, that women should be carefully educated through a balanced curriculum of the sciences and the humanities, with the greater emphasis on the former. Not since the days of Bathsua Makin, over a century earlier, had science been presented as so central to women's education.

Dr Darwin based his scheme for the science education of women on the grounds that the watered-down version of the classical regime imposed on some girls was an inefficient and unproductive mode of education. He included the education of boys in this criticism, for he regarded the classical education of the period as failing in its objectives: 'The necessity of learning some antient or foreign languages, imposes a laborious task on the youth of both sexes, which consumes years of their precious time, which might otherwise be employed in the acquisition of sciences' (p. 17). Of course he did not dismiss language teaching altogether. He wanted a modern language, either French or Italian, which as the languages of business and culture would be more appropriate. In this suggestion he was close to the policies of language teaching operating in the business schools for merchant sons and in some early girls' schools.

Although he acknowledged the importance of the cultivation of good taste and appreciation of the arts in schools, the aspects of female education that truly interested him were what might be described as the hard-core curriculum of mathematics and science. In Darwin's opinion, the education of all women should be anchored firmly in a thorough and complete training in mathematics. Once that was achieved, the scientific curriculum, which Darwin suggested should cover all the standard subjects, physics, astronomy, mechanics, hydro-statics, optics, electricity and magnetism, should be incorporated into the timetable.

Darwin foresaw no difficulties with such a proposal. Mathematics was a subject well within the abilities of women. He knew of cases where women had demonstrated a natural affinity with the subject. However, if they wished to progress in a systematic way, their mathematical studies required some formalization.

Darwin was obliged to acknowledge that there were obstacles to the realization of the ambitious reform of women's education that he was suggesting. There were neither teachers to teach it in the organized way that was desirable, nor suitable books from which to study it. He suggested as a solution to the first problem an extension of and improvement on the current system of employing the available itinerant teachers. Eventually graduates of this school and others like it would be expected to fill these vacancies.

The second problem, the lack of books, appeared to pose more serious difficulties. Part of Darwin's *Plan* comprised a full bibliography of suitable textbooks required by any young woman attempting the science education that he had outlined. He declared that devising this reading list had caused him great difficulty. There seemed to be so few appropriate works available. He issued a challenge to all 'writers of juvenile books' to take on themselves the task of adding to the woefully inadequate number of books available to girl students. We know that his challenge was more than adequately answered by the swelling numbers of authors, many of them women, who liberally fed the market for decades to come.[35]

In the meantime, Darwin himself, with the help of his wide female acquaintance, had selected those volumes that he thought would assist the female tyro. He pointed out that they had often been written with more expert readers in mind, but that their careful use would be rewarding. His list provides an invaluable insight into what amateur women scientists were reading in the last decade of the eighteenth century.

In botany the list included Mrs M.E. Jackson's *Botanical Dialogues for the Use of Schools*, James Lee's *Introduction to Botany*, a translation of Carl von Linne's *Families of Plants*, Curtis's *Botanical Magazine* and Mardyke's translation of Rousseau's *Letters on Botany*.

Darwin noted the long popularity of chemistry with women. Despite that, it was not very well served with textbooks. He was obliged to recommend such standard works as Lavoisier's *Elements of Chymistry*, Fourcroy's *The Philosophy of Chemistry* and Watson's *Chymical Essays*. In fact, the first suitable chemistry textbook in English was not published until 1803. It was by Frederick Accum, assistant to Humphrey Davy at the Royal Institution. Mrs Jane Marcet's better known *Conversations on Chemistry* was published, as has been noted, in 1806.

The problem with mineralogy was even more acute. Darwin had an interesting view on this subject as part of the curriculum. He saw it as an important foundation subject to be studied in preparation for chemistry and agriculture. Both of these subjects were often accepted as being of especial interest to girls in the 1790s, so it was obviously particularly important to offer a thorough instruction in the courses. Unfortunately, Darwin had been unable to find books he could truly recommend. The authorities in the field, whom he named as Kronstadt, Bergman and Kirwan, were to his mind 'too exact and prolix', but in the absence of anything more suitable he was obliged to include them in his bibliography. Young ladies were once more encouraged to read the foremost authorities in a scientific field.

Natural history, another popular subject, presented fewer difficulties. Darwin unhesitatingly recommended a comprehensive reading list, which included both simple introductions, such as 'Mrs Teachwell's' elementary textbook, *History of Quadrupeds*, and his friend Samuel Galton's *Treatise on Birds*, Goldsmith's *Animated Nature* and Newbery's *Natural History of Beasts*. But the ladies were also encouraged to read the standard work in the field by the great French naturalist Buffon. This was indicative of the high standard Darwin expected from his young ladies. It also illustrated Darwin's conviction that women must approach their education without any of the squeamishness often affected by their sex. Many women, like Mrs Vesey for example, had read Buffon, but others, typically Hannah More, who did not wholly approve of higher education in a woman, thought it an unsuitable book for ladies. Goldsmith's *Animated Nature* was more acceptable, although Miss More thought it was time for a new edition, 'purified from the indelicate and offensive parts'.[36]

Darwin was all for variety in the curriculum. Anything that relieved the monotony of study for the young was welcomed. He even included the growing fashion for shorthand and memory training, although with some reluctance. He was not to know that within three or four decades young women would begin to find employment as clerks, chemists and telegraph operators where such skills would be of some use.[37]

He was, however, particularly enthusiastic about the necessity of taking the girls on field trips as an integral part of their scientific education. He was of the same mind as men like Dr Johnson, who regarded a knowledge of the industrial processes of the country to be of essential interest to women. To Dr Johnson, as to Darwin, R.L.

Edgeworth and many others, these processes were a source of true fascination. When they travelled together, Dr Johnson and Mrs Thrale visited iron and brass foundries, silk mills, and ceramic and glass works.[38] Darwin suggested visits to cotton works, potteries, iron foundries and factories to see science in action. As has been noted, this was no new idea in the late 1790s, but this appears to be the first time the idea was formally incorporated into a school curriculum. Darwin further encouraged parents to devote time during the summer holidays to opening the eyes of their female young to the glories of modern technology.

All that he suggested above was aimed at women and girls who merely wanted to come to grips with an all-round general education. For those few who would wish to probe deeper into science, Darwin suggested additional reading, this time his own book, *The Botanic Garden*. This work, a long scientific poem, was a best-seller in the 1790s and it was its publication that had catapulted Darwin to his status as national celebrity. His first major scientific poem and probably the earliest scientific potboiler, *The Loves of the Plants*, had been published in 1789. The unprecedented nationwide sensation that it created was clearly reflected in the publishers' advance of a phenomenal 1,000 guineas for a sequel. It appeared in 1791 under the somewhat unpromising title of *The Economy of Vegetation* and was to be Part I of *The Botanic Garden*.

As a survey of the current state of scientific knowledge and research, *The Botanic Garden* is an astonishingly comprehensive work. In its 2,400 lines, all branches of science and technology are described and then further explained in 126 closely written octavo pages of detailed notes which form a supplement to the many long intertextual notes. It included detailed reports on the uses of electricity, the development of the steam engine, the formation of limestone, salt, coal, sand and clays, the use and design of water pumps and the best schemes of marsh drainage, water circulation, the function of vegetables and much more. If all this sounds rather forbidding, it must be said that the poem itself remains a highly readable and often extremely amusing piece, a fascinating combination of skilfully constructed rhyming couplets, full of striking visual images, and at times dancing with wit and humour. After such an introduction, the many women who were among Dr Darwin's delighted readers could not help but step on the road to scientific womanhood.

Darwin's programme of female education aroused the interest of many. His daughter's school became a place to visit for all those who were interested in the progressive education of girls. In 1799 Darwin was delighted to show members of the Edgeworth family, well known for their pedagogical preoccupations, over the school.

Maria Edgeworth (1767–1849), the famous novelist, and her father, Richard Lovell Edgeworth (1744–1817), were ardent supporters of scientific education for women. Despite her literary avocation, it was well known that Maria preferred scientists to literary men. She had a particular interest in astronomy and helped to entertain Sir John Herschel, William Herschel's son, when he visited Edgeworthstown. A friendship blossomed between the two, and in March 1831 Maria visited Herschel at Slough and discussed his work. She had the special pleasure of being shown how to use the 20-foot telescope by the astronomer himself, and she saw 'Saturn and his rings, and the moon and her volcanoes'.[39]

Chemistry was another subject she enjoyed, and Humphrey Davy was a welcome visitor when he made his lecture tour to Dublin. As might be expected, she was to become acquainted with the two ladies who had produced, each in her own way, the best books in the field, Mrs Marcet and Mrs Somerville. They enjoyed each other's company when the occasion offered, such as at the scientific house party at the home of Sir John Sebright, agriculturist and Member of Parliament, in mid-January 1822.[40]

Maria's father, Richard, to whom she was indebted for her scientific curiosity as well as her concern for the education of women, had long taken a personal interest in educational theory in general. It was often noted, and not always kindly, that he had provided himself with the raw material for such experiments by begetting nineteen children during four successive marriages. His earliest views on education were quite different to the theories he finally adopted and put into practice. As a young man he had been influenced by the theories of Rousseau, whose back-to-nature notions had been much approved by Edgeworth's eccentric friend Thomas Day (1748–89).[41] Day was the author of a trendsetting educational best-seller in the 1780s, *Sandford and Merton* (1783–9), which transmitted to enthusiastic English readers the essence of the new European thinking on the dignity and virtue of unsophisticated simplicity.

In the 1760s Europe was agog with popular versions of these theories, derived from the writings of Jean Jacques Rousseau. For a brief period, there was a flowering of interest in and cultivation of the unbridled feelings and passions of men untainted by the restraints of society. Out went restraint, convention and self-control. In came feeling, emotion and spontaneity. Worried parents and self-appointed custodians of society's morals anguished over the damage being done to the fabric of society.[42]

A fashion for the tranquillity and supposedly tangible reality of life in the country took hold. The countryside and its rustic customs acquired a charm that must have astonished its labouring inhabitants. It became fashionable for people like Edgeworth to take houses in the remote countryside, in his case in Hare Hatch in Berkshire, to grow their own vegetables and inadvertently to pine away for intellectual stimulus. But the ruling idea was splendid simplicity, the very antithesis of the restraint of conventional education.

Influenced directly by Thomas Day, Edgeworth decided that his eldest son, Richard, should be allowed to experience this liberating freedom from restraint. The child was never to be restricted or limited in any way and no attempt was to be made to inculcate into him even the rudiments of education. Before very long, Edgeworth reaped the reward of his too literal acceptance of another man's ideology. He found he had a truculent, self-willed and tempestuous child on his hands, and this product of the Rousseauesque experiment was unceremoniously packed off to the Jesuits in France. The poor little boy was already doomed. He changed very little during the rest of his frustrating and disappointing life.

As his interest in science grew, Edgeworth dropped Rousseau in favour of the carefully controlled but nevertheless inspiring and invigorating scientific education that his new-found friends in the Lunar group advocated for their children. By this time, too, Edgeworth had found the release he had long desired from a hastily contracted early marriage. Anna Maria Elers, his wife and the mother of his first four children, died, unmourned, in childbirth, after a difficult and unnecessary trip to Europe insisted on by Edgeworth. With classic Romantic haste he flung himself into the arms of one Miss Honora Sneyd, to whom he had been introduced while still a married man and a frequent visitor at the house of Dr Darwin in Lichfield.

The newly married Edgeworths repaired to the family mansion at Edgeworthstown in County Longford in Ireland, for Edgeworth had decided to take up his duties as an estate owner and he also wished to put into effect his new and more rigorous concept of education. The new Mrs Edgeworth was everything a wife should be, and she had also devised a plan to give all her children a sound scientific education. This was not surprising, for she had long been a member of Darwin's circle in Lichfield. Unfortunately, she soon succumbed to consumption, but the marriage bed was refilled almost immediately and, apparently at her suggestion, by her sister Elizabeth. Society was scandalized, but the marriage lasted for another twenty years and produced nine children, until that Mrs Edgeworth too was overtaken by the dreaded disease. The last Mrs Edgeworth was Frances Beaufort, an Irish girl from County Louth, whose labours added another six, bringing the total number of Edgeworth progeny to nineteen living children.

Of the four ladies of Edgeworth's choice, Honora and Frances were the most appropriate consorts. Honora was reckoned to be an outstanding theoretical mechanic and it was she who was responsible for initiating and supervising the Edgeworth brand of education. Frances Beaufort was already an adept artist when she married the man old enough to be her father. A bright and intelligent girl, she quickly worked up an interest in science and taught herself to make engineering drawings for her husband – as much from personal inclination as from diplomacy towards her elderly, but still energetic spouse.

When Frances' long-delayed honeymoon took place, the trip to England included an introduction to the ageing Lunatics in whose work, especially those aspects relating to industrial research, she was particularly interested. When she met Watts and Boulton, she pronounced their inventions 'sublime'.[43] A favourite story of Maria's recounted how, on a later trip in 1813, her young stepmother's scientific interests scandalized the classical preserve of Cambridge. On a visit to King's College, the party horrified the Revd Edward Smedley, their host, a donnish man with a negligible interest in science, by preferring to discuss the merits and possible defects of the wood and stone that had been used in constructing the chapel roof, oblivious to the Handel anthem being played on the organ as they talked. It was always the more tangible pleasures that held the attention of scientific ladies. After some three-quarters of an hour, the frustrated academic and music lover turned to Maria and exclaimed, 'Mrs E., seems to have this taste for mechanics too!' 'He spoke of it,' commented Maria wryly, 'as a kind of mania. So I nodded at him very gravely and answered, 'Yes, you'll find we are all tinctured with it more or less.'[44]

Maria was her father's constant companion and helpmate in all his educational endeavour. It was she who put into practice in the education of the growing family his and Honora's theories. Maria's first effort in scientific education for children was to complete the Harry and Lucy stories, elementary science textbooks for young children, begun by her father, which were eventually published as *Early Lessons* (1801). The primary purpose of these stories was to initiate the elementary instruction of children in science. According to Maria, her father expected that science would become a growing passion among the young, and he wished to prepare them for it: 'My father long ago foresaw that the taste for scientific as well as literary knowledge, which has risen so rapidly and spread so widely, would render it necessary to make some provision for the early instruction of youth in science.'[45]

Her major work on science education, on which she again collaborated with her father, was *Practical Education*. This imposing manual of education appeared initially in two large volumes in 1798, and later, in 1801, as a three-volume set, with the revised title of *Essays in Practical Education*. Although Maria did not write all of it, the book was generally attributed to her in contemporary reviews. The work embraced the whole of a child's educational existence and dealt with its intellectual physiological and moral development. A point of particular importance was that boys and girls should be educated in the same way. The Edgeworths stipulated that, although a boy's career prospects differed from his sisters', this should not be reflected in differences in their education. Boys and girls equally must cultivate the fundamentals of a good education. According to their definition, that was the ability to reason clearly and soundly.

The main argument of the Edgeworths' theory of education was the importance of training children to think clearly and to reason carefully. To achieve this goal they devised what they considered the only appropriate curriculum in the circumstances, one that laid greatest emphasis on mathematical and experimental science. Like Darwin, the Edgeworths accepted that mathematics should form the foundation of any educational system. According to these writers, scientific subjects could profitably usurp the important role in mental training traditionally assigned to Latin. The first steps in a child's education should be the acquisition of a thorough understanding of the rudiments of mathematics. In the advertisement to the third edition, father and daughter wrote:

> The author ... strongly recommends the most minute attention to the first rudiments of arithmetick; – if he has succeeded in forming the good sense of any of his pupils, he attributes it chiefly to having given them clear notions on whatever he had taught, and not to the quantity of what has been committed to memory. [*Practical Education*, 1811 edn, I, p. xiii]

They recommended that education should begin from the earliest moments in the nursery, when children should be encouraged to develop a scientific curiosity by learning to discover through play. Some of the most vital aspects of the educative process could be introduced by this method. Maria, in particular, was strongly against confining a child to a desk simply to memorize a taught lesson. She thought such a system self-defeating. Instead each child should be encouraged to develop his or her powers of discovery and deduction. A teacher who encourages this method of learning will

> discern the symptoms of a love of science, and ... he will admire the activity which they display in the pursuit of knowledge. He will feel that it is his business to direct this activity, to furnish his pupil with materials for fresh combinations, to put himself in situations where he can make useful observations and acquire that experience which cannot be bought, and which no masters can communicate. [I, pp. 18–19]

In proposing that girls be obliged to acquit themselves as adequately as boys, the Edgeworths felt they were stemming a fast-flowing current that was threatening to wash away the hard-won gains of previous decades. What they had observed was a subtle, but inevitable realignment of spheres of interest. Now it was becoming more acceptable for women to seek to employ themselves and amuse others with 'wit and superficial acquirements in literature'. Indeed many women who ventured forth in this way were already earning the admiration and enthusiasm of a growing and voracious readership. Maria herself was shortly to be hailed as a popular novelist. But whereas before women had turned to the sciences rather than to literature, now, according to the Edgeworths, 'Sentiment and ridicule have conspired to represent reason, knowledge and science, as unsuitable or dangerous to women.'

To defeat the endemic inclination of women to be superficial on the one hand, and to preserve the traditional grasp of women on the sciences on the other, the Edgeworths exhorted the female sex to put all their energy into training and developing their powers of clear thought. It is only by developing this ability, they argued, that women can ever hope to change or improve their inferior status. And at all costs they must eschew what is superficial and frivolous. Science was therefore to be preferred to the arts:

> let a woman know any one thing completely, and she will have sufficient understanding to learn more, and to apply what she had been taught so as to interest men of generosity and genius in her favour. The knowledge of the general principle of any science is very different from superficial knowledge of the science. Perhaps, from

not attending to this distinction, or from not understanding it, many have failed in female education. [I, p. 31].

Maria Edgeworth singled out chemistry as the subject in which she would most expect young girls to excel. It was so nearly allied to the domestic arts of food preparation with which most women are closely concerned that the move from one art to another could be almost imperceptible. It certainly would be, if cooking were taught in a more scientific way. Like her father, Maria was particularly anxious that chemistry should be taught to girls in as complete and thorough a manner as possible. She begged her readers to note that merely priming girls to perform a few party tricks would be worthless, and it would alienate serious-minded children. A course of chemistry for girls in which they were to be thoroughly and carefully instructed should comprise of the 'first single operations of chemistry, evaporation, crystallization, calcination, detonation, effervescence and saturation and related experiments'. Maria's fundamental aim with this course was to interest and inspire young ladies to 'exercise their reasoning and inventive faculties upon every object that surrounds them' (*Practical Education*, I, p. 31).

On the basis of their own experience, the Edgeworths were able to suggest the pursuits of natural history and the collecting of fossils and minerals as appropriate diversions for children. In pleading for time and space for youngsters to develop their particular interests, 'most well ordered families allow their horses and their dogs to have houses to themselves; cannot one Room be allotted to the children of the family' (*Practical Education*, I. p. 38), the Edgeworths were somewhat in advance of their time. In their home in Edgeworthstown the children had their own space in which to leave their treasures, maintain their collections in cabinets and have their microscopes and drawing materials handy.

The Edgeworth's educational theories were controversial probably because of the strongly feminist and secular tone in which they were presented. It was an attitude at odds with the increasing religiosity of the time. More people were concerned with church going and the teaching of religion. In fact it was no longer unfashionable to be religious, as it had been earlier in the century.[46] An education, particularly one with women in mind, that was purely secular was unlikely to win many adherents. Even quite adventurous ladies, such as Catherine Hutton and her friend Mary Anne Coltman, both with many scientific interests, worried about this aspect of Maria Edgeworth's thoughts. Some time later Miss Hutton wrote to Miss Coltman, 'I have heard the objection made to Miss Edgeworth's system of education that you make against her novel [the novel was *Helen*, 1834] – that she advocates morality but not religion. In education this is unpardonable; in a novel I think it is not.'[47]

But Miss Edgeworth's popularity as a serious novelist ensured that the public remained aware of the theories on the value of scientific education for women that she shared with her father and stepmothers. Increasing numbers of schools for girls were extending their timetables to allow the pupils opportunities for developing some degree of scientific literacy. Charlotte Lennox (1720–1804), playwright and novelist and a close friend of Dr Johnson, took up teaching when her income dwindled. At one time she taught Anne Welch, daughter of one of the members of Dr Johnson's circle, who was an accomplished linguist. Anne 'made a considerable proficiency in the mathematics' and eventually became 'an erudite botanist', kept a school herself, and ultimately applied herself to conchology.[48] Letitia Mathilda Hawkins was also a keen student of botany, an interest she developed of her own accord. Her general education had been undertaken by her father, Sir John Hawkins, one of Dr Johnson's biographers. He used her as an unofficial secretary and ghost writer. It appears from her *Memoirs* that she had to undertake whatever academic tasks he disliked. He was no arithmetician and 'for convenience he made me a tolerably good one', wrote Miss Hawkins, and, without any signs of gratitude, 'This knowledge added much to my labour' (*Memoirs*, I, p. 144).

Another schoolmistress with a scientific vocation was Meribah Lorrington, who kept a girls' school in Chelsea sometime in the late eighteenth century. The daughter of a schoolmaster, she was reckoned a 'perfect arithmetician and astronomer' and one of her former pupils, Mary Robinson (1758–1800), the notorious 'Perdita', complimented her as 'the most extensively accomplished female that I ever remember to have met with'. But Miss Lorrington had her problems. She drank![49]

There was another famous school which was established in London and presided over by a keen working woman scientist. She was Mrs Margaret Bryan. With the exception of two very pleasing portraits, the frontispieces to her books, very little information about her is extant. If the portraits are taken as accurate likenesses, she appears as a young and extraordinarily pretty mother, for in one she is accompanied by two equally attractive little daughters. The portraits prefaced her two published works, *A Comprehensive System of Astronomy* (1797) and *Lectures on Natural Philosophy* (1806). In these books she incorporated a certain amount of autobiographical information which is all that is known of her. She gives few details, apart from the fact that she had spent eight years studying the sciences followed by seven years' practical application and experiments. She says nothing of her marriage to Mr Bryan, who may have had Irish and, possibly, military connections. Unlike many lady writers who frequently sought the support of friends by their hard luck stories, she never refers to her personal circumstances, and a positive and enthusiastic interest in science teaching as a chosen vocation illuminates her writing. Her reputation must have been considerable. When Mrs Marcet's anonymous *Conversations on Chemistry* was published to great popular acclaim, it was widely accepted that Mrs Bryan was the most likely author. Her work in education attracted the influential support of an important scientist at the time. He was Charles Hutton, the editor of the *Lady's Diary* and therefore a perfect source of help and encouragement for a woman scientist and teacher. In her preface, Margaret Bryan gave him all credit for the supportive assistance he had given her in having her works of science published.

Her school was founded in the closing years of the century, and its changes of address may well have indicated the growing prosperity of its proprietress. Begun at Blackheath, it removed to 1 Gloucester Place, Portman Square. Later the premises at 27 Lower Cadogan Place near Hyde Park corner were leased by Mrs Bryan. The school's last move, so far as it is known, was to the more salubrious airs of Margate where Mrs Bryan already had many acquaintances.

Her books were the published versions of the science classes she delivered in her school to her young ladies. She admitted that the girls who came to her often required considerable coaching and remedial work before they were ready to undertake the programme laid out in her books. They were often weakest in mathematics, but a few years at her school usually remedied this deficiency.

The science classes in Mrs Bryan's school concentrated on physics, mechanics and chemistry. It was obviously in her own best interest to make her school as attractive as possible to prospective parents. The whole course, as laid out in her books, was distinctly decorous and ladylike. Her words and thoughts were neither flamboyant nor eccentric, and she made no extravagant claims for the 'liberating' effects of studying science on the condition of women. She also very deliberately avoided the secular bias that coloured the work of many women science writers through the decades. Instead she carefully linked the study of science with a belief in the revelation of the existence of God in nature. She often explained to her attentive students that the study of science, revealing as it did 'the evidence of the nature and attributes of the

Deity', was the very best armour any young woman could develop as 'a defence against the vain sophistry of the world'.

Science and religion

Coming as it did at the end of the eighteenth century, this brief for the importance of science to women was the summation of a long tradition. So many influential writers had repeated their belief that science was not only a way to salvation, but also a useful antidote to the wayward vices of womanhood. It was a commonplace in the seventeenth century and in the succeeding decades, from the contribution of Richard Steele, who, in an essay appropriately named 'Modesty', had suggested that women could acquire that virtue through the study of science, through to Dr Johnson who thought that natural history would 'excite a Curiosity after the Works of God ... and the Providence which governs the Vegetable and Animal Creation'. Dr Johnson put personal salvation and a moral life above everything else. Within this framework he attached a profound religious significance to the study of science. At an advanced level, it could benefit the whole of mankind, but even the humblest amateur would be provided with a useful and rewarding occupation which would divert him or her from idleness and temptation.[50] In his preface to Robert Dodsley's *Preceptor*, which Boswell called 'one of the most valuable books for the improvement of young minds that had appeared in any language' (*Life*, I, p. 192), Johnson recommended the fusion of religious devotion with scientific curiosity.[51]

Some women writers refined on this physico-theological value of science by asserting not only that it should make science a subject of great appeal to women, but that its particular religious implications had relevance for certain social classes. Elizabeth Hamiliton (1758–1816), a writer on educational matters, thought this relevance should be limited to the upper ranks in society, and consequently entitled her work *Letters addressed to the Daughter of a Nobleman on the Formation of Religious and Moral Principles* (1806). The first volume dealt entirely with moral and spiritual matters. The study of natural history was of central importance in religious education:

> As the works of nature tend much more than the works of art to raise our thoughts to heaven, I would earnestly recommend it to you to pursue the study, for which you appeared to have such a decided taste. Natural history, in all its branches, leads the mind to a perpetual admiration of the wisdom and power of the Supreme Being. [I, p. 71]

Jane West, another writer on the religious and educative value of science for women, also thought that only ladies 'above the lower classes' should seek the Lord through the wonders of natural history.[52] She warmly recommended to this same class that, through a 'temperate pursuit' of experimental philosophy, botany and astronomy, they should allow themselves to be diverted from 'frivolous objects' and to form 'habits of close attention and argumentative deduction; qualities in which women are supposed to be defective' (II, p. 425).

Other elements entered the equation of science and sober womanhood. There was a theory, much prized by those who saw themselves as custodians of female manners and morals, that science was a suitable subject for women because it was not as dangerous for the female brain as the study of the classics. It had always been thought that the classics were 'unwomanly'; in the words of the Reverend John Bennett, 'They would damp that vivacity and destroy that disengaged ease and *softness*, which are the very *essence* of your graces.'[53] Mr Bennett directed young ladies to safeguard their womanliness, their beauty and their social graces by dabbling gently in scientific matters, specifically natural history, geology and botany: 'They do not require so much time, abstraction or comprehensiveness of mind; they bring no wrinkles, and they will give a polish to your manners, and such a liberal expansion to your understanding, as every *rational* creature should endeavour to attain' (pp. 167–8).

The great exponent of the ladylike appeal of science was Mrs Hester Chapone. Mrs Chapone was an influential voice and her *Letters on the Improvement of the Mind addressed to a Young Lady* (Dublin, 1773) propounded the view that young women should avoid the dangers of becoming engrossed in any subject that would divert them from their primary concern, the acquisition of a husband. Their usual frivolous pursuits, however, were a poor self-advertisement. In order to avoid projecting such a flawed image of womanhood, they could resort to the study of science. This provided a suitable and acceptable alternative to the usual despised female pursuits which were counterproductive in the search for a husband. At the same time, it brought none of the contumely associated with cleverness or scholarliness in a woman. It needed little serious application, and yet was known to be capable of 'enlarging' the mind. In addition, Mrs Chapone confirmed that science had the power to excite in the mind 'the most ardent gratitude and profound adoration towards the great and good being' (II, p. 202).

Mrs Bryan's curriculum and publications, combining all these elements, made science a most acceptable subject for a woman. Small wonder then that her subscriber lists were so large. The books were offered to the public as handsome volumes exquisitely illustrated with Mrs Bryan's own drawings. A wide and appreciative readership supported her venture into print. It included libraries, Oxbridge colleges, booksellers and provincial book clubs like the Bocking Book Club and the Sittingbourne and Milton Book Society, as well as a very large number of women from all over the kingdom and as far afield as Calcutta, many past and present pupils among them. Even some of the most popular and eminent mathematicians of the age, such as John Bonnycastle and Charles Hutton himself, supported this lady scientist by buying her books. It seems, too, that the tradition of buying scientific material as presents for women had not declined either, at least on some occasions. Books like Mrs Bryan's made very suitable gifts for women friends. On 9 June 1813, one James Murray presented to Margaret Hamilton the gift of Mrs Bryan's *Lectures on Natural Philosophy*.[54]

Science: recreation and research

Ever since Bishop Thomas Sprat, in 1667, had commended the virtues of 'Working Nature' as a source of inspiration, 'one of the best and most fruitful soils for the growth of Wit', and as a source of knowledge, natural phenomena had excited the curiosity of many people. With leisure and money at their disposal, more and more people during the eighteenth century, following the example of Mrs Celia Fiennes, took time off to escort their families and friends around the sights of the British Isles and occasionally abroad. The age of the tourist and the sightseer had begun. What motivated these tourists was a scientific curiosity about the workings of nature which was usually combined with an engrossing interest in the advances of industrial science. Although there were already some stirrings of an early ecological awareness, it was more common to express an enthusiasm for the glories of industry.

It was not the beauty of the landscape that was of primary interest. Indeed it was not often recognized. Nature, untamed and wild, had not yet been accorded the aesthetic attractions that inspired later generations. Areas that would become famous for their great natural beauty were often shunned in that age as barbarous and inhospitable. Charles Cotton was untypical only in his choice of simile when he compared the mountains of the Peak District to 'Warts and Wens' and 'imposthumated boyles', and declared the whole district 'a Country so deformed' that the Traveller 'would swear those Parts Nature's pudenda were'.[55]

The approbation of the English tourist was reserved for the landscape that demonstrated man's success in taming and subduing its wildness. When, in 1730, William Hay climbed Mount Caburn to admire the view, it was the abundant traces, in the iron works, the buildings and the forestry plantations, of the transforming and controlling power of man that pleased him. In the technological harnessing of what had been wild and dangerous, he perceived a new and hopeful harmony in nature:

> Then Industry, Earth's handmaid, threw apart
> Her rural Attire, and dress'd her Charms with Art.
> From second Chaos, order did produce,
> From useless Things, Things of the noblest Use. [*Mount Caburn*, 1730]

Mines and quarries were typical goals for the traveller, particularly for women travellers, for whom they seemed to hold some special allure. It seems to have been taken for granted that women would like to know the intimate details of intricate industrial processes. In 1755 the two ladies who visited the mines near Whitehaven, and received the special compliment of having a poem addressed to them, were treated to a lengthy disquisition and a weighty body of notes that explained in greater detail the mining procedures they had observed.

Educationalists appeared to accept that such outings had a serious pedagogic value. Dr Johnson recommended 'all opportunities of learning, however remote the matter may be from common life or common conversation', to youngsters like Susannah Thrale. As has been noted, Dr Erasmus Darwin was particularly enthusiastic about the importance of field trips as an integral part of scientific education. He was of the same mind as Johnson. All of them regarded a knowledge of the industrial processes of the country as of essential interest and importance to women. He suggested visits to cotton works, potteries, iron foundries and factories to see science in action. All this was to be formally included in the school curriculum, and, in addition, parents were urged to devote time during the summer holidays to opening the eyes of their female young to the glories of modern technology – as indeed some of them, like Mr and Mrs Girle, were already doing.[56]

Exhibitions and collections had long attracted massive audiences. When, for example, the 'Microcosm, a Mechanical Exhibition' was put on at Chester in 1765, it was noted that it was 'frequented by everybody' (*Memoirs of Richard Lovell Edgeworth*, 1820, I, p. 110). What it purported to demonstrate was the motions of the heavens in moving pictures.[57] Johnson's suggestions for enriching the education of Susannah Thrale had included the imperatives, 'Look in Herschel's telescope; go into the a chymist's laboratory; if you see a manufacturer at work, remark his operations' (*Letters*, No. 994, 25 March 1784, III, p. 144). This, it seemed, was the programme that almost the entire population was attempting to put into practice.

Herschel's telescopes were a potent attraction for ladies interested in astronomy. In 1786, when William and Caroline were organizing the construction of the 40-foot telescope at Windsor, everyone, including the King, the Archbishop of Canterbury, the dukes, princesses, lords and ladies, came to walk through it. Fanny Burney, the novelist, was one of the throng. She and her father called in July 1786, 'to see and *take a walk* through the immense new telescope'. Fanny went on to describe her stroll through the great tube: 'It held me quite upright ... and without the least inconvenience; so would it have done had I been dressed in feather and a bell-hoop.'[58]

Viewing exhibitions, museums, factories and workshops, all part of the scientific education of the leisured classes, acquired a certain social prestige. By the early 1800s even debutantes did it. As soon as she had been presented at court in 1835, Ada, daughter of Lord Byron, was escorted by her mother on a tour of the manufacturing cities of Coventry, Ashby de la Zouch, Derby and Sheffield to acquire a better understanding of the operations of industry.[59]

Annabelle Milbanke, the estranged wife of Lord Byron, was a devoted amateur scientist and mathematician. She considered such activities essential in the education of any well-brought-up young woman. Her daughter had been carefully educated in mathematics and the sciences. Other dedicated young scientists enjoyed similar excursions. Caroline Fox, for example, took her friend Clara Mill (John Stuart Mill's sister) on a visit to a Cornish coal mine in the neighbourhood of Falmouth in order to give her 'a thorough insight' into the workings of the mines and the lives of the miners.

While many ladies enjoyed the recreational pleasures of nature walks, tours of interesting landscapes and visits to industrial centres, some women developed a more professional approach to what they observed and, in quite a few cases, ended by contributing to current scientific research. Geology was a particularly fruitful field.[60] Among the amateur lady geologists of the late eighteenth century were women of humbler birth whose profession as 'fossilists' earned them a living. Those who worked in and around Lyme Regis, a coastal town remarkable for its rich fossil deposits, are best known. Demand for specimens was growing and their extensive geological skills and good fortune ensured a good supply of specimens for their customers at the Geological Society and other places.

There were the Misses Philpot, Mary, Margaret and Elizabeth, whose clients included William Buckland, Richard Owen and James Sowerby. Their contribution to geology was acknowledged when the great Louis Agassiz named a species of fossil fish after Elizabeth.

But the most famous of all was Mary Anning (1799–1847). Her career began in earnest when she was twelve. On her father's death, she insisted that she could contribute to the upkeep of her family, not by the unrewarding drudgery of sewing, but by digging for fossils along the cliffs. She proved her point with her astonishing finds, among which was the first complete skeleton of an ichthyosaur, which went to a London museum, and a nearly complete skeleton of a plesiosaur which she auctioned off at £150 to the highest bidder. Even allowing for overheads, this was a handsome sum. In 1823 she made her third great discovery, a pterodactyl or gliding reptile. It has been noted that the lias around Lyme Regis is a marine deposit; had there been terrestrial deposits of the correct age in the vicinity, Mary Anning would doubtless have found land dinosaurs too.

Despite her humble origins, Mary Anning had managed to acquire a reasonable scientific education. She was well versed in comparative anatomy. In fact, one geologist wrote of her, 'she is perfectly acquainted with the anatomy of the fossils'. When the plesiosaur was sent to London to be viewed at a special meeting of the Geological Society, the ship was delayed for ten days. The meeting was not postponed, however, for the Society held Mary Anning's drawings of that reptile and they were displayed instead.

Mary Anning's reputation as a palaeontologist grew. She was made an honorary Fellow of the Geological Society, so that she had the right to be addressed as Miss Mary Anning, FGS. When Lord Melbourne became Prime Minister, she was awarded a research grant by the government. She never underrated herself as a scientist. Like Caroline Herschel, she took pride in her own efforts. In 1844, when the King of Saxony came to her and bought an ichthyosaur, he asked her to autograph his pocket book. She did so and added, 'I am well known throughout the whole of Europe.' She died in 1847 and a stained-glass window was placed in Lyme Regis church in her memory.[61]

Not all women geologists were forced into the field to ward off penury. More secure middle-class ladies responded to the intellectual challenge as well as the pleasures of field work. Caroline Fox included it among her interests and was fortunate enough to be acquainted with many of the leading men in the field. They were always willing to undertake an informal tutorial or expedition.

Other ladies were independently occupied in making valuable contributions to the earliest geological surveys undertaken by the Geological Society in the first decades of the nineteenth century. In some cases it was their efforts alone which allowed certain areas to be mapped. Glamorganshire was in the hands of Lady Mary Cole and the Talbot sisters. They were expected to complete the map, recording in detail the known geological observations. Their reputations were so high that their work could be forwarded directly to the engraver without any intermediate corrections.[62]

Miss Jane Talbot, in particular, was frequently consulted by William Buckland. Her botanical expertise was greater than his. Among the tasks he set her was the making of lithographs of specimens of mosses from the Carpathian Alps and the Apennines, explaining the British distribution of *Lobelia urens*, and, on one occasion, to devise a nomenclature for marine plants.[63] It seems she was a brave and daring woman. Nothing held her back in her search for specimens. She undertook an investigation of the fossils of the South Wales coal fields and produced accurate lithographs of the 'most perfect vegetables of the Welsh coal strata'.

Another of her exploits was to examine the famous cave of Pavilant or the Goat Hole near Penrice Castle in Glamorganshire. Geologists had begun to realise that answers to the many queries that perplexed them might lie in the inaccessible depths of the underground caves. The Goat Hole was one such promising site. It could only be entered at low water or, at other times, by climbing up almost vertical cliffs. Miss Talbot attempted the feat and she and her companion, Mr L.W. Dillough, were rewarded by the intriguing find of two molar teeth of an elephant and a curved tusk. Her greatest satisfaction was in telling Buckland that her intuition had been correct.

Buckland knew many of these women geologists and those he did not know he often sought out. It was on precisely such an expedition that he met Mary Morland, his future wife. She had been reared in Oxford, in the house of Sir Christopher Pegge, the famous physician. She was well educated and had acquired a rounded scientific education before specializing in geology. On the coach, travelling to meet this young woman, Buckland noted that the other occupant, a lady, was engrossed in a new and weighty work by Cuvier, a copy of which he was also reading. When he remarked on the coincidence, she told him that she had worked for Cuvier, had corresponded with him and had illustrated his books, and that the work in question had been a personal gift from the author. Buckland was impressed, and more so when he discovered that this surprising young woman was none other than the Miss Morland to whom he was carrying a letter of introduction. Not surprisingly, a deeper understanding soon developed and they were married on 31 December 1825.

Their honeymoon was a year-long geological tour of Europe, all of it accurately recorded by Mrs Buckland. Later, back in Christ Church College in Oxford, she divided her time between rearing a large and energetic family, philanthropic work and scientific studies. She continued her geological investigations and, when possible, accompanied her husband on field trips, particularly to sites of special interest, such as landslides. And, of course, by and large, whatever illustrations were required in her husband's books were supplied by her. She was still working on her scientific research within hours of her death.

Buckland had been impressed by the work of women geologists he knew. When he became Professor of Geology at Oxford in 1819, he showed his appreciation by initiating the tradition that allowed women to attend geological lectures at the university. By 1873, when the Royal Commission on Scientific Instruction and the Advancement of Science was taking its reports, it was noted that Professor Buckland's gesture had acquired the status of custom at Oxford.

Notes

1. E.V. Hamilton, *The Illustrious Lady* (1980), p. 71.

2. E.V. Hamilton, *William's Mary* (1972), p. 140.

3. Quoted in Hamilton, p. 259.

4. D.G.C. Allan and R.E. Schofield, *Stephen Hales: Scientist and Philanthropist* (1980), pp. 110–16.

5. Allan and Schofield, p. 114; D.E. Allen, p. 43.

6. In the nineteenth century Mary Somerville presented her books to Princess Victoria and to Queen Adelaide. See above, p. 115.

7. Lucy Hutchinson, *Memoirs of the Life of Colonel Hutchinson* (1806), p. 14.

8. All quotations are from *The Diary of Samuel Pepys*, ed. by R.C. Latham and W. Matthews, 11 vols (1983).

9. See above, pp. 82–3.

10. Richard Ward, *The Life of the Learned and Pious Dr Henry More* (1710), ch. XVI.

11. Compare with other writers who saw science as a healthy antidote to the triviality of women's lives. See above, p. 46.

12. The quotations from Swift are taken from *Journal to Stella*, ed. by Harold Williams, 2 vols (Oxford, 1974).

13. See R.E. Schofield, *The Lunar Society* (1963), p. 107. See also *Annals of Science*, xiii (1957).

14. Benjamin Franklin and Roger Boscovich were typical guests. See James Boswell *The Life of Dr Johnson*, (1791, Dent 1964), I, p. 292.

15. Anna Williams, the friend and dependant of Dr Johnson, once acted as an assistant to Stephen Gray and claimed to have been the first to observe the emission of an electrical spark from a human body. She wrote a poem to commemorate his death which was revised by Johnson, 'On the Death of Stephen Grey, F.R.S. The Author of the present Doctrine of electriticy' in *Poems*, p. 335, II.9–22. See R.B. Schwartz, *Samuel Johnson and the New Science* (Wisconsin, 1971), p. 42.

16. *Memoirs of the Life of Mrs Elizabeth Carter* (1807), p. 6.

17. 20 March 1747 in *Letters* (1809), vol. I, p. 194.

18. Her fame and her intellectual achievements, particularly her Epictetus, inspired mid-eighteenth-century feminists, notably the authoress of *Female Rights Vindicated* (1758), p. 37.

19. Charles Hutton, editor of the *Ladies Diary*, had been mathematics tutor to Elizabeth Surtees, later wife to Lord Eldon, the Lord Chancellor.

20. See the poet Alexander Pope's attack on cruelty to animals in the *Guardian*, no. 61 (1713); William Melmoth's advocacy of pesticide-free farming in *Letters on Several Subjects, by the late Sir Thomas Fitzosborne* (1748), p. 29.

21. Mary Somerville's powers of concentration were remarkable. She worked in the family living room apparently not much disturbed by family or callers. See Harriet Martineau's account in her *Autobiography* (1877), I, p. 433.

22. Compare Harriet Martineau's experiences in *Autobiography*, I, pp. 100–1.

23. For Johnson's interest in science see R.B. Schwartz, *Samuel Johnson and the New Science* (1971).

24. Catherine Macaulay suffered a similar fate when she married a man twenty years younger than herself.

25. James L. Clifford, *Hester Lynch Piozzi* (1941, 2nd edn 1952, reprinted 1987), p. 413.

26. Elizabeth Mavor, *The Ladies of Llangollen. A Study in Romantic Friendship* (1971), pp. 160–7.

27. James L. Clifford, *Hester Lynch Piozzi*, p. 90.

28. James L. Clifford, *Hester Lynch Piozzi*, pp. 78–9.

29. All quotations are from *The Letters of Samuel Johnson*, ed. by R.W. Chapman, 3 vols (Oxford, 1952).

30. *The Herschel Chronicle*, ed. by Constance Lubbick (1933), p. 160.

31. *Memoir and Correspondence of Caroline Herschel*, ed. by Mrs John Herschel (1876), p. 31.

32. *Diary*, 1786, quoted in *The Herschel Chronicle*, p. 169.

33. The most complete account of the Lunar Society is to be found in R.E. Schofield, *The Lunar Society of Birmingham. A Social History of Provincial Science and Industry in Eighteenth-Century England* (Oxford, 1963).

34. *Life of Mary Anne Schimmelpennick* (1858), pp. 36ff.

35. See above, pp. 104–17.

36. *Strictures on Female Education* (1799), p. 195. This was an important book; there were 13 editions by 1826.

37. L.P. Brockett, *Woman* (1869), p. 197. Georgiana Hill, *Women in English Life* (1896), II, pp. 178–9.

38. Schwartz, p. 33.

39. Marilyn Butler, *Maria Edgeworth* (1972), pp. 192–3, 444.

40. Maria Edgeworth was 'one of my most intimate friends': Mary Somerville, *Personal Recollections*, p. 155. See Butler, p. 415.

41. *Memoirs of Richard Lovell Edgeworth*, 2 vols (1820), I. pp. 177–9.

42. There was a great scandal in the 1760s when one Miss Kitty Hunter, aroused by Rousseau's *Julie*, ran off with the married Earl of Pembroke. See *Mrs Montagu, 'Queen of the Blues'*, ed. by Reginald Blunt, 2 vols, I, p. 15.

43. Butler, p. 142.

44. *Maria Edgeworth. Letters from England. 1813–1844*, ed. by Christina Colvin (Oxford, 1971), p. 38.

45. Desmond Clarke, *The Ingenious Mr Edgeworth* (1965), p. 179.

46. L.M. Hawkins, *Anecdotes* (1822), p. 91.

47. *Catherine Hutton and her Friends*, ed. by Mrs Catherine Hutton Beale (Birmingham, 1895), p. 221.

48. Letitia Mathilda Hawkins, *Memoirs* (1824), I, p. 63.

49. *Memoirs of Mary Robinson. 'Perdita'*, ed. by J. Fitzgerald Molloy (Philadelphia, 1894), pp. 21–2. Mary Robinson's notoriety derived from her much-publicized affair and its termination with the Prince of Wales, later George IV. She was an actress and a poet. Her poetry was much admired by Coleridge. See E.K. Chambers, *Samuel Taylor Coleridge* (1938), p. 128. For other schools teaching science and mathematics to girls at the turn of the century see Hans, *New Trends*, chs VII and X.

50. *Ramblers*, nos. 73, 83, 177; Schwartz, pp. 114–15.

51. *Prefaces and Dedications*, quoted in Schwartz, p. 130.

52. *Letters to a Young Lady* (1806), II, pp. 169ff.

53. *Letters to a Young Lady* (1789), p. 167; see also Dr James Fordyce, *Sermons to Young Women* (1765), who advocated similar ideas.

54. Inscription on flyleaf of copy in the Bodleian Library, Oxford.

55. *The Wonders of the Peak* (Nottingham 1725); see also M.H. Nicolson, *Mountain Gloom and Mountain Glory: The Development of the Aesthetics of the Infinite* (Ithaca, NY, 1959).

56. In 1757 that inveterate scientific tourist Caroline Girle visited a coal mine. Later she took in the joys of industrial Birmingham. See *Passages from the Diaries of Mrs Philips Lybbe Powys*, p. 20.

57. Caroline Girle visited the British Museum shortly after it opened to the public in 1759. See *Diary*, p. 5, and above, p. 132.

58. *Memoir and Correspondence of Caroline Herschel* (1876), p. 38; see also *The Herschel Chronicle*, p. 157.

59. Doris Langley Moore, *Ada Countess of Lovelace* (1977), p. 55.

60. Alic, pp. 114–16.

61. This information was supplied to me by the late Dr E. Nevill, Department of Geology, University College, Cork.

62. Elizabeth Gordon, *The Life and Correspondence of William Buckland D.D. F.R.S.* (1894), pp. 16–17.

63. Gordon, p. 21.

PART III

Women and Science in the Nineteenth Century

Introduction

During most of the nineteenth century, women so interested maintained and seemed to gain ever more widespread acceptance of their scientific predilections. As each new move to disseminate science to the public was initiated, the claims of the ladies were taken into consideration. The scientific society was one such move. Begun in a small way during the eighteenth century, it flourished in the nineteenth century. The two best known, the Royal Institution and the British Association for the Advancement of Science, extended the tradition of the participation of women in the scientific world by permitting women to become members, to attend lecture courses, to utilize the library facilities and to meet on social terms with leading scientists and other interested amateurs.

By the middle of the nineteenth century, women were no longer content to be supplied with their science in a haphazard manner. They recognized that consistency and continuity were necessary. All over the country organizations for the improvement of women's education sprang up. Many more women were drawn into the process. Science teaching acquired a special place in the studies that these associations encouraged. Ultimately, this movement stimulated the founding of University Extension, which had enormous consequences for the liberation of women in the last quarter of the nineteenth century.

Meanwhile, girls of the industrial classes were also being encouraged to develop the sorts of scientific skill that could be exploited in the workplace. The need to raise education standards among the working classes was felt to be of such importance that the government of the day agreed to put money into the project. As a result many girls from the lower social orders completed scientific courses that were more comprehensive and consistent than anything on offer to the better-off women.

The extent and depth of the scientific education developed over many years and enjoyed by at least a section of the women and girls in the British Isles was the subject of a government report in the 1860s. This report, coming on the eve of major changes in girls' educational ambitions and in attitudes to education in general, stands as a fitting valediction to the long tradition of women's interest in science.

CHAPTER 7
Scientific Societies and Lady Members

By the end of the eighteenth century, many of the major towns of the British Isles could lay claim to a learned 'Literary and Philosophical' society.[1] The function of these societies was both social and educational, and entry was often conceded to women. That constant drive to extend the scientific education of the population continued into the nineteenth century. Two institutions were founded then that set as their goals the improvement of the reputation of science and its effective dissemination. The Royal Institution was followed a little over thirty years later by the British Association for the Advancement of Science. Both these bodies approached the question of the participation of women in scientific study in quite contradictory ways. However, the end result was the same. It had to be accepted that women's interest in science existed and that their demands for support and encouragement could not be balked.

The Royal Institution

The Royal Institution was the brainchild of Massachusetts-born Benjamin Thompson, later Count Rumford, and, in its early stages, was conceived as a noble vision of universal education. Thompson's intention was to establish a college of further education that would attract all sections of society, artisans and masters, men and women. He felt strongly that the pursuit of scientific knowledge was an activity in which all social classes and groups should participate. Through this universalization of scientific interest, he hoped to benefit the whole nation.

In the event, the lower classes were quickly edged out and the Royal Institution, 21 Albemarle Street, London, was soon set on its distinguished career of bringing science to the public – from the middle classes upwards. However, the exclusion of women was never even discussed. On the contrary, their membership was welcomed from the beginning. Indeed, the positive advantages of the lady membership were self-evident. The Institution was to be self-supporting and the fees and investment of members and shareholders constituted an important part of the Institution's economic viability.

The decision that ladies should be admitted on equal terms, both as proprietors and subscribers, was taken at the second meeting of the managers, convened on 23 March 1799 to discuss the constitution, form and aims of the Institution. Ladies were to be entitled to all the same privileges as the gentlemen members. The only exception, which must be seen in the context of contemporary decorum, was that 'the ladies will not be called upon to take any part in the management with the officers of the Institution'.

As proprietors, they were required to invest fifty guineas. For annual subscribers, the fee was two guineas. After a short time this was raised by a guinea. But another fee increase, to five guineas, was not applied to the ladies. A sizeable number of women became members. By 5 April 1800 women constituted about one-third of the lists of annual subscribers, although there do not seem to have been any females among the proprietors or life subscribers.[2] Their preference for annual membership may well have been dictated by the smaller fee involved, and by the fact that many of them would only expect to attend the lectures while in town during the season.

According to the original statutes, nominations for membership could only be enacted on the proposal of a manager. But there were so many women wanting to be proposed during the first year of its existence that, at a meeting of the managers on 10 February 1800, it was decided to alter this procedure to hasten the admittance of ladies. A Ladies' Committee was formed to expedite applications. This pioneer body consisted of approximately eight ladies, chosen from among the seventeen or so that had been nominated for membership at the meeting. They were the Countess of Bessborough, the Countess Spencer, the Duchess of Devonshire, the Viscountess Palmerston, Lady Campbell, the Hon. Mrs Bassington, Mrs Sulivan and Mrs Bernard, 'with such other ladies as may be hereafter named'. These were requested by the meeting to 'suffer books to be sent to them for the Admissions of the Names of such Ladies, as may wish to become Proprietors or Subscribers to the Royal Institution'.[3]

The timetable of lectures, as devised at these early meetings, was carefully organized to dovetail with the busy life of a lady in town for the season (November-June). There were to be lectures on Tuesdays and Thursdays at 2 p.m. and on the other weekdays at 8 p.m. The lectures were to last one hour and were to be of a 'general and popular' nature, concentrating on natural and experimental philosophy and chemistry (6 January 1800).

By the end of January 1800 it was clear that Count Rumford's college was answering a deep need. 'The R.I. is not only the fashion, but the Rage,' crowed the Count gleefully.[4] As the fashionable carriages thronged the narrow confines of Albemarle Street at the hours appointed for the lectures, all traffic ground to a halt in the impenetrable confusion. The drastic measures needed to modify these major traffic jams produced a new solution to traffic problems. Albemarle Street was turned into the first one-way thoroughfare in London. The ladies who turned out in such numbers for lectures on galvanism, modern tanning methods and sugarbeet production soon posed the managers another serious problem of congestion. The minutes for their meeting on 27 January 1800 noted their disquiet with the arrangements made for the ladies. The room that had been set aside for the purposes of the lectures was now seen to be woefully inadequate:

> We invite Ladies to subscribe; and our Professor informs us, that the Fair Sex constituted a large Proportion (and not the least observant) of his numerous auditory, which sometimes bordered on 1000 persons. The ladies of this *Metropolis* are not the earliest attendants at public Assemblies, and with us, unless they should be early enough to occupy the two or three lowest ranges of seats, no female of Condition or Delicacy can find suitable Accommodations.

At this stage, the lower orders were still filling seating in the upper areas of the room, accessed by an outside staircase, so that their betters need in no way be inconvenienced. Although a new lecture theatre was soon under construction, it was obvious that this seating was needed for those of 'Condition and Delicacy'.

By the meeting of 24 February it was obvious that yet another problem connected with the ladies had arisen. Concern to ensure that only ladies from the acceptable ranks of society gained admission to the Institution was noted in the minutes as a matter of some importance. As the crowds of females continued to pour in, the managers had become worried lest the selection procedure should prove faulty. From the tone of their communication to the proprietors, it seems possible that some 'doubtful' ladies had found their way into the lectures:

To preclude the Possibility of any improper Female name being found amongst the subscribers to the Royal Institution, the managers deem it necessary to inform the Proprietary that they have come to the Resolution of not electing any Ladies as Subscribers unless they are recommended by one of the Ladies, who has obligingly accepted Books for the Insertion of such Ladies Names as may be desirous of becoming subscribers. The managers have the fullest confidence that the Proprietors will take care that their transportable Tickets shall not by any accident fall into improper hands.

On 24 February 1800 there were five new lady subscribers, on 3 March five more, and on 10 March twenty-four, which was followed on 17 March by twenty-one, and so it continued. This snowballing popularity of the Royal Institution among women was eventually to wane, but not before it had introduced several generations of girls and women to scientific subjects.

In the meantime every provision was made to make the lady sub-scribers comfortable. They were encouraged to 'bring or send' their children (9 April 1802), at the cost of two guineas for a year's lectures. If a mother and daughter chose to attend together, they were offered a special fee of two guineas. No such reduction appears to have been offered to fathers escorting sons. Ladies who wished only to attend 'the Lectures and Public Experiments' during the season were charged only one guinea. The economic benefits of using the Royal Institution merely as a means of scientific education were obvious.

Although frequently ridiculed both for its fashionable image and for the inclusion of women among its regular membership, the Royal Institution regarded the serious pursuit of scientific education, not least among women, as its most important aim. In his introductory lecture on 20 January 1802, Dr Young, the resident lecturer, described the valuable function of the Institution particularly in the lives of women who had been excluded from the usual channels of education:

The many leisure hours which are at the command of females in the superior order of society may surely be appropriated with greatest satisfaction to the improvement of the mind, and to the acquisition of knowledge, than to such amusements as are only designed for facilitating the insipid consumption of superfluous time. The Royal Institution may in some degree supply the place of a subordinate university to those whose sex or situation in life had denied them the advantage of an academical education in the national seminaries of learning.[5]

Among the Institution's great attractions were the lecturers chosen to deliver the daily talks. In the early years it was the charismatic Humphrey Davy who held the ladies' attention. He was not only a gifted speaker, but young, handsome and charming to boot. When he began lecturing in the early months of 1801, it was soon being reported that 'Men of the first rank and talent, the literary and scientific – bluestockings and women of fashion – eagerly crowded into the Lecture room.'[6]

Like other scientists before him, Davy regarded science less as a profession and more as a life philosophy. It has often been remarked that Davy partook of some of the poetic spirit that is usually termed 'Romantic'. Indeed some of his literary contemporaries felt he had thrown himself away in becoming engrossed in the triviality of science. William Godwin (Mary Wollstonecraft's husband) once wrote to Coleridge, 'What a pity such a man should degrade his talents to chemistry.'[7] He was almost as interested in poetry as he was in chemistry. He was a close friend of William Wordsworth and Robert Southey, and through them knew Coleridge. Their common bond was poetry and science. The poets consulted with Davy on their scientific studies. In 1801 Coleridge appealed to him for advice on how to set up a proper laboratory.[8]

In passing, it may be noted that Percy Bysshe Shelley too shared this scientific interest. The early years of the romantic run-away marriage of Percy Bysshe Shelley and the fifteen-year-old Harriet Westbrook were enriched by various programmes of study among which chemistry was a particular favourite. Shelley horrified the neighbours and nearly blew the roof off their rose-covered bower in Keswick with experiments that were more enthusiastic than scientific.

Later another child of the Romantics, Sara, Coleridge's beloved daughter, who was better educated than poor Harriet Shelley, followed some scientific pursuits. Her inclination was primarily literary, and it was not until she had endured several difficult births and pregnancies that she followed Coleridge's example and her husband's urging and turned to science for intellectual stimulation. She took to the study of geology, botany and animal and vegetable physiology with great delight.[9]

When Davy began his lectures on 21 January 1802, he brought to his subject the idealism and aesthetic fervour usually associated with the 'revolutionary' poets of the age. He was firmly convinced that science could and should be the primary concern of all intelligent and sensitive people – and this was the topic of his introductory discourse.

Science, he announced to his rapt audience, should carry within it all that is of significance to intelligent and sensitive people; it was connected with the finest aesthetic passions, 'the love of the beautiful and the sublime'; it could stimulate and nurture 'the more powerful passions and ambitions of the Soul'; it could compensate for the deprivation felt by those, shut up in the weary uniformity of urban life; and, finally, and most importantly, it could become 'a source of consolation and of happiness'.[10]

In these words Humphrey Davy summed up the therapeutic pleasures of science, a factor that had long enhanced its attraction for many women. Going back over a century, we find that even then women were conscious of the escapist dimension of science. Mary, Lady Chudleigh (1656–1710) confessed that her scientific studies had alleviated the unhappiness of an unsatisfactory marriage.[11] The great Dr Johnson, who was himself far from immune to the agonies of melancholy, suggested chemistry as an antidote to depression: 'If you could get a little apparatus for chimestry [*sic*] or experimental philosophy, it would offer you some diversion' (letter to Revd John Taylor of Ashbourne, 31 August 1772). And there must have been many ordinary women like Marianne, wife of Sir Charles Mordaunt (1771–1823), who had cultivated science as a temporary release from the cares and tribulations of life. Lady Mordaunt was confident that her intellectual efforts, which included chemistry and mineralogy, had helped her through life. As a young woman she had doubted whether 'a much refined and cultivated education in women conduced to happiness', but having coped with the exigencies of a long life, she could then write with confidence, 'under the experience of the great and lengthened trials of life, I am quite enlightened on the subject and perceive that every power of the mind can be called in at different moments and will conduce to good and happiness in proportion to its sound and solid cultivation'.[12]

It may be surmised that Humphrey Davy furthered this tradition of the healing powers of science among his female audience. He certainly had other positive effects. The impact he had on Mrs Marcet has already been noted. To Maria Edgeworth, he was a source of inspiration and idealism. She heard him speak when he travelled to Ireland in the winters of 1810 and 1811 to lecture on electrochemistry in the fine new laboratory of the Dublin Society and to deliver six lectures on agricultural chemistry to the Farming Society of Ireland. The current Mrs Edgeworth, Elizabeth, reported on the enthusiasm that Davy's visit had aroused in the Edgeworth family as well as in the intelligentsia of Ireland, who had all crowded into Dublin to hear him: 'Davy's Lectures not only opened a new world of knowledge to ourselves and to our young people but were specially gratifying to Mr Edgeworth and Maria, confirming by the eloquence, ingenuity and philosophy which they displayed, the high ideas they had clearly formed by Mr Davy's powers.'[13]

When Davy's place at the Royal Institution was taken by Michael Faraday, the ladies continued to be pleased. Faraday's own incomplete education had convinced him of the importance of the art of communication for those involved in popular education. He paid great attention to his lecturing skills and carefully evolved an attractive and effective technique. The women who came to hear him were appreciative. Years later, Lady Holland remembered the enthusiasm he could generate and the numbers of women who, following his gentle guidance, turned to an exploration of chemistry:

> Whatever might be the afterthought or the after-pursuit, each hearer for the first time shared his zeal and his delight; and with some listeners the impression made was so deep as to lead them into the laborious paths of philosophy in spite of all the obstacles which the daily life of society opposes to such undertakings.[14]

That dedicated young scientist Caroline Fox (1819–71) gave a description of one of Faraday's lectures, at the same time conveying something of her own unorthodox scientific education. She lived at a time when young girls, at least those with scientific acquaintances, might expect demonstrations in the family kitchen:

> We went to Faraday's lectures on 'Ozone'. He tried the various methods of making Ozone which Schönbein had already performed in our kitchen, and he did them brilliantly. He was entirely at his ease, both with his audience and his chemical apparatus; he spoke much and well of Schönbein, who now doubts whether Ozone is an element, and is disposed to view it simply as a condition of oxygen, in which Faraday evidently agrees with him. [*Diary*, II, p. 172]

The Royal Institution performed an important function in the introduction of many women to science. It permitted a greater freedom and equality to women than had been allowed them hitherto. Its class consciousness and its location in London, however, limited its overall influence. Another society was responsible for stimulating a greater interest in science among women in general.

The British Association for the Advancement of Science

The foundation of the British Association for the Advancement of Science was an important landmark in the history of women's interest in science. BAAS, as the Association soon came to be known, put down its roots at a meeting at York in 1831. As far as the women were concerned, it began inauspiciously. In the presence of a large group of men and women, the rules of the Association were drawn up. But only the men who were present were asked to sign the document. No woman in the room was invited to add her name. This regressive action was neither overlooked nor accepted by the ladies, who, in the spirit of the times, clearly thought that their support and compliance should have carried equal weight with the men.

Their displeasure grew. By the following year, at the Oxford meeting, the problem had become acute. The two parties drew up their battle lines. The President-Elect of the Association, William Buckland (1784–1856), had been hard at work behind the scenes to marshal support for his views. He had no notion of allowing women to become involved in the society. He described his machinations to his colleague, Roderick Murchison:

> Everybody whom I spoke to on the subject agreed that if the Meeting is to be of Scientific utility, ladies ought not to attend the reading of the papers – especially in a place like Oxford – as it would overturn the thing into a sort of Albemarle dilettante meeting instead of a serious philosophical union of working men. [27 March 1832][15]

His trump card was to have been an endorsement of his views by the 'Queen of Nineteenth-Century Science' herself, Mary Somerville. But the result of his attempt to enlist her support was ambiguous to say the least. Mrs Somerville declined to see him in person. Instead her husband met him, and Buckland was obliged to extract what comfort he could from the bland message transmitted to him by Somerville: 'I did not see Mrs Somerville, but her husband decidedly informed me that such is her opinion of this matter, and further, I fear she will not come at all.'

Buckland's fears were well founded. She did not attend the Oxford meeting of the BAAS, nor any other future meetings. There could have been many reasons for this. A busy wife and mother, as well as an extremely productive mathematician and author, she simply may not have had the time to travel to the meetings that, according to the policy of the Association, were arranged on an annual basis in different provincial cities. The Somerville family's straitened circumstances may have been another deterrent. In view of her participation in the somewhat indecorous attempt to force King's College, London, to open its doors to women at about this time, it is unlikely that her absence had anything to do with a wish to exclude women from these scientific bodies. It may well have been that it was President-Elect Buckland's own tactless reluctance to welcome women, especially one of her reputation, into the BAAS that induced her to protest in her turn, by resorting to a determined but dignified boycott. In noting that he thought Mrs Somerville would not patronize the Association, Buckland was surely aware that his appeal to her to prevent other women coming had been offensive.

Despite his efforts to rally support in favour of the exclusion of women at the Oxford meeting, Buckland was not entirely successful. As it turned out, women were admitted, perhaps somewhat grudgingly, to some of the sections. In view of the number of men involved in the setting up of the Association who were married to women of reputable scientific ability, this was not surprising. Buckland's own wife, Mary Morland, was, it will be remembered, an accomplished naturalist and geologist. Part of her wifely duties was to edit and illustrate her husband's books, including eventually his famous Bridgewater treatise, *Geology and Mineralogy Considered with Reference to Natural Theology* (1858). Mrs Charlotte Murchison (1789–1869) was also a working geologist. She kept extensive diaries of her field trips and made useful drawings. G.A. Mantell's wife illustrated his *Fossils of the South Downs* (1822). Mary Kater, a close friend of Mary Somerville, assisted her husband with his calculations and results as a matter of course. Annabella Smyth took care of her growing family at the same time as she worked closely with her husband, W.H. Smyth, the astronomer. As a girl, Caroline Clift, who later married Richard Owen, had devoted herself single-mindedly to a demanding education. She eventually specialized in comparative anatomy, facilitated by her father's position as curator at the College of Surgeons. Charles Lyall's wife, Mary Elizabeth Horner, was another practising geologist who accompanied her husband on field trips and expeditions as a matter of course. Her expertise as a conchologist was useful in documenting the antiquity of geological formations. General Sir Edward Sabine, the explorer who established magnetic observation, married a lady known as a magnetist, prompting the joke 'married magnetists'.[16]

With so many other women also known to be taking an active, if not quite so professional interest in science, it seemed churlish to deny them entry. In fact, by the end of the Oxford conference, it was generally agreed that the presence of the ladies had probably contributed significantly to the high tone and dignified respectability which had distinguished the proceedings. But, despite this compliment from the gentlemen, nothing was done to resolve the dilemma of female membership. At the next meeting, in Cambridge in 1833, the ladies turned up again, and this time in such numbers that the organizers were taken unawares. The limited seating reserved for them proved totally inadequate. The only course open to the harassed officials was to ask the gentlemen present to forgo the comfort of their own seats.

Once again the women were treated with the same combination of patronizing chivalry and benign tolerance. This comfortable complacency was rudely shattered when it became known that the official transcripts of the proceedings could not compete with the accuracy and insight of the records made during the meeting by a seventeen-year-old local girl, Pauline Jermyn. In particular, her masterly account of the impromptu and highly complex inaugural address given by Professor Adam Sedgwick raised many eyebrows.

Pauline Jermyn was the eldest daughter of Dr George Bitton Jermyn, the incumbent of Swaffham Prior vicarage. Her father's circle of friends included many of the Cambridge dons, all in holy orders, who led the field in the different branches of science. Pauline was popular with these distinguished clerics. They appreciated her personal charms and her precocious cleverness. She was well acquainted with Adam Sedgwick, the Woodwardian Professor of Geology, and familiar with his idiosyncrasies of style and delivery. She had other supporters among the leading scientists of the day. William Whewell was a tutor at Trinity College and its future master. He was a friend to many intellectual women, including Mary Somerville. He had already permitted Pauline Jermyn to attend his classes at Cambridge. In fact, his respect for her intellect was such that, in the following year, he asked her to read and comment on the manuscript of his famous work, *Inductive Sciences*. There was also the great John Stevens Henslow. He became Professor of Botany at Cambridge in 1827 and was one of the pioneers in the teaching of natural history at the university. There was an immediate intellectual accord between him and the bright young girl whose field work in the Cambridge fens he regarded as highly accomplished. He encouraged her to attend some of his lectures at the university.[17]

In fact, many of the men in the BAAS sympathized with the ambitions of the women who wanted to be part of the organization, and felt that their exclusion was untenable. Quietly some of them ensured that women gained access to whichever section meetings they desired to attend. Caroline Fox, still a teenager but with serious scientific predilections, found her male friends helpful in furthering her ambitions. Of course, she probably shared in the persuasive powers famous in her family. She was a cousin of Elizabeth Fry and a more distant relation of Priscilla Wakefield, and as strong-minded as most Quaker women. She too grew up in an environment in which the sciences were cultivated not only for intellectual edification, but for entertainment as well. A typical day for Caroline was the one on which Professor Richard Owen visited in the afternoon, for 'lesson No. 1 on the primary divisions in Natural History'. They were later joined by others and 'we had some talk over Wordsworth, Carlyle and collateral subjects'. That same evening, the gathering was augmented 'to listen to a very beautiful lecture on Light which Professor Lloyd was so good as to give us ... [He] told us wonderful facts and exhibited beautiful phenomena, and gave an interesting sketch of the progressive views of Light which have been held by our greatest men.'[18]

Falmouth, where Caroline was born, provided ample opportunities for the pursuit of science. It had a polytechnic and many scientific men passed through, paying their respects to the Fox family as they did so, and bringing them up to date with scientific research. Caroline and her sister Anna Maria, who was an ornithologist, taxidermist and artist, were enthralled by the revelations of Dr Calvert when, on one of his visits, he treated them to an

> instructive exhibition of comparative anatomy of the stomachs of a Brent goose and a diver: the former lives on fuci, and is accordingly provided with amazingly strong muscles of digestion: the other depends on fish, and though a much larger bird, its stomach is far smaller and less muscular. Dr. Calvert took seventeen fish out of it. [*Diary*, I, p. 222]

Caroline was one of the women who was determined that the BAAS would open its doors to them. She was part of a group that at every meeting sprang into action and demanded places for women. There was the occasion of the BAAS meeting in Edinburgh in 1834. The committee had come up with a plan which they were sure would foil the hopes of the women who wanted to attend. Their attention was to be diverted by a series of social gatherings and evening parties which the good gentlemen of the committee were sure would be adequate compensation. But the ladies were not to be bribed. They would have none of it. They disdained the charms of dancing and late dinners.

What they wanted was the scientific stuff of the lectures. They were not to be deterred and, taking the matter into their own hands, simply occupied the lecture theatres by force. A curious situation then arose in which the male members were effectively dispossessed by the women determined to hear the lectures at all costs. Of the 1,500 or so people who crowded into the auditorium, most were women. While they listened avidly to the lecture, the members were forced to kick their heels in the stairwell and adjacent rooms. Their only hope, as the *Athenaeum* reported drily,

> was that heat and pressure might compel the ladies to resign their posts, and afford them an opportunity of hearing the lectures or seeing the speakers. But they had badly calculated the powers of female endurance, and the love of science possessed by the ladies of Edinburgh; able-bodied philosophers gave way and left posts in which they were boiled – literally boiled – but not a lady stirred.[19]

At Bristol in 1836, further attempts were made to prevent women from gaining access. At one lecture, on 22 August 1836, as the ladies milled around the doors trying to get in, they were told that all available places had been taken and were summarily dismissed. But the 'Scientific Fair' in the 1830s were not so easily dissuaded. They used elbows and effort; they pushed and they shoved in a manner that is rarely associated with popular notions of nineteenth-century womanhood. Caroline Fox, who was part of this seething mass of femininity, related the escapade, with some relish, in her *Diary*: 'the ladies, dear creatures, would not hear of that [going home], so by most extraordinary muscular exertions, we succeeded in gaining admittance' (I, pp. 6–7).

The gatecrashing of the ladies became such a problem that it was obvious some action must be taken. The gentlemen began to turn in retreat, although slowly at first. They still held that women should be excluded from most of the meeting, but conceded that they might be admitted to certain sections. Geology, the old favourite, was an obvious choice, and natural history could be permitted, with certain reservations. By 1837, when the Association arrived in Liverpool, formal admittance to these two sections had been extended to the ladies, on condition that they sat in carefully cordoned-off areas. In practice, however, the ladies had their own way again, and went about the meeting as they pleased. Caroline Fox, for example, met with no obstacles when she attended the section for the physical sciences.

At the 1838 meeting in Newcastle, the women were there in even larger numbers. No fewer than 1,100 ladies' tickets were issued. When

Adam Sedgwick went to the podium to give his geological lecture, he complimented the ladies on their excellent showing to hear him speak on their favourite subject. They were, he said, so numerous and so beautiful that it seemed to him as if every sunbeam that had entered the windows in the roof had deposited there an angel. Some of the gentlemen in the audience were amused by this gallantry. Charles Babbage tried to count the panes of the windows to estimate the number of angels present. He applied to Sir John Herschel for help in estimating the number, to which Herschel replied, 'I can't guess, but, if what Sedgwick says be true, you will admit that for every little pane there is great pleasure.'[20] Herschel reported his *bon mot* to his wife, confident, as every husband is, of her appreciation. But the attitude to women that prompted this flippancy and Sedgwick's fulsome condescension annoyed many of the women in the room. One delegate, Harriet Martineau, found the atmosphere unbearable and resolved never to attend again:

> I heard two or three valuable addresses; but, on the whole, the humbugs and small men carried all before them: and, I am sorry to say, Sir John Herschel himself so far succumbed to the spirit of the occasion as to congratulate his scientific brethren on the 'crowning honour' among many, of the presence of the fair sex at their sections![21]

In fact, at Newcastle, the women had won the war. Their impressive turnout finally succeeded in extracting, for the first time, formal permission from the organizers to attend all sections. The only exception to this new ruling was to be Section D, the zoological section, and it was put out of bounds to ladies on the grounds that some of the papers contained matters 'of a delicate nature'. However, even this modified ban was not acceptable to the lady delegates. Richard Owen arrived to deliver his paper on the reproductive system of marsupials only to find that the ladies had not observed the restrictions. Looking around the room, he was shaken to observe a vast number of women, 'mostly Quakeresses' and including Mrs Buckland among the audience. The sight of so many sedate matrons, presumably all ignorant of the mysteries of the reproductive system, was too much for him, and although he really should have known better, he delivered a greatly modified version of his talk.[22] At least one male member of the audience was unimpressed by his squeamishness. J.D. Hooker noted, 'I was afterwards much surprised to hear that ladies were precluded from attending this section of Botany and Zoology on account of the nature of some of the papers belonging to the later division.'

Nevertheless there were objections to the impropriety of the unblushing Amazons and they continued to be strongly expressed. The Hull doctor James Alderson wrote that he was 'much disappointed to find that the Sections of the Association in Newcastle had been *monopolized* by *ladies*; what they did there ... it would be difficult in our unenlightened condition to imagine'. He was so cross that he refused to have anything to do with the Association when it came to Hull.[23] And there were women who agreed with him. Harriet Martineau thought the other women at the meeting were much too frivolous in their demeanour: 'I was in truth much ashamed of the ladies; and I wished they had staid [*sic*] at home, preparing hospitalities for the tired *savans*, and showing themselves only at the evening promenade in the Green Market and at the ball.'[24]

In the end, what counted in favour of ladies being admitted to all sections of the BAAS was not any reversal of attitudes to women as a whole, nor any new appreciation of their intellectual or scientific abilities, but the hard facts of economic reality. The 1,100 or so ladies who had attended the Newcastle meeting had been the dominating presence at the general lectures. It was the profits from these expensive ladies' tickets that counted with the organizers. In the period 1841–4 the proceeds from ladies' tickets amounted to 9–10 per cent of the Association's income. If the BAAS was to grow and prosper, it needed the continuing generous support and interest of the 'fair sex'.

The acceptance of women, and soon of families, was ultimately responsible for the famous 'carnival' atmosphere that has long been associated with the annual meetings of the BAAS, and which was also, and unexpectedly, responsible for turning the Association into a powerful link between professional and layperson in the scientific world.[25] But there was no hope that women would remain satisfied for very long with the limitations of their status under the new arrangement. It was to be 1853 before the first female, a Miss Bowlby of Cheltenham, was admitted to full membership of the BAAS.[26] Soon a steady agitation to be considered eligible for election to the sectional committees, the General Committee and other offices was under way. The Association stonewalled and prevaricated as of old. Committees were set up to discuss the issues, and reports were presented to the Council. Eventually, in 1913, the botanist Miss Ethel Sargant (1863–1918) took her seat as the first woman president of a section, the botanical. In the following year, Miss E.R. Saunders of Newnham College became one of the first members of Council, and in 1966, when

Kathleen Lonsdale became the first woman president of the BAAS, the last embargo on women was finally lifted.

Some nineteenth-century lady lecture-goers

Among the hundreds of ladies who attended scientific lectures in the nineteenth century, some have a particular claim on our attention. I have selected four, whose lecture-going, it seems to me, helps to illustrate the broad appeal of scientific lectures at the time: Augusta Ada Lovelace was a woman passionately interested in science and mathematics, and frustrated in her attempts to forge a career in the field; Mary Somerville, although a professional scientist, was a keen lecture-goer and wished to open up every available opportunity for all women to study science; George Eliot became a famous novelist, but her scientific interests had blossomed early and she was the typical woman amateur scientist; Elizabeth Garrett Anderson was one of the few women to attempt to exploit public lectures for professional purposes – she was determined to become qualified as a medical doctor, the first woman to do so in England.[27]

Ada, Lady Lovelace

Augusta Ada was the child of the short-lived marriage between Miss Annabelle Milbanke and Lord Byron. Before her disastrous marriage to Lord Byron, Miss Milbanke had studied astronomy, algebra and geometry under the guidance of William French, a Cambridge don. As a single parent, she later lavished a great deal of attention on her little daughter. Ada's scientific education in particular was carefully structured. By the time she was presented at court in 1835, the young debutante was committed to her scientific interests. What she really would have liked was a professional career in some scientific field. She attended lectures at the Royal Institution and at the Mechanics' Institute, and tried to catch the attention of the well-known people in the field. She and Charles Babbage corresponded, and she had the frequent companionship of Mary Somerville, whose books she eagerly read, and of her daughters.

For all her mother's devoted attention, the girl longed for companions of her own age who might share her esoteric interests. On 10 November 1834 she wrote to one candidate, Lady Annabella Acheson, one of her mother's goddaughters, hoping to initiate some form of scientific communication: 'So this you see is the commencement of "A Sentimental Mathematical Correspondence between two Young Ladies of

Rank" to be hereinafter published no doubt for the edification of womankind ... Ever yours mathematically.'[28]

Even after what was a very happy marriage to Lord King and the beginning of motherhood, she was still trying to continue with her mathematical studies, and was still looking for women friends to share her interests. Only Mrs Somerville and her daughters provided the stimulation she needed. Her cherished friend Charles Babbage did try to help, but finding a mathematics and science tutor for her proved impossible. As her frustration grew, not even the joys of her marriage and family could heal her sense of isolation. The compulsive gambling to which her fascination with numbers led her, together with the pain and anguish of the cancer that killed her in her mid-thirties, is a well-known story. That so much talent and energy should have been destroyed for want of a coherent and acceptable form of scientific education for women remains a tragedy.

Mary Somerville

While she still resided in England, Mary Somerville was an active supporter of equality of educational opportunity for women. As she grew older she was more frequently content to sign petitions or write letters, but in the 1830s she and her scientific women friends spearheaded an informal movement to open the opportunities of scientific education to women. Change was in the air and, in the light of contemporary political events, it is not really so surprising that respectable matrons in their early middle age were prepared to make demands and follow them through with a degree of force if necessary.

1832 was the year of riotous agitation and the Reform Bill. The country was split along traditional social lines over the Whig attempt to redraw parliamentary boundaries in order to take into account the new industrial cities, to abolish decayed and unrepresentative boroughs and to update the franchise qualification. The middle classes stood on the threshold of a new era of political power. The Prime Minister, Lord Grey, and the leader of the House of Commons, Lord John Russell, attempted to pilot the Bill through Parliament. It was defeated in the Upper House by a combination of Tory lords and the bishops. There was an explosion of popular fury. The homes of the Bill's opponents – lords and bishops alike – were attacked. Effigies of the bishops were burned on Guy Fawkes Night. Revolution seemed imminent and the army was ordered to stand by.

In the midst of this turmoil, women were once again becoming conscious of their own unenfranchised state. It was the scientists among them who felt their inferior status most keenly. It was also they who seemed prepared to act to improve their condition. They had their opportunity when, in the spring of 1832, the newly opened King's College offered a course of lectures on geology, to be given by Charles Lyall who had just been appointed first Professor of Geology.

As geology was a popular preoccupation with women, a surprising number of whom were well-known researchers, it was not unexpected when some women decided to force the issue of female education. A committee, with Mary Somerville and Charlotte Murchison as ring-leaders, decided the moment had come to challenge the establishment. They demanded to know if they would be admitted to the lectures. The young Professor Lyall, an academic fledgling, was nervous and stated bluntly that, in his opinion, the presence of females in a classroom was 'unacademical'. This cut no ice with the ladies. They carefully organized a large group of enthusiastic friends to turn up on the first day. Mary Somerville even took her two young daughters along. Complete success rewarded their courage. When Mary Somerville wrote later that day to her old friend William Whewell in Cambridge, she was jubilantly militant: 'It is decided by the Council of the University that ladies are to be admitted to the whole course, so you can see what in[va]sions we are making on the laws of learned societies. Reform is nothing to it.'[29]

But this heady victory was short-lived. Although Charles Lyall had, in the event, been persuaded by the strength of female interest, the traditionalists had regrouped by June 1832 and the Council of King's was persuaded to forbid the future admission of women to the lectures on the grounds that the young men who attended might be distracted. In 1848 women tried again to gain entry, this time to Wheatstone's lectures on electricity, but a strict ban on their presence was effectively enforced. It was not until 1878 that a series of lectures for ladies was instituted, and in 1881 King's admitted women as students. Other educational institutions in London were just as dilatory. The London Mechanics' Institute, later Birkbeck College, had admitted women in 1830, but three years later was still agonizing over the propriety of allowing the women who were attending the lectures to use the front door. University College had permitted two women to register for a course on natural philosophy in 1832, but there was no further registration of women until 1861. Seven years later, in 1868, the college opened its lectures to women, and finally, in 1878, it permitted them to take degree courses.[30]

George Eliot

The interest of George Eliot (i.e. Mary Ann Evans) (1819–80) in science runs like a bright connecting thread through the varied scenes of her life. In 1828, at the age of nine, she was sent to a boarding school in Nuneaton run by a couple of fervently religious Irish women. Four years later she continued her education at the Miss Franklin School in Coventry. From these two educational establishments she gleaned a fair acquaintance with English, history, French and arithmetic, and the accomplishments of music and drawing. If there were any formal lessons in science, she never mentioned them, but her teachers were liberal and intelligent women, so it is not unlikely that some intro-ductory instruction was on offer.

Mary Anne Evans was an intellectual girl, as indeed were several of her women friends. Even after she left school she sustained a scheme of rigorous study which included teaching herself Latin. When her brother Isaac married, she and her father surrendered the family home to the newly married couple, as was customary, and moved to a smaller establishment in a village near Coventry. In the manner of so many women before her, Mary Anne, now her father's housekeeper, filled her time to the best of her ability with domestic chores, charitable works in the neighbourhood and ever-extending intellectual pursuits. Her reading at this time was impressive and implied some earlier and intensive scientific instruction. It ranged widely through mathematics, astronomy, chemistry, geology and entomology. Even the popular pseudo-science of phrenology triggered her interest.

She brought to her studies a critical awareness of the importance of science, a conviction that followed a period during which she had experienced and subsequently rejected an intense evangelical awaken-ening. Equipped with her new scientific outlook, she turned a ques-tioning eye on the literal interpretations of the Bible, still a relatively outrageous action in most sections of society.

The new discoveries in geology excited and disturbed her just as much as they did the main scientific community. It was clear to her that the human race was arriving at a new and more accurate version of its history. Without trepidation for the consequences, she was pre-pared to cast aside old myths. She had no time at all for that powerful movement that was attempting to stem the flow. When she read Vernon Harcourt's *Doctrine of the Deluge*, a vindication of the scriptures over geology, she was not persuaded. A little later she carefully studied John Pye Smith's *Relation between the Holy Scriptures and some Part of Geological Science* (1839), only to find that his arguments against geology merely encouraged the secular speculations that they had set out to dispel.[31] In due course she laid aside all religious belief and proclaimed herself a 'free-thinker'.

When she and her father moved to the outskirts of Coventry, Mary Anne discovered new ways in which to supplement her private scientific studies. She met more interesting people. The bookshops were better, although when they could not supply her with what she wanted, she simply ordered from London. She was also able to attend whatever public lectures were available, which would have given her the necessary personal contact with science teaching.

At this time her favourite subject was astronomy. In letters to friends she let her enthusiasm bubble forth, describing how she 'revelled' in the subject, winging her flight 'from system to system, from universe to universe'. Her favourite author was John Pringle Nichol, a former clergyman who had withdrawn from the ministry when his religious beliefs had altered, and who was currently Professor of Astronomy in Glasgow.[32]

During the 1840s, boredom was kept at bay by taking on teaching, writing and translating. It was only after her father's death in 1849 that Miss Evans had the time to concentrate her energies. She joined her closest friends Mr and Mrs Bray on a European tour, and when they turned for home she chose to remain in Geneva. For eight months she lived alone in a comfortable *pension* and sought to come to terms with her hopes and ambitions, and with her new identity as a spinster on the verge of somewhat penurious middle age. She had not, as yet, tried her hand at fiction and seemed to have felt no inclination to do so. While this presumably none-too-comfortable stocktaking was in progress, she continued her scientific studies, taking advantage of the facilities of that foreign city. Twice a week she went to the Athenée to hear the lectures on experimental physics that were organized that winter for the benefit of Geneva's women scientists. The lecturer was Professor A.A. de la Rive, the inventor of electroplating.[33]

On her return to London, Miss Evans was established in January 1851 as the editor, albeit anonymous, of John Chapman's *Westminster Review*. Now living in the metropolis, she was able to take advantage, when her editorial duties permitted, of the many and varied opportunities for scientific study that the capital could offer. So, for example, she enrolled in Francis Newman's course in geometry at the Ladies' College in Bedford Square. Bedford College, as it came to be known, had been established in 1849, a year after Queen's, by Mrs Elizabeth Reid, a leading figure in the anti-slavery movement. It differed from

Queen's in ways that the self-proclaimed free-thinker would have found significant. Of particular importance was the stress that was laid on its undenominational character, and, in addition, the women students were expected to participate in the government of the college.[34]

Gaining admission to many of the places where science teaching was offered was still usually a matter of luck, pull and money. The price of the ticket was often the most effective deterrent to scientific study. For all his philandering, John Chapman was a keen enthusiast for women's studies in science. He would certainly have encouraged Mary Anne, as he did other young women, to go to these lectures.[35] On at least one occasion he presented her with a ticket, but she, perhaps only too conscious of his weakness for young ladies, refused to accept it as a present, but paid for it herself. Someone else got her a ticket for Faraday's lecture on the magnetism of oxygen. This may have been the first time she heard him teach. What he made of her is not recorded, but she certainly seems to have thought a great deal of him. He was one of the nine people to whom she had her publishers send presentation copies of her first work of fiction, *Scenes from Clerical Life* (1858). In his acknowledgement of this anonymous work, he wrote of the two volumes, 'They have been, and will be again, a very pleasant relief from mental occupation among my own pursuits. Such rest I find at times not merely agreeable, but essential.' Of all the letters of compliment she received, George Eliot (as she now was to her readership) treasured Faraday's letter particularly. In due course he became a devoted reader of all her novels.[36]

There was yet another scientist who meant a lot to Mary Anne Evans. He was Herbert Spencer, the biologist. During her first years in London, he was one of her most ardent admirers. Together they pursued romance and science over many years in a way that foreshadowed Mary Anne's later, more serious rebuff to convention. She would certainly have liked to marry, but that was apparently beyond Spencer's powers of decision. He died when he was eighty-four years old – still a bachelor. However, what he could offer, a scientific mentorship, he did give, and generously for many years.

Under Mary Anne Evans's editorship, the *Westminster Review* developed and maintained a strong scientific section. Among the articles on biology, geology and chemistry which appeared were such seminal works as the first publication of Spencer's theory of evolution. Assuming that she read, or perhaps even edited, these pieces, it was clear that she was well placed to keep abreast of the most advanced scientific thought of her time.

It was her momentous liaison with G.H. Lewes, considered by both as a solemn, if unorthodox marriage, that not only brought to maturity her development as a great writer of fiction, but also opened up yet another area of scientific study for her. Lewes, a one-time medical student, was an enthusiastic zoologist and naturalist. George Eliot described her feelings for Lewes and his scientific interests as having herself 'a slight zoological weakness' and therefore not being alarmed by 'the society of a zoological maniac'. When they set up house in East Sheen in 1855, they began immediately on their studies in biology and zoology with the help of a borrowed microscope. Astronomy had been demoted as a lesser interest. When Charles Lewes, one of G.H. Lewes's sons, joined their household after his schooling in Switzerland, she paid as much attention to developing his scientific interests as she did to his musical and artistic avocations. The boy was taken to a course of lectures on chemistry at the Museum of Economic Geology. George Eliot felt it was incumbent on the individual to become well informed on scientific matters.

Their work kept them in London, but as Marian, as she now called herself, jokingly remarked, when the slightest opportunity presented itself they were ready to 'run away to mountains and molluscs and seabreezes'. Holidays were an opportunity to make field trips in pursuit of some zoological rarity. In September 1855 they went to Worthing in search of polyps. Still a friend, Herbert Spencer, as well as lecturing them on his biological theories, fired them with interest in the unique marine life to be found at Tenby. Ilfracombe was yet another goal. In May 1856, Marian recorded that they spent most of their time there 'naturalizing' along the shore.[37] As she and Lewes settled down contentedly together, Marian, a happy woman at last, described her days as spent 'reading Homer, science and rearing tadpoles'.[38] Only after Lewes's death, which she experienced as total devastation, did she appear to surrender her scientific interests. When she was sufficiently recovered, one of her first actions was to put away his microscope and other scientific apparatus.[39]

Elizabeth Garrett Anderson

In the 1850s it seemed that, for as long as they were content to accept their amateur status in the scientific world, women had at least some degree of access to the advantages and opportunities offered by the scientific community. When they decided to turn their scientific interests into a career, however, they were less welcome. The experience of Elizabeth Garrett Anderson, who became England's first qualified female doctor, not only reveals the nature of this struggle, but also casts further light on the efforts being made by other young girls to increase their scientific knowledge and what opportunities there were for them to exploit.

The deficiencies of the system that permitted women to study science for recreational purposes, but not with any professional end in view, were immediately apparent when Elizabeth Garrett decided to become a doctor. Rejected by all teaching hospitals, she was finally able to persuade the only other examining body, the Society of Apothecaries, to accept her. This it did, but only because it was legally bound by its charter not to turn away any student. The examination requirements, the minimum necessary for a general practitioner, included courses in *materia medica*, chemistry, anatomy and physiology, botany, dissections, midwifery and diseases of women, as well as sessions of clinical practice.

By dint of personal obstinacy, contacts and money, Elizabeth succeeded. Excluded from all official medical schools, she was able to use many of the courses put on for the recreation of women in a more professional way. Thus her certificate for botany was acquired by attending courses at the Pharmaceutical Society which included demonstrations at the Physic Garden in Chelsea, and which placed no ban on the attendance of women. The accessibility of the Pharmaceutical Society to women remained a curious anomaly. Both lectures and examinations were opened to women in 1873. A course completed successfully entitled women to register as 'Chemists and Druggists and as Pharmaceutical chemists, under the Pharmacy Act'.[40]

Elizabeth Garrett utilized the physics courses given at the Royal Institution by the then Professor of Natural Philosophy, John Tyndal, which was an acceptable enough course of action. What seems to have outraged convention most of all was her appearance at T.H. Huxley's course on natural history and physiology, given for teachers at the South Kensington Museum. Elizabeth had been personally introduced by John Chapman. Huxley apparently had doubts about admitting women to scientific meetings. In his opinion five-sixths of all women were 'in the doll stage of evolution'. But he was also prepared to admit that much of their apparent mental deficiency could be attributed to the limited education and the enervated regimen that society ordained as suitable for women. He had refused to let his own daughters be so constrained. They were not to 'be got up as mantraps for the matrimonial market', and his educational ideal was to educate women as comrades, fellows and equals of men.[41]

His first lecture in the course dealt with the tricky subject of the physiological differences of sex, something which up till then Elizabeth Garrett's private tutors had sedulously avoided. Elizabeth was thrilled to have had at last a clear, logical and scientific exposition, but it was a daring step for a respectable young lady to attend such lectures publicly and alone. John Chapman, knowing how she would feel, kindly permitted his own daughters to accompany her. The girls were introduced to Huxley, who took the trouble to show and to explain to them the specimens in the museum.

A little later in the lecture series, more women appeared, two sisters of the renowned Octavia Hill, and the extraordinary Sophia Jex-Blake who was also aiming for a medical career. On the same evening, 19 October 1861, Huxley recognized the novel composition of his audience and began his lecture, 'Ladies and gentlemen'. Amidst so much forceful and continuing opposition, it was a small triumph.

Eventually Elizabeth Garret qualified as a doctor, though to obtain an MD she had to travel to Paris. Her own contribution to furthering education for doctors commenced almost at once. In May 1872 she began to give a course of lectures for women on anatomy and physiology. She charged a substantial fee and was determined to make the lectures vivid and practical.[42] Her main goal was to establish a women's medical school and a teaching hospital as well. In October 1874 the London School of Medicine for Women opened its doors. It was her work that finally broke down the barriers of resistance to the idea of women doctors.[43] It was a tough struggle. In 1876 an Act of Parliament permitted, but did not require, medical examining boards to admit women. In fact only the Royal College of Physicians of Ireland acted immediately to facilitate the entry of women into the profession.

Shortly some eight English women were named on the Medical Register. Despite these signs of change, in 1878 the British Medical Association voted by a substantial majority not to allow women doctors to become members. Elizabeth Garrett Anderson mustered all her rhetorical strength to try and dissuade her fellow members from this course, but in vain. She herself was grudgingly allowed to remain a member, however, and continued thus, the only woman in the BMA, for a further nineteen years.

In her *Annual Report* of 1878 for the New Hospital for Women, Elizabeth Garrett Anderson summed up what progress women had made in the medical field up to that date. She recognized that for women hope lay in the future:

Parliament has expressed a decided opinion in favour of allowing women to practice medicine; the highest medical examining body in the United Kingdom has declared its willingness to confer its degrees upon them; a complete medical school, with a large hospital, a museum and a library has been organized for the use of female students; and we believe that when these facts are fairly considered the change must be accepted as accomplished, and that women must, from this time forth, be left to make the best mark they can for themselves in the practice of the medical profession.[44]

She had advice, too, for other women neither rich nor fortunate enough to be able to contemplate a medical career. These women, usually ageing spinsters, immured through economic necessity in the parental home, must come forth, ensure that they acquire some form of education and seek their own salvation in independence. The pressing need for women of this category to be encouraged to do something for themselves was behind many of the mid-nineteenth-century educational movements.

Women's educational associations and university extension

The scientific societies of the nineteenth century offered women an admirable introduction to the various branches of the subject. But for women who nurtured serious educational ambitions the obvious defects of a piecemeal system of occasional lectures sporadically planned were a serious deterrent. The structured educational continuum that men of the privileged classes enjoyed made a telling contrast. It was obvious to many reformers that, until a more consistent and systematic process of education was open to women, they would continue to be unable to support themselves by useful work and be frustrated in their desire to pursue independent lives.

In the middle of the nineteenth century a new sense of self-determination among women was evident throughout the country. For the first time they began, on a large scale, to take upon themselves the responsibility and obligation to improve the educational opportunities of their sex. In the autumn of 1867, in the northern counties, these pioneers swiftly and efficiently organized themselves under a parent body called the North of England Council for the Education of Women. More than any other group at the time, it was responsible for opening up new educational ventures to women and for encouraging the study of science at least among middle-class women.[45]

Its committee members were prominent women who left their mark on the history of the women's movement in the nineteenth century.

Mrs Josephine Butler was the President. The Secretary was Anne Jemima Clough and active members included Miss Wolstenholme in Manchester, Theodosia Marshall in Leeds and Miss Keeling in Sheffield. The Council's aim was to improve the education of women in the northern towns. It had in mind two particular groups of women. The first group were those who had left school and, although obliged by convention and economic restrictions to remain at home, still wished to continue with their education. The second group, to which the Council gave priority, were those women who wished to qualify themselves as governesses and schoolmistresses and who required high standards of teaching. Since no other outlet was available to fulfil the evident needs of such women, the members of the Council saw it as their duty to provide a more systematic approach to education for women over the normal school-going age, by hiring teachers and by arranging a coherent timetable of classes spread over several seasons. It was taken for granted that the Council and the classes it organized would be financed by the women themselves.

With an amazing display of organizational ability the Council very quickly established branch offices in Manchester, Liverpool, Sheffield and Leeds, which set an inspiring example for other towns to follow. Some of the most active daughter associations were the Liverpool, the Birmingham, and the Leamington Ladies Educational Associations. Soon effective associations had appeared in Bradford, Huddersfield, Bowden, Birkenhead, York and other northern provincial towns. Other areas of the country followed suit. There was the Windsor and Eton Association for the Education of Women, the Rugby Council for Promoting the Education of Women and the Brighton Association for Promoting Higher Education, as well as branches at Cambridge and Clifton, Plymouth and Falmouth, Edinburgh, Dublin and Belfast.

They were strong-charactered women who ran these organizations, and jockeying for power could not always be avoided. Edward Carpenter, a lecturer on the ladies' circuit, reported somewhat gleefully the competitiveness between Miss Lucy Wilson, the local secretary of the Leeds branch, and Miss Heaton, another committee member.[46]

Initially, the associations experienced considerable difficulty in finding teachers to undertake the work of teaching these female students. Few qualified men were willing to undergo the privations of months spent teaching in northern towns. Fortunately, the Council and other educational bodies working for the improvement of education among the lower classes, such as the Rochdale Equitable Pioneers, the first co-operative in the country, and the newly founded mechanics' institutes, managed, around 1867, to secure the interest of James Stuart.

James Stuart was the son of a flaxmill owner in Balgonie in Fifeshire. As a young boy he had spent many years working in his father's mills. Whether this contact with the artisan and labouring classes was the key to his later concern with broadening the base of higher education is not clear. Whatever the case, when his studies at Trinity College in Cambridge were over, he became involved in various educational experiments, all tending towards the modification of the power and prestige of the age-old tradition of residential university education. His liberal reputation grew and it was to him that the ladies of the North of England Council turned for teaching assistance.

Initially, what they wanted from him was a series of lectures to their lady members, most of whom were aspiring teachers, on the theory of education. Reluctant to tackle such a subject, Stuart decided that something a little less abstruse would suit his purpose. So, as he explained in his autobiography, *Reminiscences* (1911), what he actually delivered was a series of eight lectures on the history of astronomy. Once again, almost inadvertently, another effort on behalf of women's education came to concentrate on the scientific subjects. While the ladies' associations lasted, the scientific content of these extra-mural classes remained significant.

As well as being the subject closest to his heart, Stuart saw astronomy as an excellent introduction to a necessary and fundamental study of the laws of nature. In his autobiography, he described astronomy as

> the only really complete science. Its history is well defined, and involves interesting personalities, and it affords the best example of the discovery and application of what is called a law of nature, and my lectures were really confined to the very narrow limit of elucidating the discovery and the meaning of one law – that of gravitation. [*Reminiscences*, p. 161]

It was not only the scientific classes that became a tradition in the ladies' associations. On the basis of this introductory series, various study techniques and lecture formulae were established which continued to characterize this type of education for decades. To begin with, Stuart discovered that convention would not permit him to employ the question and answer method of teaching. It would have been socially unacceptable for a young woman to have joined in conversation with an unknown young man. To cope with this ticklish point of etiquette, Stuart prepared a sheet of written questions which he distributed after his first lecture, announcing that, if any of those in attendance wished to send him their answers before the following week's class, he would discuss the questions on the basis of those written replies. The result was astounding. From the six hundred or so ladies who had sat and listened to him at the four centres in Leeds, Liverpool, Manchester and Sheffield, he received not the handful of brief scribblings that he expected, but completed papers from half that number:

> I expected twenty or thirty answers, but from the four centres, which consisted of about 600 pupils, I got about 300 answers. I had a very hard time getting these corrected in readiness for the next lecture. But I got very valuable assistance from these replies, as I saw where my explanation had been insufficient. [p. 162]

In addition to the lectures and the set questions, the ladies were also provided with an outline of the talk to assist them in following it, instructions on how to take notes intelligently and a comprehensive reading list to assist their further study.

This indefatigable teacher was much pleased with his efforts in the area. His circuit embraced the mechanics' institutes, the co-operatives and the ladies' associations. He himself noted wryly that it was only the ladies who invariably paid his lecturing fee. In the case of the first lectures series it amounted to £200. 'I have always found women more ready to pay than men, and more considerate' (p. 164).

It was not only middle-class ladies who benefited from Stuart's teaching. He recalled giving a series of weekly lectures on physical astronomy to which over a thousand working people came, many of them straight from the factory floor. What stayed in his mind was not simply the attentiveness of the men, but the numbers of their wives who had also crowded on to the benches in the lecture room: 'Some of the women brought their babies, as they needed to lock up their house in order to come. Sometimes the babies cried. However, the mixture was better than that at a public house, where many of the men might otherwise have been' (*Inaugural Address*, 1871).

Some statistics convey both the breadth and scope of the science lectures and the numbers of ladies who attended them. The timetable of the Liverpool centre between autumn 1867 and spring 1873 was typical of many associations. During the first session (1867/8), 186 ladies studied astronomy and 214 history. In the next session (1868/9), physical geography was taught to 185 women and the history of science to 163 women. In the autumn of 1869, light was taught to 157 ladies, and in the following spring, electricity and magneticism to 173 ladies. In comparison, the available course during the session 1870/1 concentrated on English literature, which attracted two groups of 227 and 190 respectively. Meteorology was offered to 166 women in the autumn of 1871, while during the following three sessions, 164 women studied the history of the USA, 301 read contemporary poetry and an impressive 310 examined the plays of Shakespeare. Although the numbers of women tended to shoot up when literary subjects were on the timetable, the general bias of the courses was heavily scientific. It seems that it was always more difficult to persuade literary men to lecture.

Other examples of locations where women could study a scientific curriculum included the North London Ladies Educational Association which, in the 1872/3 session, offered astronomy, algebra, English and French grammar. The Cambridge Association included chemistry, astronomy and maths among its course subjects, while Clifton promoted natural philosophy and botany together with other studies, although a course on heat had to be suspended for lack of interest.

At Bradford in 1872 approximately 93 ladies attended a series of lectures and wrote papers on electricity, mathematics, Latin, German, French, zoology and physiology. The ladies in Birmingham were fortunate in that the Birmingham and Midland Institute, which had opened in 1867, welcomed women to its lectures. There the timetable included chemistry, physiology, physical geography, experimental physics, botany and geology – all taught by well-qualified university men.

Out of this successful, if quaint, programme of women's education grew the more sophisticated idea of the University Extension lectures system. James Stuart was at the centre of a group who believed that the ancient universities should adapt their educational obligations to a rapidly changing society. One of the main complaints against the old university system was its residential requirement. Men who needed to work for their living were automatically excluded from university life because they could not take the requisite number of months away from their work in order to meet the requirements of the university statutes. Since so few could come to Oxford or Cambridge, Stuart argued that the universities should extend their academic provision to people out in their homes in the provinces.

The women in the educational associations joined vigorously in the agitation, standing shoulder to shoulder with the co-operatives and the mechanics' institutes. In 1871 they united with the other pressure groups, the Crewe Mechanics' Institute, the Rochdale Equitable Pioneers and the Mayor and citizens of Leeds, to present a memorial to the Vice-Chancellor and the Council of the University of Cambridge.[47]

The North of England Council for the Higher Education of Women concentrated on putting a strong case on behalf of the two groups of women who needed access to higher education – would-be teachers and ladies obliged to reside at home. In its submission, the Council proposed a scheme similar to the recently instituted local examinations. It was to consist of two or three courses of study to be prescribed by the University, which would then send out teachers to supervise the courses and examiners to control the results.

As regards the cost of such a scheme, the Council recognized that the lower the costs, the more persuasive the argument. It referred to its own experiences of running a similar system over several years. Its officers believed that women would be willing to pay a suitable fee for the lectures, as they had done in the past, and because these moneys could be augmented by others, any systematic teaching organized by the University would soon become self-supporting. They were also careful to point out that there need be no great outlay involved in setting up a series of lectures in provincial centres since most of these places already possessed lecture rooms, museums and laboratories which, at a small cost, could be opened for lectures and classes in the afternoons, the time usually set aside for women's study. The willingness of women to shoulder the costs of their own education was exploited by the University and the State for many decades to come.

Stuart's own suggestions were for a twice-weekly lecture plus two hours of class teaching for women. All lectures were to be accompanied by a syllabus, and questions were to be answered in writing and by discussion before and after the lecture, to solve any difficulties that might have arisen in connection with the course. He had clearly become a little irritated with the petty restrictions of feminine life. In his *Letter on University Extension, addressed to the Resident Members of the University of Cambridge* (1871) he went to some trouble to point out that 'it would be a great saving of trouble if the lectures to men and to women were not separate'.

In October 1873 the efforts of the many dedicated campaigners resulted in the setting up of the Cambridge extension lectures at Nottingham, Derby and Leicester. This novel move was ultimately to lead to the establishment of local colleges and a flowering of opportunities for many more women. In the last decades of the nineteenth century it was generally agreed that university extension was 'one of the chief liberating forces of the intellectual capacities of women in the mid-Victorian era'.[48]

The students at these classes were mostly women. They included older women looking for additional training, women living at home in need of intellectual stimulation and, not infrequently, 'young ladies' from the sort of schools, particularly Quaker establishments, which encouraged the study of science among their pupils. The pupils of the Mount Street School in York were always keen listeners at science lectures. Otherwise, elderly clerks, intelligent young men of the lower middle classes and a sprinkling of manual workers made up the audiences.[49]

It had been hoped that some at least of those who attended the university extension lectures in their own locality would eventually provide Cambridge with a new type of student. But though highly praised on many sides, it was not long before students and extension lectures alike came in for a barrage of criticism from what might be called the educational establishment. The scientific content, already noted as a particular feature of this movement, brought considerable opprobrium on both organizers and students. Detractors claimed that the now well-established correlation between science and philistinism was amply proved by the student mixture that patronized the extension lectures. Artisans, manual workers and women were still not recognized as qualified to participate in nobler educational practice. It was often observed that, while the science lectures were full, few bothered with the courses offered in literature and art. Similarly, when the summer students poured into Oxford to enjoy their brief week as real undergraduates, even *The Times* descended to cheap jibes at the expense of these deluded part-timers, most of them women, who thought they could take a short cut to a university education. One extensioner, a certain M.I.E., enjoyed the Oxford summer meeting of 1888, but had been so incensed by the sneers of the press that she took them to task in *Oxford Blue v. Drab* (1892). Defiantly, she claimed:

> We are especially proud of the part Extension is taking in the great movement for the education of women. Men have far fewer difficulties in getting in touch with living knowledge than have women, and the Extension system comes, therefore as an especial boon to the women of the middle and even the upper classes. [p. 7]

She attempted to pacify the opposition then, by explaining the agonies endured by women condemned to the philistinism of the suburbs, 'the sickly green of the coverings, the gloomy hue of the curtains, the Philistine antimacassars, the dead wall outside' (p. 10). These could be alleviated somewhat, she promised, by the courses in entomology, zoology, geology and so on that the summer school offered, which, of course, would also give women 'a deeper, even a fresh love for the Law-Giver' (p. 11). This woman knew she was speaking on behalf of many of the 'drab' forgotten women of the silent, outer suburbs. During the summer of 1896, 653 students attended the Oxford summer school, of whom four-fifths were women.[50]

Meanwhile, other women's organizations were continuing the struggle for better education. In 1871 the National Union for Improving the Education of Women of all Classes was founded by Mrs William Grey and her sister Miss Shirreff. Its formidable programme of reform quickly brought it to public attention, and in some cases to public condemnation as a 'widely-ramifying conspiracy'. Its first task was to publish monthly the *Women's Educational Journal* as a 'record of all efforts made in favour of women's education'. Secondly, it set up a company which established the first Girls' Public Day School in Chelsea in 1873. A few years later, in 1878, it achieved its other aim when the Maria Grey Training College for Secondary Teachers was founded.

The *Journal* also reported extensively on the state of women's education in other countries, Germany, Japan, Sweden, Finland and the USA. It also established its own lecture series from time to time and advertised what was happening in other towns for the convenience of its readers.

The National Home-Reading Union, based at Surrey House on the Victoria Embankment, was another expedient employed not only to put pressure on publishers for cheaper editions, but also to take education to house-bound women. As well as following the Union's carefully devised study plans for use in the home, its eight thousand strong membership could also participate in the summer schools it organized around the country. Students could congregate at Blackpool, Weston-super-Mare, Bowness, Ilkley, Salisbury or Chester, or at one of the many other chosen locations. There they could put into practice the studies which laid a strong stress on geology, botany and natural history.

Working girls and science studies

Although this study is concerned primarily with the interest in science among women who were seeking intellectual fulfilment rather than the means to financial and social independence, some developments in the education of working-class girls require consideration.

A fundamental and self-evident difference in the education thought natural to each class was that the higher the rank, the more likely its members might be encouraged to enjoy a liberal (i.e. non-career-orientated) education; contrariwise, the lower orders were obliged, almost always, to accept a strictly vocational training. Neither of these attitudes to class and education went unchallenged. Many reformers thought that the education of women of the upper classes ignored the financial exigencies in which these ladies often found themselves. Equally, it was frequently argued that working women had the right to education in the true sense of the word, rather than the narrow training that was all that was available for most of them.

These class differences in education had the full weight of tradition behind them. It was extremely difficult to break free from them. Even Mary Wollstonecraft's revolutionary *Vindication of the Rights of Woman* (1792) had ratified the concept of different education for women from different classes. She accepted it as inevitable that the education of girls of the working classes (and boys too), who are 'intended for domestic employments, or mechanical trades', should be channelled into vocational training at an early age (p. 186). Middle-class women, on the other hand, were to be allowed 'the steady investigation of scientific subjects' and 'the enchantments of literary pursuits' to permit the cultivation and liberation of their minds (pp. 187–8).

Priscilla Wakefield (1751–1832) made even more rigorous class distinctions in education, although she also suggested some constructive and practical alternatives to women seeking employment. Her most thought-provoking contribution to the debate was the fact that she thought working-class women ought to study science since they could put that knowledge to practical use.

She was well placed to advise on work for women. As well as writing her popular science books and travelling extensively, she was engaged in a demanding programme of aid to the lower classes. She was an interesting woman. She came of a philanthropic family. She was the great granddaughter of the famous Quaker, Robert Barclay (1648–90), and the tradition was to be continued by other family members, notably her niece, the celebrated Elizabeth Fry. Self-educated, her two specialities were science and economics. She recognized the link between poverty and dependence and, as a result, became one of the earliest promoters of the new savings bank scheme, as the first step towards self-help. Almost the first savings bank in existence was founded by her, in Ship Inn Yard, Tottenham. By 1798 she had also established a friendly society whose aims were to encourage and promote the ideal of self-reliance among the poor.

She had some very curious notions on the vulnerability of women. While she worked hard for their education and their financial independence, she appears to have always regarded the easy mixing of the sexes with the greatest unease. When this disquiet got the better of her, she seriously proposed that women should live in an all-female world, not the only time this suggestion was made by women in the late eighteenth century.[51] Women were to be well educated and to enjoy many freedoms, but they should never come in contact with the other half of society. All the jobs and offices presently held by men should be filled by women: from educating to undertaking. Male undertakers were just as abhorrent to Mrs Wakefield as male dancing teachers. She also gave her blessing to the growing movement among women at the end of the eighteenth century to establish an economic boycott of those jobs and professions, anything from millinery to midwifery, which, for reasons of modesty or money, she and other women felt should be theirs.[52] The idea had other supporters as well. Even a baronet was reputed to have endorsed the setting up of 'a female association', the first all-women pressure group, whose brief would be a total boycott of the masculine-dominated labour market. Appeals to Parliament for laws favouring positive discrimination on behalf of women had also been suggested, and Mary Anne Radcliffe, in *The Female Advocate* (1799), added her own views on the need to alleviate what she regarded as the punitive income tax legislation relating to self-employed women.

For all this sensitivity, Mrs Wakefield was inclined to take a robust view of women as nothing more or less than an economic unit in society. She saw female employment as not so much a right as a duty. She had read and approved of Adam Smith's interpretation of modern society as a vast mechanism of independent but interrelated parts and obviously felt that women might not be aware of the obligations of their economic contract with society. To drive home the point her treatise, *Reflections on the Present Condition of the Female Sex* (1798), was prefaced with Smith's remarks that 'every individual is a burden upon the society to which he belongs, who does not contribute his share of productive labour for the good of the whole' (p. 1).

Her aim was to demonstrate that women can and must undertake an active role in modern society. In her book she outlined in some detail the various types of employment open to women at the end of the eighteenth century. She noted in passing and with some regret that, although many of the upper classes were following the lead (urged on by people like Catherine Macauley Graham and Mary Wollstonecraft) and casting aside the fetters of dress and deportment to improve the health and well-being of women, the labouring poor continued to wear their leather bodices and whalebone stays.

Similarly, a 'more energetic mode of education' was necessary to produce women who could fend for themselves and who would be willing to face down the ineradicable snobbery and prejudice that blocked the woman who went into business. Naturally, Mrs Wakefield, a successful business woman herself could find no excuse for the double thinking that snubbed the wealth producers while enjoying the wealth.

In Mrs Wakefield's educational scheme the social role of the women of each class dictated the form and goal of their education. The women of the upper classes were expected to perpetuate their crucial social function as the moral leaders of society whose aims must be the 'reformation of vice, the instruction of ignorance and the promotion of virtue'. Their education should conduce to an expansion of the human personality and understanding. Her programme is one with which we are familiar:

> Whatever had a tendency to strengthen the judgment, to enlarge the compass of the understanding; to impress just principles of action, and raise the mind to the contemplation of the wisdom of the Creator, by an acquaintance with his works, deserves a decided preference. The acquisition of languages, simple mathematics, astronomy, sciences and experimental philosophy, with history and criticism may be cultivated by the sex with proficiency and advantage. [p. 74]

Mrs Wakefield had no time for the ill-executed attempts at the fine arts that were increasingly passing for education among the upper classes. These were activities for people with talent. Lesser mortals should occupy themselves in pursuing a variety of scientific studies, such as 'chemistry, electricity, botany, and an investigation of the properties and habits of the several orders of animals'. Gardening, woodwork and devising inventions were also acceptable recreations.

The women of the middle classes faced quite a different destiny and need not anticipate much time spent in self-realization or the pursuit of truth. Instead they should be well versed in the vocational training of the domestic sciences. However, if this was a retrograde thought, Mrs Wakefield did not imply that they should be kept in ignorance of their husband's business affairs. It was constantly on Mrs Wakefield's mind, as it had been on the minds of many women reformers, that widows had to acquire some means of earning their own living. Left ignorant and ill educated, their future and that of their children was bleak.

The specific training that she suggested emphasized a basic general education. Women of this social group should be competent in English, in mathematics, in drawing of the professional kind, that which was usually reserved for boys, and in natural history. If widowed or single, women of this class, and indeed of the class above, had several options. Mrs Wakefield allowed any career so long as it would not bring women into too close association with the opposite sex. At the top of her list comes the career of writer, for the very ambivalent reason that it kept women suitably cloistered. She had the grace to admit that 'the emolument is precarious'. Professional art work, colouring of prints, engraving, illustrating textbooks and working with book and print production was already in the hands of many women. Her most unusual suggestion, and one that was increasingly an option for women, was the area of agriculture and horticulture, in particular nursery and landscape gardening.

When she turned her attention to 'the duties, attainments and employments of the women of the third class', the lower trades people and those just above the labouring poor, Mrs Wakefield tailored an education for them that was solely vocational. The essence of this educational programme for working women was to be what Adam Smith had previously suggested as the most useful training for the lower orders. In *The Wealth of Nations* (1767) he had noted the need for elementary geometry and mechanics because they could be applied to every common trade. Mrs Wakefield added her own gloss. In her opinion these lowly subjects served the inferior orders well, for although they would encourage the cultivation of civic spirit they would also reinforce the unchanging nature of class distinctions and their place down near the bottom of the social hierarchy.

A careful study of arithmetic and geometry, neither subject ever having managed to acquire the marks of social prestige, was guaranteed to dissuade social climbing:

> The objects concerning which these sister sciences treat, being confined to the understanding they possess nothing in their nature encouraging to personal vanity, or to false pride which often excites one order of men to tread too closely upon the footsteps of those above them. The knowledge of things that are in themselves useful, can only be injurious when it has a tendency to break down the distinctions of society, by arousing a passion for science in the bosom of individuals of a certain condition which can seldom be gratified, but at the expense of their welfare in life. [p. 11]

Mrs Wakefield felt secure in recommending to the wives and daughters of masons and carpenters the practical skills of mathematics, for this was not a subject that would encourage social climbing.

Most of the charitable institutions that catered for the education of poorer girls, if not offering the demanding curriculum that Mrs Wakefield suggested, would have agreed nonetheless with her reservations on the dangers and the unsuitability of an excessively liberal education for the working classes. That there were exceptions has been mentioned. The Mechanics' Institutes for Working Women was one organization that attempted, in so far as it was capable on its limited resources, to expand the basic education of women. Established in Huddersfield in 1847 and later in Bradford and other towns of the industrial heartlands, these institutes appeared convinced that true education had little or nothing to do with the training, either industrial or domestic, that many authorities seemed to force on women not only of the working class, but of all classes. The case for the liberal education of women was put at the Social Science Conference in 1859:

> Women are to be educated, (it is argued), in order to qualify them for the duties of wives and mothers, of mistresses and servants. Now, it is impossible to overrate the value of education to women, as affecting the right discharge of their social functions, nor can the advocates of the cause be blamed for turning to account an argument so calculated to tell with force; but they surely ought not to be content to have the questions regarded from this point of view exclusively. How rarely is it urged that women should be educated in order that whatever capacities they possess may be completely developed, and their natures permitted to grow to the full height of which they carry in them the germ! How little weight is attached to the consideration that moral and mental culture must be of the greatest consequence to themselves as human beings, quite apart from the good results which necessarily accrues thence to others.[53]

What the Mechanics' Institute for Working Women aimed to do was to liberate the whole woman by cultivating her powers of reasoning. In the opinion of the organizers, the physical sciences were well adapted for this purpose, and by 1859 they were being taught in evening classes in the Huddersfield and Bradford institutes. The mill girls were asked to pay 1s. 6d. per quarter or 2d. a week for their science lessons.

Those other early manifestations of worker solidarity, the co-operatives, often tried to bring something more than merely vocational skills to workers in industrial cities. The very first one, as has been noted, was the Equitable Pioneer Co-operative Society, which was established in Rochdale in 1848. Its ideals were appropriately high, for it added to its liberal educational aims a belief in the improvement of the financial and social position of women. Not only did it set aside $2\frac{1}{2}$ per cent of net profits for the education of its members, but its other, equally innovative move was its decision to regard the savings paid in by women as their own money, not that of their husbands as the law maintained. The Rochdale Co-operative maintained this revolutionary stand, eventually even going to court to prove a test case. That it won was a major contribution to the change in the law that introduced the Married Women's Property Act in 1872. It is little wonder that the North of England Council for the Higher Education of Women, James Stuart and other interested parties knew they could rely on the support of the Rochdale Co-operative for the movement for university extension.

Some schools, too, defied convention and offered females of this class a more comprehensive, if not very literary, education. One was the Milldown Endowed School at Blandford, which was founded in 1862 by one T.H. Bastard, Esq. According to its statutes, the main subjects to be taught in the school were the structure of the human body, physiology and the laws of health. Of secondary interest were reading, writing, English grammar, arithmetic and geography. Not surprisingly, the founder had added

> such subjects of scientific and useful knowledge as shall be necessary for the requirements and duties of life, accounts and book keeping as qualifications for business situations, and needlework, housework, and gardening as far as practicable with the design of teaching the dignity of labour, imparting skill and handiness and training the children to self help.[54]

Science schools for girls of the industrial classes

The weight of public opinion, however, was behind the theory that the lower classes should be taught useful and practical subjects. The shock of Great Britain's poor showing at the Exhibition of 1851 prompted much haste in government circles to improve the education and training of the working classes. Over the following decades various commissions and committees brooded over ways and means in which to transform the country's industrial output and to improve Britain's ability to compete with the well-educated workforces of Germany and other European countries. Ultimately this concern was to breathe new life into the debate on the government's obligations to the education of the nation. In the short term, a considerable amount of parliamentary time in the last decades of the century was devoted to discussion on how to improve standards, to modernize the curriculum and to educate more of the country's population. This concern produced the notion of the State-aided science school for the working classes.

Science classes, funded by the government, were established in places like Torquay (1863), Barnstaple (1864) and Plymouth (1865), and later in other towns throughout the British Isles. It led to an inquiry chaired by Lord Frederick Cavendish, which was appointed to examine 'the Provisions for giving Instruction in Theoretical and Applied Science to the Industrial Classes' and whose findings were published as the *Report from the Select Committee on Scientific Instruction* (1868). By the 1870s, interest in these science schools among the working-class population had increased considerably and the numbers of children on the registers had risen.

The science schools were taught according to a plan laid down by the Science and Art Department of the Committee of the Council on Education. The curriculum included twenty-three subjects. The subjects, each designated with a Roman numeral from I to XXIII, were practical, plane and solid geometry; machine construction and drawing; building construction; naval architecture; pure mathematics; theoretical mechanics; applied mechanics; acoustics, light and heat; magnetism and electricity; inorganic chemistry; organic chemistry; geology; mineralogy; animal physiology; elementary botany; general biology; mining; metallurgy; navigation; nautical astronomy; steam and physical geography.

Nationwide, physical geography was the most popular option. In 1873 15,238 students were examined in it, compared with 6,845 in animal physiology, 7,943 in magneticism and electricity, and 7,635 in pure mathematics.[55] To achieve a rapid improvement in scientific literacy, the government had opted for a payment by results scheme which was generally deemed to have been very efficient.

Concealed within the statistics is the interesting fact that many working- and lower-middle-class girls were studying science and were being taught by women teachers. At the end of 1873 there were approximately three dozen women science teachers being paid, by government grant, on the basis of examination results. They were teaching in schools all over Great Britain and Ireland. Of the twenty-three science subjects open for examination, these women teachers most often taught physical geography (Subject XXIII). Mrs A. Biggs of the Clifton National School put all her girls in for the physical geography examination and made £4 that year. Ann Prosser, teaching pupils in the Camberwell

British School, made £5. Mrs Catherine W. Hunter had similar results at the Tennant Street National School in Belfast. Further south the subject was taught in the Sunday's Well School in Cork by Mrs Mary Dwyer. Miss Tamar Gold put the students of the Lifford Female Schoolroom in for the examination, with the excellent result of £5.

If the girls took two subjects for the state examination, physical geography was usually one and animal physiology (Subject XIV) was often the other choice. This combination was taught by Annie Oakes at the Southlands Wesley College in Battersea, by Catherine Bowles at St Mary's School in London (who received £21 from the Department for the year 1873), by Mary Coram at the Stepney National School (whose results made £5), and by Sarah Yelf at the Technical School in Salisbury.

Sometimes general biology was the alternative second subject. This was the case at the Catholic Liverpool Training College where five women teachers, Mary Winfield, Maria Short, Elizabeth Lomax, Catherine MacGarvie and M. Adela Lescher, worked over a long period of time. Their income for 1873 was £101. Catherine MacGarvie did very well with £22.

In some of these science schools the girls occasionally undertook a more demanding examination schedule. Of the 80 children at the Well Street Girls' School in Bedford, 15 took the pure mathematics course (Subject V); 12 took the course in acoustics, light and heat (Subject VIII), 20 took magneticism and electricity (Subject IX); 25 took inorganic chemistry (Subject XI); 15 took geology (Subject XII); 15 took animal physiology (Subject XIV) and 60 took physical geography.

Other schools had equally striking notions of what was appropriate in a vocational school for girls. There were 10 children at the Girls' National School in Seaham Harbour who took the examinations. All of them studied practical, plane and solid geometry, while 8 took building construction (Subject III) as well. At the Girls' National School in Bexley Heath where there were 9 pupils, 4 of them studied geometry while all 9 took building construction. At the Bradford Girls' Middle School, with 40 pupils, 20 were studying magneticism and electricity, 20 took animal physiology and at least 20 took metallurgy (Subject XIX).

Promising pupils and teachers were offered scholarships by the Department of Science and Art which permitted them to come to London for further education in South Kensington. Not many women or girls did achieve this distinction, so when a young teacher from the Roscrea YMCA institution in Ireland, Mary Anne Gahan, won one of these prized scholarships, the *Journal of the Women's Education Union* reported it triumphantly (15 August 1873). Her brother William P. Gahan had won a Royal Exhibition to the Royal School of Mines in Jermyn Street in 1872, when he was about seventeen and had been teaching some time.

However, the goal of the science schools scheme, the improvement of technical and scientific education, was never achieved. Despite all the effort, the results overall were disappointing. Each new government initiative seemed to founder on the congenital uninterest of the British population in science. This debilitating 'want of interest in scientific instruction, which has hitherto characterized the people of this country' and the government's apparent inability to replace it with some of the enthusiasm for science expressed by the country's European competitors, was summed up by Mr J.F. Iselin in his *Report on the Inspection of Schools* (1872):

> Every now and again the alarm note is raised that our industries are suffering in competition with foreigners, and the superiority of the technical schools abroad is pointed out as the cause of our inferiority; but the note soon dies away again without apparently having stimulated any permanent effort. [p. 44]

Leaving aside the more general politico-economic point made by Mr Iseline (and repeatedly by many others), as far as the study of science by girls and women was concerned the identification, by the government and other educational bodies, of science studies and the labour of the 'industrial classes' was, in due course, to amalgamate with other influences to produce a powerful disincentive to study science among girls of the middle and upper classes. In the meantime, just on the eve of that alteration in women's longstanding interest in science, the government produced a report which demonstrated the strength of that interest.

Notes

1. Jack Morrell and Arnold Thackray, *Gentlemen of Science. Early Years of the British Association for the Advancement of Science* (Oxford, 1981), p. 12.

2. There were 248 proprietors and 259 life subscribers, none of whom was a woman.

3. Minutes of Managers, 10 February 1800. The high social status of the seventeen or so ladies nominated was indicative of the social cache of the Royal Institution. Their number included one duchess, five countesses, one viscountess, four right honourables, two honourables, and four untitled ladies.

4. Gwendy Caroe, *The Royal Institution* (1985), p. 16.

5. Henry Bence Jones, *The Royal Institution* (1871), pp. 241–2.

6. Caroe, p. 23.

7. Caroe, pp. 26–7.

8. L.S. Boas, *Harriet Shelley* (1962), p. 71.

9. E.L. Griggs, *Coleridge Fille: a Biography of Sara Coleridge* (1940), pp. 77–8, 193.

10. Sir Harold Hartley, *Humphrey Davy* (1966), pp. 84–5.

11. See *The Ladies Defence* (1701) and *Of Knowledge* (1710). See above, pp. 45–6.

12. Elizabeth Hamilton, *The Mordaunts* (1965), p. 254.

13. Quoted in Hartley, pp. 84–5.

14. *St Paul's Magazine*, vol. 6 (1870), p. 293.

15. Quoted in Morrell and Thackray, p. 150.

16. Caroline Fox, *Diary*, I, p. 257.

17. Raleigh Trevelyn, *A Pre-Raphaelite Circle* (1978), pp. 12ff.

18. *Diary*, I, pp. 263–5.

19. *Athenaeum* (1834), p. 694, quoted in Morrell and Thackray, p. 153.

20. J.W. Clark and T.M. Hughes, *The Life and Letters of the Reverend Adam Sedgwick*, 2 vols (Cambridge, 1890), I, p. 156.

21. *Autobiography*, II, p. 137.

22. Morrell and Thackray, p. 155.

23. Morrell and Thackray, p. 155.

24. *Autobiography*, II, p. 137.

25. Morrell and Thackray, pp. 156–7.

26. Morrell and Thackray, note on p. 149.

27. The professionalization of women as doctors is beyond the scope of this book. I have restricted my comments to indicating how useful general public lectures were to the first woman to attempt to qualify in England.

28. Quoted in Doris Langley Moore, p. 55.

29. 4 May 1832, quoted in Patterson, p. 93.

30. Negley Harte, *The University of London 1836–1986* (1986), *passim*.

31. *Letters*, I, p. 34, quoted in G.S. Haight, *George Eliot* (Oxford, 1968), p. 29.

32. Haight, p. 35.

33. Haight, p. 77.

34. This unsectarianism made it suspect in many quarters. When the first school boards were to be elected in 1871, the only woman candidate to stand in Oxford was Miss Eleanor E. Smith. Her connection with Bedford College and her preference for 'secular' over 'sectarian' education for girls in her evidence to the Schools Inquiry Commission furnished her rivals with ample propaganda. The *Oxford Journal* (21 January 1871) remarked, 'We have in London Dr Elizabeth Garrett and Miss Davies. Oxford may wish to follow suit. But, excellent as ladies are in their own sphere, we take leave to doubt whether public government is the place for them.' Miss Smith came fourth in the polls and was elected.

35. See below, pp. 246–8.

36. Haight, pp. 82–3, 246, 251. Faraday's comment on *Adam Bede*: 'How clever the book is', unpublished letter to Mrs Pollock, 14 April 1859. This reference was pointed out to me by Dr Frank James of the Royal Institution.

37. Haight, p. 197.

38. *The George Eliot Letters* (1954), II, pp. 202, 335.

39. Haight, p. 521.

40. *Journal of the Women's Education Union* (15 December 1873), no. 12, p. 225.

41. Jo Manton, *Elizabeth Garrett Anderson* (1965), pp. 119–20.

42. Manton, p. 225.

43. Manton, pp. 240–60.

44. Manton, p. 260.

45. Working women were to benefit from the Mechanics' Institutes for Working Women. See Fanny Hertz, 'Mechanics' Institutes for Working Women', *Transactions of the Social Science Association* (1859), pp. 347–54. For the science education of working class girls see below, pp. 223–32.

46. *My Days and Dreams* (1916), pp. 80–1.

47. Stuart, p. 170.

48. *University Extension Bulletin*, Lent term, 1909.

49. Carpenter, p. 81.

50. C.S. Bremner, *Education of Girls and Women in Great Britain* (1897), p. 221.

51. One such all-female Utopia had been dressed up as a novel: Sarah Scott (and Lady Barbara Montagu), *A Description of Millennium Hall, and the Country Adjacent: Together with the Characters of the Inhabitants, And such Historical Anecdotes and Reflections, As May excite in the Reader proper Sentiments of Humanity, and lead the Mind to the Love of Virtue* (1762).

52. Another advocate of this boycott was Mary Anne Radcliffe in *The Female Advocate or An Attempt to Recover the Rights of Women from Male Usurpation* (1799).

53. *Transactions* (1859), p. 348.

54. *Report of the Schools Inquiry Commission* (1868), XIV, p. 165.

55. These figures and those quoted in the following pages are taken from the *Twentieth Report of the Science and Art Department of the Committee of Council on Education* (1873).

CHAPTER 8

The Demise of Science as a Female Interest

In the mid-1860s those who were working to improve the status and conditions of women in British society began to reap the first rewards of their efforts. Over the next decades girls' education was improved; institutions of higher learning opened their doors to women; women took their first steps in political life by standing for election to the newly founded school boards; married women gained greater control over their lives; careers that had previously excluded women now welcomed them. Women had begun to make concrete the dreams of earlier generations.

In every aspect of women's lives there was evidence of female energy and action, and a determination to erode the inequalities of the past. The Mechanics' Institutes for Working Women and the educational associations for middle-class women, the employment agencies and career advice centres, the printing and publishing organs to disseminate national information and to keep women abreast of changes in Europe and America, were just some of the bodies founded and operated by women themselves to spearhead the movement or to reinforce its gains.[1] Many of these ideas had first been mooted decades, even centuries, earlier. What was new was the organization and commitment of women and the sympathy and support of certain key figures in government.[2] Their gains undoubtedly laid the foundations not only of the suffragette movement, but of twentieth-century feminism in general.

It is ironic, then, that it was these very improvements in the condition of women and the aspirations which they fuelled that were eventually responsible for a decline of interest in science. As women set out on the road to equality, they resigned the scientific identity that had been theirs since the seventeenth century.

Science studies in girls' school in the 1860s

One of the most momentous decisions taken in the 1860s by the movement to improve the education of women, spearheaded by Miss Emily Davies, was to persuade a government inquiry into the education of the middle classes that it ought to include the conditions in girls' schools in its investigation. It was an extraordinary twist in the history of women's education. For the government of the day to take such a step was unprecedented. That it was persuaded to do so almost by default was irrelevant in the light of the acceleration in change and improvement that followed in the wake of this crucial decision. Following the directions of the Commission, efforts were made to finance a greater number of girls' schools and to improve existing ones, to systematize teaching and to raise standards, to open examinations to girls, to give them access to higher education and, in due course, to require that all girls be granted access to the same sort of education that boys enjoyed.

For four years (1864–8) the appointed inspectors quartered the land, interviewing headmistresses, sitting in on classes, examining the girls and enquiring into school finances. Their brief was comprehensive. These had been their instructions:

> You will, therefore, report on the more important girls' schools in your district, and particularly on any which possess endowments. You will endeavour to ascertain what amount and kind of education is generally considered necessary for girls, what time is given to it, what it annually costs, and how far it appears to fit the girls for their after life.[3]

This massive educational inspection was known as the Taunton Commission. Its brief was a thorough investigation of the schools of the middle classes – that three million of the population occupying houses assessed at an annual value of £20 or over. These were, in the main, private, proprietary or endowed schools funded from sources other than government grants. There were reckoned to be about 974,000 children between five and twenty in this social class. The Commissioners recorded 10,000 educational establishments, of which the great majority catered solely for boys.

Government interest in education was not, of course, restricted to the middle classes. Groups above and below had already been examined. The Newcastle Commission (1858–61) had looked at the provision of 'sound and cheap elementary instruction to all classes of the people'. The Clarendon Commission (1861–4) had investigated the nine leading public schools. The recently established Department of Science and Art kept a close eye on the government science schools.

The reason for this new-found interest in education was not so much philanthropy as anxiety. Increasingly Britain was becoming painfully aware of the shortcomings and inconveniences of mass illiteracy and innumeracy. It was slowly being recognized that the classical education favoured by the middle and upper classes must be modified in favour of greater emphasis on sciences and modern languages. To expedite reform, the government had been persuaded to set up and finance a Department of Education, which was to oversee and to encourage improvements in arts and sciences in the schools.

It was by no means only the poorest classes who were assessed as far gone in illiteracy and ignorance. In fact, many decades of charity work among the poor had often produced very satisfactory results. Disagreeable as it was to acknowledge, the servant class often seemed better educated than the masters.

Of the young men who failed the Civil Service examination (1856–64), only a tiny minority was found to be competent in the three Rs. This prompted a bitter comment in *The Times*, 28 April 1864: 'It is nothing less than disgraceful for gentlemen's sons, at the age of eighteen or twenty, to be ignorant of that in which thousands of charity school children are proficient.'

So it was to investigate and suggest improvements in this state of affairs that the Taunton Commission was established. The Commission's particular obligation was to suggest ways in which the education available to middle-class boys might be made more relevant to the conditions pertaining in the industrial and professional roles needing to be filled.

It would not have occurred to them of their own volition to look into the state of girls' education, for what has that to do with the communal well-being of the country? Had it not been for the inspired efforts of Miss Emily Davies, a tireless campaigner on behalf of women's educational equality, girls would have been left in their educational limbo.

In its initial indifference to girls' schools, the inquiry was somewhat out of touch with contemporary thought. The developments in the recent past among women's educational bodies had, in fact, drawn public attention to the interesting differences between girls' education, at its best, and boys' education, as it was currently provided. The fact that many girls' schools had chosen to ignore the classical curriculum in favour of a varied timetable which paid particular attention to modern languages and the sciences was sometimes held up as an example of how education should be allowed to develop for both sexes. These ideas were summed up in an article in *The Times*:

> Schools for girls are free from the heavy incubus of an antiquated routine, whereby boys are forced to spend the greater part of ten or twelve of their best years in the vain pretence of learning Latin and Greek; of neither of which two languages, after all this expenditure of time, do 19/20s of them, at the end of their school life, know anything beyond a smattering, inaccurate as well as superficial; while for their sake have been neglected, more or less entirely, many other subjects easier for boys to learn, more important for them to know, more useful even as educational agencies in the process of learning. I am no enemy to Latin and Greek; I should wish much to see one, if not both, taught in the highest classes of girls' schools; and I think it would be easy in the course of two years, with two, or at most three lessons per week, to submit to examination a class of average girls, vastly superior in attainments to the great mass of lads who now present themselves at the universities for matriculation, after the usual long curriculum of a public school.[4]

In the opinion of this writer and others of the same persuasion, the best way to raise standards would be to take the model established in girls' schools, improve on it and make its practice universal.

The Taunton Commission and science teaching in boys' schools

The outcome of the inquiry was not a surprise. The assistant commissioners reported that almost all the schools they inspected had low standards – and that girls' schools had, in general, the lowest of all. In their reports to the inquiry they laid bare all the sins of the broken-down system: lazy and lax teaching; learning by rote by uncomprehending pupils; a dismal lack of educational material; and a striking absence of any attempt to accommodate education to social and industrial needs.

But they noted that they had also uncovered considerable evidence to support the contention that two very different educational systems were applied in boys' and girls' schools. In the boys' schools, with a few notable exceptions, the classics continued as the staple fare and anything else was strongly opposed by the teachers, mainly university-educated clergymen. In the girls' schools, on the other hand, there was a varied timetable that included modern languages, arithmetic (sometimes mathematics) and, almost invariably, one or more scientific subjects. It was noted that a school of the calibre of Queen's College offered a full scientific curriculum to its students (roughly two hundred in the first years, of whom Dorothea Beale and Caroline Fox were two). Schools like these were, of course, in a small minority. The assistant commissioners also mournfully documented the more general and enduring popularity of the 'accomplishments'. It was a sad fact that many girls were still subjected to little more than music, needlework and French.

Turning again to boys' schools, the assistant commissioners laid particular stress on the resistance to change that they found there. Aware that the aim of the enquiry was to lay the foundations for an alteration in the importance attached to science, technology and modern languages, they had tested the waters to assess strength of feeling among parents, teachers and boys on these changes. They were well aware that they were looking for a most unconventional departure from tradition. Indeed, it was commonly known that the more industrialized Britain became, the more entrenched on the matter of a traditional education were parents, schools and pupils.

When the Clarendon Commission investigated the nine great public schools, it found that parents 'have no wish to displace the classics from their present position in the forefront of English Education', although they would have accepted the addition of 'modern languages and natural sciences' (Schools Inquiry Commission, 1868, I, P. 16). When the newer schools, such as Marlborough, Cheltenham and Clifton, attempted to incorporate the modern subjects by bifurcating the curriculum into classical and modern departments, few parents were willing to risk their child's future and academic reputation by allowing him to take the modern timetable. The boys themselves were just as conscious of the implications of such a choice. Not many of them wanted to forgo the prestige that their classical studies, however desultorily pursued, brought them. Epsom College was one of the few schools to offer natural science to its students. The boys could choose between science and drawing. Five-sixths of them chose drawing. These modern departments quickly acquired a reputation as the 'refuge for boys whose inferior ability or diligence has prevented their success in classical studies'.

Quite simply, parents did not wish to experiment with their own children and their children did not wish to be guinea pigs. As the assistant commissioners noted, the conviction of these parents that 'to learn the classics was a definite mark of an upper class and clearly separated the education of their sons from that of a merely commercial school' could not be modified. Not until the two great universities had altered the system confining almost all important exhibitions and scholarships to those who displayed distinguished ability in the classics or mathematics was a major deterrent to the study of science removed. Only then, and indeed only in part, was science able to cast off its low academic reputation and begin to attract stronger students.[5]

In the meantime, a powerful lobby continued to bolster the reputation of the classics. Dr Thomas Arnold of Rugby was among the influential contemporary educators who unreservedly threw their weight behind the traditional syllabus. Arnold was quite aware of the claims of science to be included in the school timetable. He just could not see how it could be done. It was 'too great a subject' to be studied 'in parts' and so must either occupy the chief place or be left out altogether. As well as that, he had no respect at all for science as an educative instrument. Only the classics could fulfil that function adequately: 'the study of language seems to me as if it was given for the very purpose of forming the human mind in youth; and the Greek and Latin languages seem to me the very instrument by which this is to be affected'. Scientific literacy had no place in schools: 'rather than have physical science the principal thing in my son's mind, I would gladly have him think that the sun went round the earth, and that the stars were so many spangles set in the bright blue firmament'.[6]

Most schoolmasters heartily concurred that Latin was the chief and ideal educational instrument. That this was not an objective stance did not go unnoticed. The assistant commissioners tartly observed that these teachers' opinions should be weighed against their well-known inability to teach anything else. Their training as Latin grammarians had not prepared them for any of the demands of a modern education. Their answers to the questions posed by the Commission verified their ignorance.

The questions were searching and were intended to discover attitudes to science among schoolmasters. These men were asked, for example: 'How far ought a boy to be advanced in language, mathematics and physical science (a) who leaves school for business at 15; (b) who leaves school for a profession at 18?' The Revd E. P. Vaughan of Wraxall gave a typical answer. The fifteen-year-old 'should know his grammar, English and Latin, be able to construe Caesar and Virgil with a dictionary and work any common sum in decimals, proportion and practice'. The eighteen-year-old 'should be able to read Caesar and

Virgil easily, translate English into Latin fairly, and know three or four books of Euclid, and algebra to quadratics'. The question of ability in physical science was dismissed in silence.

Answers to another question further emphasized the poor esteem in which science was held by those of a firmly classical stamp. When asked 'What value do you attach to chemistry as an educational instrument?', headmaster Gabriel Poole of Bridgwater replied succinctly, 'None.' The Revd Vaughan elaborated somewhat further, identifying the most fundamental premise in the argument against including science in schools. According to him, these subjects did not assist in the mental training of youth. Put simply, chemistry was 'a poor educational instrument' (VII, pp. 85–6).

It took a progressive like Mr W. Tothill of Bristol City School (Bristol had a long tradition of school science for both boys and girls) to disagree – but then he held minority opinions on many matters. He was a keen advocate of equal education for both sexes where possible (VII, p. 89).

In their reports the assistant commissioners noted that there was one section of society that was demanding change and reform. This section was identified as the business and professional classes whose sons would not normally go to either of the universities: 'They think the classics good, but other things indispensable; and they want the classics either to make room beside themselves, or to give way altogether' (I, 1868, p. 17). When interviewed by Mr Fearon, one of the commissioners, some of these parents claimed that 'though classics may be excellent, yet, mathematics, modern languages, chemistry, and the rudiments of physical science are essential, and we do not find time enough for all' (p. 19).

In their demands for the type of education that suited their needs, this class unwittingly or indifferently ruffled the classical sympathies of the inspectors. Mr Fearon noted ruefully and a little sorrowfully that these parents, whom he might have called Gradgrinds, 'will not allow any culture, however valuable otherwise, to take the place of English, arithmetic, sometimes natural science, and modern languages' (p. 20).

Mr Fearon's regretful criticism of what was an eminently modern education betrayed his own pedigree. The assistant commissioners were excellent men and they were committed to the notion of reform in education. However, they were products of their own class and education, which was in most cases typically classical and unscientific, and often, even more true to tradition, unmathematical. Charles Holbrow Stanton, the assistant commissioner for the southern counties, was aware of the poor standard of mathematics in the boys' schools he inspected, but he honestly admitted his own elementary and inadequate knowledge of the subject. J. E. Fitch was the one exception, but he belonged to a different class. He had been an elementary school teacher and took his degree at London University. Later, he became external examiner in mathematics at Cheltenham Ladies College.

The Taunton Commission and girls' schools

For the government to take notice of education was a new departure; for it to attempt to investigate the condition of girls' education was remarkable. In view of this, the sensitivity and sympathy with which the commissioners approached their task was admirable. Through the pages of their reports gleams an interest in and an appreciation of the alternative forms of education that women had evolved over many generations. Naturally they were obliged to dismiss the many schools of 'accomplishments' with a few well-chosen words of condemnation. Their conclusions were quite different, however, when they examined some of the best girls' schools and interviewed the mistresses.

What struck them particuarly was the contrast between their varied and 'modern' timetable and the rigidly classical structure of the boys' schools. Even though most of the inspectors were products of traditional education and were not well placed to appreciate the alternative time-table, and science subjects in particular, they still managed to report on their findings with a commendable modesty and lack of prejudice. When Mr Giffard, one of the assistant commissioners, noted his approval of the science lectures that he had monitored in some girls' schools, he added a personal comment: 'But I was unable, from ignorance of the natural sciences, to test the proficiency of their pupils' (VII, p. 207).

However, he provided the Commission with a comprehensive analysis of what he had found in the schools he had examined. Only 21 per cent of the girls learnt Latin, but almost all of them studied French. Arithmetic and music were also taken by a majority of girls. Only 8 per cent attempted mathematics, compared to 52 per cent of boys. A mere 50 per cent of girls studied drawing, which was firmly categorized as a boys' subject.[7] What was most significant, however, was the 72 per cent who studied some branch of natural science.

This popularity of science in girls' schools repeatedly struck the assistant commissioners as they went about the country on their inves-tigations. They admitted to some surprise. Apparently the fact that the teaching of science was so widespread in girls' schools was not previously known to them. They frequently compared its popularity in these schools with its almost total absence in boys' schools. In view of current efforts on the part of the government to stimulate science teaching and study, it was apparently a shock to them to discover that women had already divined the value of science some time previously. Mr Stanton, who visited twenty-two girls' schools in his region, was very impressed:

> Some of the upper schools I had permission to examine. The work of some of them pleased me exceedingly and bore the marks of conscientious and intelligent labour on the part of those that taught. Many of them were in the habit of attending lectures on natural science, physics etc. and showed a knowledge of these subjects, and of the elements of astronomy, which I rarely found in boys' schools. [VII, p. 71]

In Brighton, where more than two-thirds of the female pupils studied some branch of natural science, Mr Giffard, the inspector, visited at least three schools where several scientific subjects were taught. It seems that botany was the most popular subject, indicating a new development in women's scientific interests since the beginning of the century. But chemistry, natural history and physics were also prominent. The girls were taught very well, he noted approvingly. He reported an interesting sociological observation as well. The interest of the Brighton girls' schools in science was so well known and the reputation of their schools so high that 'a large body of resident professional teachers' had been attracted thither and was highly regarded by pupils and parents alike (VII, p. 207).

In addition to examining schools and pupils, the inquiry called witnesses before it to give testimony. From these accounts it is quite evident that many girls' schools opted for science as a natural part of their timetable. How science lessons were arranged in these establishments, in an era before there were many science teachers available to undertake the work, was also revealed. It seems that the schools exploited whatever opportunities fell their way, as was well illustrated in an anecdote told to the inquiry by Mr J. Buckmaster, a science teacher.

He informed the committee that he had, for some time, observed with concern the slow progress of science in boys' schools. He had been among those who had hoped for great things from the stimulus to science aroused by the Great Exhibition of 1851, but his hopes were to be deflated. In his view the educational establishment had scuttled any attempts at change. In the typical boys' school,

> every difficulty was thrown in the way of science teaching, and, in a short time, nothing was left, but the broken remains of a little apparatus. Latin and Greek swallowed up the science and, at this time ... science as a means of training a boy to think and observe occupies a less important position than it did ten years ago. [II, p. 82]

In the opinion of Mr Buckmaster, this was not the case in girls' schools. They were as anxious as ever to continue and extend the science teaching available on their timetables. He informed the committee that he had decided to advertise himself as a chemistry teacher. He wrote some two hundred letters of application to the masters of grammar and commercial schools in and near London, 'offering to give gratuitously twelve lessons on chemistry'. The only school that accepted his offer was a ladies' school near Hyde Park, which had heard of his proposal by the merest accident.

Among the many girls' schools examined by the assistant commissioners, those run on Quaker principles were most often singled out for commendation. Quaker schools had, of course, a long history of girls' education. As early as 1717 the Friends in Witney, for example, had promised a prospective master six boarders and twelve weekly scholars besides 'young women that may be willing to improve their learning'.[8] Their principles stressed the equality and intellectual potential of both sexes, and their girls' schools were conspicuous for the way in which they avoided any contamination from the 'accomplishments'. Instead the girls were rigorously trained in experimental science, 'well and intelligently taught', opined the inspector who visited the Friends' school at Ackworth near Pontefract.

The Mount School in York, another long-established Quaker girls' school, also enjoyed a reputation for its mathematical and science training for girls. It had always devoted a considerable proportion of the timetable to science subjects, resorting to co-operation with neighbouring boys' schools or exploiting what public science lectures there were available, to secure adequate teaching. During the 1830s, one of the periods in which women's interest in science flowered, the school's determination to provide science teaching for its pupils was attested by some of its current students. A young Irish Quaker, Anna White, wrote enthusiastic letters home to her parents in Cork, describing her studies and school life. Her timetable included Greek, Latin, geometry and algebra, which were taught between 6.30 and 8 a.m. French and science were also on the curriculum. Anna noted the increasing interest in science among her teachers and school fellows. Her letter implies that her father had already taught her something of the subject: 'H. Brady [the headmistress] and the older girls are very much interested about Chemistry and Natural Philosophy. I wish Dada could tell some simple experiments we could do without much trouble. I find the little knowledge I have of it, of great use to me.'[9] Eventually the headmistress resolved the difficulty by sending her girls to the boys' school nearby for chemistry lessons. Anna White was very pleased because her brother was a pupil there.

Soon after, the girls were able to avail themselves of the growing number of public lectures in York on science subjects. In 1839 another pupil recorded the geology lectures given by Professor Phillips at the museum in the city. The girls also attended and greatly enjoyed public lectures on chemistry and practical experiments. As has been noted already, a generation later the girls at the Mount School became a familiar part of the audience during the years when the Ladies' Educational Association in York arranged public science lectures.

The school's lively scientific tradition encouraged many activities within the school itself. There were scientific clubs and committees in mineralogy, botany and conchology, which encouraged the girls to undertake simple scientific research by making collections and writing reports.

At the time of the inquiry, the headmistress was Lydia Rous who herself had had the benefit of an excellent education at the Friends' school in Croydon. There she had been given a thorough grounding in mathematics. During her time as headmistress in York, the girls were encouraged to include Latin and advanced mathematics as an integral part of their education.

Another school that could be proud of its academic and scientific tradition was the Moravian Seminary for Young Ladies in Bedford, which had been established in 1800. It had a resident teaching staff of women teachers and the curriculum was supplemented by visiting masters. The school's stated object was 'to afford a Christian and useful education to girls of the middle classes'. The subjects taught included English language and literature, geography, history, astronomy, the use of the globes, natural philosophy and plain and ornamental needlework. Extras were music, French, drawing and German. There were forty-one pupils and the fees were thirty guineas per annum. In contrast, St Anne's School, Rewley House, Oxford, restricted itself to the traditional timetable of 'French, music, drawing and English'. A slight variation was permitted to five girls who studied Latin.

Among the other witnesses appearing before the inquiry were the two young headmistresses Frances Mary Buss and Dorothea Beale, who were busy stamping their indelible image on the recently founded progressive schools for girls, the North London Collegiate School and Cheltenham Ladies College. Their testimony strengthened the view that science had been an integral part of girls' education in many places for a long time.

Dorothea Beale was still in the early stages of her famous career as the headmistress of Cheltenham Ladies College. Yet, during the previous decade or so, she had succeeded in transforming the college from an academically undemanding establishment for the better-off of Cheltenham into a dynamic school for hard-working and ambitious girls and a pace-setter for other schools aspiring to similar status.

Miss Beale's fostering of science in her school stemmed from her own scientific studies in girlhood. In the 1840s, as a teenager, she had attended the scientific lectures available in London. Among the most exciting were the lectures on astronomy given by Mr Pullen. She wrote later that 'they inspired a passionate desire to know more of mathematics, and to understand all the processes described'.[10] Like other young women, she was hampered by having no teacher to assist her through her difficulties with the subject. Trying to study alone was frustrating. 'I obtained books on mechanics and spelt them out as well as I was able, but was often baffled.'

It was not until she became a student at the newly established Queen's College that she managed to overcome her mystification. Under the guidance of the mathematics teacher of the college, Mr Astley Cock, she studied trigonometry and differential calculus successfully. In 1849 she was duly appointed as Queen's first lady mathematics tutor. Her father's anxiety lest she accept a salary for her work indicated how long the road to educational equality really was.

Ironically, despite the economic pressure on middle-class women to join the workforce, almost equal social pressure was exerted on them in the matter of receiving money for their labours. The convention that women from a certain class should not earn money was a powerful one. At an 1861 meeting in Dublin of the Society for Promoting the Employment of Women, the organizers described as 'rampant' the 'feeling that earning money was discreditable'. Women declared 'that though glad enough to receive payment, their perceptions of delicacy were so refined that they would shrink from taking it openly, and required it to be conveyed to them in some secret and unusual way, which would prevent the disclosure of identity to the employer'.[11]

Happily, Dorothea Beale resisted this pressure, as she was to resist everything that smacked of empty custom. Yet she was always tactful. When she was appointed head of Cheltenham, Miss Beale had every intention of altering the character of the school as she found it, in favour of a more rigorous educational regimen. But she diplomatically bore in mind the fears of conservative parents and moved with some stealth. Her explanation was simple:

> Had I [not] done so, I might have been the death of the College, so I had to wait for the tide. I began my innovation with the intro duction of scientific teaching, and under the name of physical geography I was able to teach a good deal. This subject was unobjectionable, as few boys learned geography. [Raikes, pp. 113–14]

Mathematics was introduced in the same cautious manner. Parents were informed that their daughters were learning geometry. The term 'Euclid', with its associations with classical education, was never used, for that would have aroused suspicions that the girls were wasting their time on inappropriately masculine subjects.

They were lucky girls, that early generation of Cheltenham ladies. Miss Beale was a gifted mathematics teacher. Her classes were a far cry from the learning-by-rote method favoured by teachers universally. The Schools Inquiry Commission noted with approval that her methods and her pupils far outshone even the great public schools.

Miss Beale ensured that her pupils worked towards a goal of achievement. At a time when few girls were permitted to be examined in any form of open competition, Cheltenham Ladies College, together with a few other schools of repute, had instigated its own internal examination system. Men of intellectual substance, such as Charles Bloxam, the Professor of Chemistry at King's, the mathematician J. E. Fitch, examiner at the University of London and an assistant commissioner on the Endowed Schools Enquiry, the Revd Charles Dodgson, another mathematician, and Dr Wright, the scientist, were persuaded to examine the young ladies.

What was expected of the girls in these examinations, remembering that this was still the era when competitive examinations were deemed too stressful for girls in general, can be illustrated by the not untypical results of one of the young ladies involved. Caroline Birch Dutton attended the college during 1866–71. She was awarded a first-class certificate in the following subjects: scripture, history, literature, geography, French, German, geology, chemistry, Euclid, arithmetic and algebra. This was surely a most acceptable advance on society's standard expectation of female education – a little dancing, music and French.

The other well-known school, the North London Collegiate School (founded in 1850 during that wave of enthusiasm for women's education that resulted in the establishment of several famous schools for girls, particularly Queen's and Bedford College), also demonstrated to the inquiry that it offered a demanding and modern curriculum. In her evidence, given on 30 November 1865, Frances Mary Buss, the head-mistress, described how the school coped with the illiterate and innu-merate girls who came to it. Usually between thirteen and fifteen years old, they could 'scarcely do the simplest sum in arithmetic'. Remedial teaching was often necessary before the pupils could undertake a varied syllabus similar to what was offered at Cheltenham. If anything, Miss Buss laid even greater emphasis on science subjects, without appearing to have received complaints from parents. She informed the inquiry that her school offered 'complete courses of teaching in natural science', which in practice included the property of matter, the laws of motion, mechanical powers, simple chemistry, electricity, geology, botany, natural history and astronomy. Miss Buss also favoured the corrective stimulus that only public examinations could supply. She had been in the vanguard of the movement to open the Cambridge Local Exam-inations to girls on the same terms as boys, and had entered twenty-five girls as early as 1863. After these first tentative steps, so much at odds with public opinion, she claimed that she had noted that a great improvement had occurred in the girls' training in arithmetic.

In their conclusions to their report on girls' education to the inquiry, the assistant commissioners expressed their admiration at much of the work being done in the best girls' schools. They were most sympathetic to the efforts they had witnessed among girls and their mistresses. Yet they were shaken by the overall inferiority of the education that fell to the lot of girls. They were convinced that the women of the country deserved better. What they sought to alter was a system that wasted the intelligence and brains of women. They stated categorically that they had found no evidence to sustain any claim that girls need not be educated in the same manner as boys. Mr Giffard, one of the most thoughtful and appreciative of the assistant commissioners, spoke for all when he said that he could find 'no natural inaptitude in girls to deal with any of the subjects which form the staple of a boys' education'.

It was the next step in the inspectors' thinking that was to have serious consequences for the place of science in the timetable of girls' schools. Like most of the assistant commissioners, Mr Giffard was a man educated in the classical tradition. He had little or no scientific education. So, as far as he was concerned, there was only one way to improve matters. When he noted that in his opinion the mental training in even the best girls' schools was unmistakably inferior to that found in the best boys' schools, he unhesitatingly assigned that deficiency to the unclassical nature of girls' education: 'the absence of classical teaching would alone account for much of the inferiority'. In the eyes of Mr Giffard, and of many of his contemporaries, the only way to improve the standards and the prestige of girls' education was to introduce the classics.

Notes

1. The achievements were catalogued in the *Journal of the Women's Education Union*, established in 1873. Its first editors were Miss Shirreff and George T. Bartley.
2. See Sheila Fletcher, *Feminists and Bureaucrats. A Study in the Development of Girls' Education in the Nineteenth Century* (1980).
3. Schools Inquiry Commission. General Reports by Assistant Commissioners. Southern Counties (1868), VII, p. viii.
4. Quoted in the *Victoria Magazine* (May–October 1864) III, p. 270.
5. It took a long time for things to change. In 1903 a secret meeting at Cambridge revealed that the University had just lost an endowment of £100,000 for the education of naval engineers through its insistence that Greek would remain a study requirement: *The Universities in the Nineteenth Century*, ed. by Michael Sanderson (1975), p. 234.
6. Quoted in Lytton Strachey, *Eminent Victorians* (1918, Penguin reprint 1977), p. 172.
7. Many women reformers complained bitterly at this total usurpation of drawing as a masculine subject. See C. S. Bremner, *Education of Girls and Women in Great Britain* (1897), p. 49.
8. *Victoria History of Oxfordshire* (1939), I, p. 135.
9. H. Winifred Sturge and Theodora Clark, *The Mount School York* (1931), p. 47.
10. Elizabeth Raikes, *Dorothea Beale* (1908), p. 13.
11. *Victoria Magazine* (1864), p. 459.

CHAPTER 9
Conclusion

In many respects the finding of the Taunton Commission benefited girls' education and the academic status of women. Government intervention meant that, at last, the demands of women for their educational rights had been recognized. At least some efforts were made to finance a greater number of girls' schools and to improve existing ones. There were new moves to organize teaching and to raise standards, as well as to open examinations and higher education to girls. But in one major way, girls' education lost through this process. Its scientific stamp was shortly to disappear.

For all the enthusiasm and approval for the modern and scientific education they had observed in the best of the girls' schools, the assistant commissioners were influenced in their final conclusions by their own unavoidable educational prejudices. With the best will in the world, they suggested that the way in which girls' schools might be improved was to increase the quota of classics taught there.

This opinion might have been resisted had it not been shared by Emily Davies and her supporters. She believed passionately that the goal of equality could be achieved only if female education was allowed to be a reasonably exact copy of what boys' education had always been. She consistently rejected any suggestion that separate but parallel systems for men and women might be more compatible with their different spheres of activity. She recognized only too well that any such duality would invariably perpetuate the slur of inferiority on the strand favoured solely by women. Central to her campaign was her conviction that women could and must justify their claims to equality by competing only in the arena traditionally reserved for men, the classics. It must be said, too, that she belonged to that tradition, reaching back to the Bluestockings and beyond, which accepted without question the superiority of the classical studies. In her opinion, the classics remained the only system that merited the name of education. In the struggle to gain a place of real merit for women in the educational system of the country, science could not be taken seriously.

Ultimately the founding of Girton College, Cambridge, by Emily Davies was to ensure that women would gain access to the privileged preserve of the classics. When the historic moment arrived with the first intake of three women students into Girton, she acted as she thought best. She positively discouraged the girls from choosing the natural sciences tripos or the moral tripos, for these were the courses with low prestige and reputation. In the event, the new students did as they were told. Two of them chose the classical tripos and one the mathematical.

Emily Davies's commitment to traditional educational values eventually won the day, but it was not wholly unopposed. The long tradition dating back to Bathsua Makin and Mary Astell in the seventeenth century, which disputed the prestige enjoyed by the classics as undeserved and unconstructive and considered it as unfit for the female intellect, still had its adherents. At Cambridge, James Stuart and some of his Cambridge colleagues, such as Professor Henry Sidgwick, had hoped that the 'modern' curriculum that girls studied might become a blueprint for reform of education in general.[1] They regarded with some dismay the rigorously classical image that Miss Davies had effectively stamped on Girton. More than one supporter of women's education censured her decision as retrograde. In August 1870 Professor J. R. Seeley withdrew his teaching support from Girton. He wrote to Miss Davies, 'I hope for times when you may feel able to be bolder and more progressive.'[2]

It was left to the ladies of the North of England Council, Anne Jemima Clough, Josephine Butler and Miss Wolstenholme, together with James Stuart and their other supporters, to attempt to found an educational forum of a sufficiently high standard which would yet encompass the liberal tradition of science and modern languages that women had evolved. To this end they established the Cambridge Lectures for Women, which were to be the genesis of Newnham, Cambridge's second women's college.

The next step was to petition the University itself, to establish a higher examination that would take into account the varied curriculum typical of women's education. James Stuart described their aims:

> We were desirous of making this examination one that would embody the best ideas of an examination which we had then developed in

our minds, and many of us hoped that it might lead to the degree examinations for men being more upon the same lines. There is no doubt that it has influenced the degree examinations, but not so much, I think, as we then expected. The work of the Cambridge Lectures for Women was largely directed to preparing for this examination and when Newnham came on the scene it continued the same work, so that the teaching at Newnham and at Girton went rather upon different lines, and was based on somewhat different ideals. [*Reminiscences*, pp. 181–2]

The men and women who continued to reject the old classical curriculum took a very serious risk. By insisting on developing a modern educational system, which many people believed would be inferior to the traditional one, they played into the hands of those who dismissed women's educational aspirations as trifling or pretentious. This pitfall was fully appreciated by campaigners and reformers in the other camp. When the excellent results were announced of the first three girl students, those whom Emily Davies had counselled to take either the classical or the mathematical tripos (two would have been on the classical honours list and one on the mathematical, had they been men) the *Journal of the Women's Education Union* pointed out that those who had believed that women could not compete in the same arena as men were now confounded. The editor noted that their achievement was unassailable in a way in which that of women who opted for the alternative could never be:

It must be evident, without entering into any discussion of that objection, that those students who have left the College, holding a certificate that records their having passed the examination for mathematical or classical honours at Cambridge, stand in a position in which no special examination for women upon any specially arranged course of studies could possibly have placed them.

The editor went on to warn women that it was still too soon for them to try to stamp their special identity on the educational system. If they succumbed to the temptation to deviate from the educational precedents decreed by tradition, they would place their newly won intellectual reputations in jeopardy: 'The time may come when women may have won the right to choose another curriculum should another seem more suitable, but at present their only wise course is to take what advantage they can of the prestige of old established or deserved authority' (*Journal of the Women's Education Union*, 15 July 1873, pp. 114–15).

It is clear that many women and girls heeded this warning. When the Royal Commission on Secondary Education, the Bryce Commission, investigated the state of girls' schools in 1894–5, it was observed that, although many of the schools were adequately equipped to teach science, those girls who were going to sit for higher examinations were discouraged from taking the science classes.[3] Any girl hoping to study for the equivalent of an Oxbridge degree was advised to concentrate on the classics.

Among the witnesses who appeared before the Bryce Commission was Miss Rogers, who was tutor in classics to the Oxford Association for the Education of Women. In her pertinent testimony to the Commission, she summed up the dilemma facing educators. Although many of them, including herself, had no wish to change the nature of the general education that girls received at school, which they considered much more satisfactory than boys', it was necessary to condone the almost exclusive study of the classics by those girls aiming for higher education:

> It is not possible to ignore classics in girls' education while the subject holds the place it does in boys' schools and at the universities; girls will not leave them alone. They feel that if they are to get the full good out of their university they must study the subject in which men win most credit, and in which the best teaching is to be procured. Those who direct their studies cannot conscientiously make them the object of educational experiments beyond a certain limit, nor will the general public think much of a course of work which is followed mainly or entirely by women ... The claim of women students to the degree is strong in proportion as they are qualified in the same way as men. So long as classics are compulsory at Oxford and Cambridge women who do not take them put themselves at a disadvantage and diminish their chance of being admitted to the BA ... if the BA cannot be got without classics, we must accept classics, for we cannot acquiesce permanently in the withholding of the degree. [p. 56]

Miss Rogers acknowledged that she would prefer a greatly diminished emphasis on the classics and a university course more in keeping with the curriculum generally in favour in girls' schools, but she had to admit that at that time, in the closing years of the nineteenth century, she saw little reason to suppose 'that Oxford is as yet prepared to take women into consideration in prescribing a curriculum for its undergraduates'.

It seems that women had learnt the value of the prestige of the classics only too well. They accepted unequivocally that, to be admitted within the masculine precincts of learning and culture, they must demonstrate their familiarity with the works that were the essence of that tradition. The old equation of the classics with culture had won new adherents. Sophie Bryant, headmistress of the North London Collegiate School in the late 1890s, observed that, since classics were the sole 'instrument of culture' for educated men, it would be unwise for women to substitute alternatives: 'To cut ourselves off abruptly from Latin and Greek would be to break with a tradition of centuries' standing – a tradition that unites with each generation of scholars the next generation as it arises.'[4] The suffrage question, in which women were once again going to seek the support of men, was looming ahead and was one very likely factor dictating the need to underline the community of culture between men and women.

The intellectual disenchantment with science that affected many of the brighter women who were now setting their sights on the universities was exacerbated by further evidence of its low social prestige. Women of high mental calibre were now just as sensitive to science's menial reputation as men had always been, and its inferior social status seemed to be confirmed by the interest shown by artisans and factory workers in the government-funded science schools. The status of science teachers was equally low, an important consideration at a time when the major area of employment for well-educated women was teaching. It had been noted many years previously, in the *Report of the Select Committee on Scientific Instruction* (1868), that science teachers were poorly treated and poorly rewarded. As a profession, the teaching of science was regarded as unprofitable and pointless (p. v).

In a later review of an article on the same subject from the *Westminster Review*, in which the decline of female interest in science in England was noted, the author, Mrs Sherriff, had also pointed out that scientific research 'can never pay in the sense of bringing a money reward equivalent to the time and labour expended' and that it also 'ranks lower in public esteem than professional knowledge that may be labelled with its marked price'.[5]

At the end of the century there was something of a revival of interest in science among middle-class women, and a fair number of women did complete the B.Sc. at Cambridge or London. Scientific societies like the 'X Club' begun by women at Oxford flourished during the early years of the twentieth century. They encouraged research, provided a forum for debate and discussion, and also allowed women interested in science to meet on social terms with each other and other professionals.

In the year from October 1904 to July 1905, the committee of the 'X Club' consisted of Miss Rogers of St Hugh's Hall (President), Miss Scott of Somerville (Secretary) and Miss Leeson of St Hilda's (Treasurer). Seven meetings were held during that year, which included talks given by a Miss Jourdain on the relationships betwen mathematics and metaphysics, by a Miss Hedley on geometrical arrangements of atoms and molecules, and by a Miss Bazeley on 'Artificial Parthenogenesis'. The other meetings included an exhibition of, botany, geology, archaelogy and geography, and talks given by Miss Webb on 'Fermentation', by Mr Jenkinson, D.Sc., on the effects of solutions of salts on frogs' eggs, and by Miss Weaver on some types of English scenery.

But the job opportunities open to women in science remained as limited as ever. As the field became increasingly professionalized by men, women were inevitably unable to progress into the higher, more lucrative and demanding scientific careers. It was noted that hardly any employment was open to female science graduates 'save that of science mistress with the modest salary of £100 ... the best posts are still closed to women in certain branches. This is not entirely due to masculine selfishness; public opinion and custom are also factors.[6]

'Public opinion and custom' were increasingly to prove a powerful disincentive to the growth of women's interest in science. In the first decades of the twentieth century the education of women and girls began to come under fire. The poor state of the nation's health and fears of a declining birth rate were blamed on the 'mischievous' nature of the education that women enjoyed. It was noted that women from all classes were inefficient and unhousewifely; that girls tended to reject their roles as mothers, by condoning 'deliberate and wicked means to avoid the legitimate consequences of marriage'; that breast feeding was on the decline; and that academic girls became unmarriageable through losing their good looks and manners.[7] It was decided that steps must be taken to ensure that girls were better trained for their most important roles in life, those of wife and mother. The result was a general introduction of and support for the teaching of domestic subjects in girls' schools. Notoriously tardy in making known their needs in the technical and science fields, girls' schools now acquiesced in the allocation of grants from the new Board of Education, created in 1899, that encouraged the replacing of science by domestic science subjects in the school curriculum.[8] It became customary for the few outstandingly clever girls to be allowed to study the classics, while their less able or less ambitious sisters were encouraged to choose homemaking in preference to science.

By 1918 the desirability of 'needlework, cookery, laundrywork, house-keeping and household hygiene' being 'substituted partially or wholly for science' in the education of girls over fifteen had become a fact of educational policy.[9]

Just as the research field was about to become highly specialized and politically and strategically important – in other words, just as science was poised to become a respectable profession – women were finally excluded. Science, after all, was soon to be a serious matter. Women had other jobs to do.

Notes

1. 'The Education of Girls, considered in Connexion with the University Local Examinations', lecture (11 June 1864) by W.B. Hodgson, reprinted in the *Victorian Magazine* (May–October 1864).

2. Rita McWilliams Tullberg, *Women at Cambridge* (1975), pp. 45, 63, 65.

3. Report by Mrs Ella S. Armytage on the County of Devon to the Royal Commission on Secondary Education (1894).

4. Special Report written for the Board of Education in 1898, p. 106, quoted in Nancy L. Blakestad, 'The Place of Domestic Subjects in the Curriculum of Girls' Secondary Schools in Late Victorian and Edwardian England', unpublished M.Phil. thesis (Oxford, 1988), p. 5.

5. *Journal of the Women's Education Union* (April 1873), p. 96.

6. C.S. Bremner, p. 221.

7. *Parents Review* (May 1906), XVII, no. 3, p. 379, quoted in Blakestad, pp. 55–6.

8. Noted by C.S. Bremner, p. 221.

9. Parliamentary Papers (1917–18), vol. 25, p. 127, quoted in D.M. Turner, *History of Science Teaching in England* (1927), p. 148.

Select Bibliography

Primary Sources

Abercromby, David, *A Discourse of Wit* (1685).
Advice to the Women and Maidens of London, By one of that Sex (1678).
Agrippa, Henricus Cornelius, *De Nobilitate et Praecellentia Feminei Sexus, ad Margaretam Austriacorum et Burgundionum Principem* (1529, translated 1542).
Aiken, Lucy, *Epistles on Women, exemplifying their Character and Condition in Various Ages and Nations. With Miscellaneous Poems* (1810).
Algarotti, Francesco, *Sir Isaac Newton's Philosophy explain'd for the Use of the Ladies in Six Dialogues on Light and Colours* (1739).
[Ames, Richard], *Sylvia's Revenge, or: A Satyr against man; in answer to the Satyr against Woman* (1688).
The Ape-Gentle-woman, or The Character of an Exchange-wench (1675).
Artemisa to Cloe. A Letter from a Lady in the Town to a Lady in the Country; Concerning the Loves of the Town (1679).
Astell, Mary, *A Serious Proposal to the Ladies, for the Advancement of their True and Greatest Interest. By a Lover of her Sex.* (1694, third edition 1696).
The Athenian Gazette: or Casuistical Mercury Resolving all the most Nice and Curious Questions Proposed by the Ingenious of Either Sex (ninth volume 1693).
Athenian Mercury (1693).
Athenian Society, *The Young Students Library* (1692).
Baker, Henry, *The Microscope made Easy* (Third edition 1744).
Ballard, George, *Memoirs of British Ladies* (1775).
[Bancke, Richard], *A Discourse of Women, shewing their Imperfections Alphabetically* (1673).

259

Barber, Mary, *Poems* (1734).

Barksdale, Clement, *A Letter Touching A Colledge of Maids; or a Virgin Society* (1675).

Beauty's Triumph: or the Superiority of the Fair Sex Invincibly Proved. etc. (1743, reprinted 1751).

Bennett, Revd. John, *Letters to a Young Lady on a Variety of Useful and Interesting Subjects, Calculated to Improve the Heart, to Form the Manners, and Enlighten the Understanding* (2 volumes, 1789).

Bercher, William, *The Nobylyte of Women* (1552; Roxburghe Club 1904).

Betham, Matilda, *A Biographical Dictionary of the Celebrated Women of Every Age and Country* (1804).

Blackmore, Richard, *The Lay Monastry* (1714).

Boswell, James, *The Life of Samuel Johnson* (1791, Everyman edition 1906, reprinted 1973).

Boyle, Robert, *New Experiments Physico-Mechanicall Touching the Spring of the Air, and its Effects* (Oxford, 1660).

——*Experiments and Considerations Touching Colours* (1664).

——*Works*, edited by Thomas Birch (1744).

Bremner, C. S., *Education of Girls and Women in Great Britain* (1897).

Brereton, Jane, *Poems on Several Occasions* (1744).

Browne, Moses, *Poems on Various Subjects* (1739).

——*The Works of Creation. An Essay on the Universe* (1752).

Bryan, Margaret, *A Compendious System of Astronomy* (1797).

——*Lectures on Natural Philosophy* (1806).

——*Astronomical and Geographical Class Book for Schools* (1815).

Buckland, William, *The Life and Correspondence of William Buckland DD, FRS*, by Elizabeth Gordon (1894).

Burnet, Bishop Gilbert, *History of His Own Time*, abridged by Thomas Stackhouse (1724 and 1734, Everyman reissue 1979).

Bury, Elizabeth, *An Account of the Life and Death of Mrs Elizabeth Bury ... Chiefly Collected out of her own Diary*, by the Revd. William Tong (1720, second edition 1721).

Carter, Elizabeth, *Memoirs of the Life of Mrs Elizabeth Carter*, edited by Montagu Pennington (1807).

——*Letters* (two volumes, 1809).

Carpenter, Edward, *My Days and Dreams* (1916).

Case, Thomas, 'Objections to the Proposed Statute for Admitting Women to The Examination for the Degree of Bachelor of Medicine'. Oxford, 13 June 1890.

Cavendish, Margaret, Duchess of Newcastle, *Poems and Fancies* (1653).

——*The World's Olio* (1655).

——*Philosophical and Physical Opinions* (1655, second edition 1663).

——*Nature's Pictures* (1656).

——*CCXI Sociable Letters* (1664).

——*Philosophical Letters: or Modest Reflections upon Some Opinions in Natural Philosophy* (1664).

—— *The Life of the Thrice Noble, High and Puissant Prince, William Cavendish* (1667).

——*Observations upon Experimental Philosophy. To which is added, The Description of a New Blazing World* (1666, second edition 1668).

——*Orations of Divers Sorts Accommodated to Divers Places* (1662, second edition 1668).

——*Grounds of Natural Philosophy* [Second edition of *Philosophical and Physical Opinions* but much altered] (1668).

Letters and Poems in Honour of the Incomparable Princess, Margaret, Dutchess of Newcastle (1676).

Chapone, Hester, *Letters on the Improvement of the Mind* (2 volumes, 1773).

Child, Sir Josiah, *A Discourse about Trade* (1690).

Chudleigh, Lady Mary, *The Ladies Defence* (1701).

——*Poems* (1703).

——*Essays upon Several Subjects in Prose and Verse* (1710).

Clerke, Agnes M., *The Herschels and Modern Astronomy* (1895).

The Diary of Lady Anne Clifford Countess of Dorset, Pembroke and Montgomery, 1590–1676, edited by George C. Williamson (1922, second edition 1967).

Collier, Jeremy, *The Great Historical Geographical Genealogical and Poetical Dictionary* (1701).

Comenius, John Amos, *School of Infancy. An Essay on the Education of Youth during the First Six Years* (1628–30; edited by W.S. Monroe, 1897).

——*A Reformation of Schooles*, translated by Samuel Hartlib (1642).

—— *The Great Didactic* (1657).

Comenius, edited by M. W. Keatinge (New York, 1931).

Comenius in England, edited by Robert Fitzgibbon Young (1932).

Conway, Anne, *The Correspondence of Anne, Viscountess Conway, Henry More, and their Friends, 1642–1684*, edited by M.H. Nicholson (New Haven, 1930).

—— *The Principles of the Most Ancient and Modern Philosophy* (1692, edited by Peter Loptson 1982).

Crousaz, Jean Pierre de, *Traité de l'Education des Enfants* (1722).

Dalton, John. *A Descriptive Poem addressed to Two Ladies At their Return from Viewing the Mines near Whitehaven* (1755).

Darwin, Dr Erasmus, *The Loves of the Plants* (Lichfield, 1789).

——*The Botanic Garden: A Poem in Two Parts* (1789–1791; two volumes, 1794–5).

——*A Plan for the Conduct of Female Education in Boarding Schools* (Derby, 1797).

Debus, Allen G., *Science and Education in the Seventeenth Century. The Webster-Ward Debate* (1970).

Defoe, Daniel, *An Essay Upon Projects* (1697).

Derham, William, *Physico-Theology or a Demonstration of the Being and Attributes of God from His Works of Creation* (1711–12, third edition 1714).

Desaguliers, J.T., *System of Experimental Philosophy* (1719).

——*A Course of Experimental Philosophy* (two volumes, 1734, 1744).

——*The Newtonian System of the World* (1728).

Discourse of Women (1673).

A Discoverie of Six Women Preachers in Middlesex, Kent, Cambridgeshire and Salisbury (1641).

Drake, Judith, 'Letter to Sir Hans Sloane', The British Library, Sloane Ms. 4047, 1 September 1723.

Duck, Stephen, *Poems on Several Occasions* (1736).

D'Urfey, Thomas, *A Common-Wealth of Women* (1686).

Edgeworth, Maria, *Practical Education* (two volumes, 1801).

——*Early Lessons* (1801).

——*Early Lessons, continued* (two volumes, 1814).

——*Letters from England 1813–1844*, edited by Christine Colvin (Oxford, 1971).

Edgeworth, Richard Lovell, *Memoirs of Richard Lovell Edgeworth. Esq. Begun by Himself and Concluded by His Daughter, Maria Edgeworth* (two volumes, 1820).

Eliot, George, *The George Eliot Letters*, edited by Gordon S. Haight (1954).

Essay on Woman (1763).

Essays on Women (1696).

Essex, John, *The Young Ladies Conduct* (1722).

Evelyn, John, *Mundus Muliebris* (1690).

——*Numismata. A Discourse of Medals, Antient and Modern* (1697).

——*The Diary of John Evelyn*, edited by E.S. De Beer (six volumes, Oxford, 1955).

——*Memoirs of John Evelyn, Esq. F.R.S.*, edited by William Bray (five volumes, 1827).

Fanshawe, Anne, Lady, *Memoirs of Lady Anne Fanshawe. By Herself*, edited by Sir N. H. Nicholas (1829).

The Female Advocate: or an Answer to A Late Satyr against The Pride, Lust and Inconstancy etc. of Women. Written by a Lady in Vindication of her Sex (1686).

The Female Advocate; or a Plea for the just Liberty of the Tender Sex, and particularly of Married Women (1700).

Female Rights Vindicated; or the Equality of the Sexes Morally and Physically Proved. By a Lady (1758).

The Female Spectator: English Women Writers Before 1800, edited by Mary R. Mahl and Helene Koon (Indiana University Press, 1977).

The Female Wits (1704).

Fiennes, Celia, *The Journeys of Celia Fiennes*, edited by Christopher Morris (1947).

Fontenelle, Bernard le Bovier, Sieur de, *Entretiens sur la pluralité des mondes* (1686).

——*The Theory or System of Several New Inhabited Worlds Lately Discover'd and Pleasantly Discrib'd in Five Nights Conversation*, translated by Mrs Aphra Behn (1688).

——*A Plurality of Worlds*, translated by Joseph Glanvil (1695).

——*Conversations on the Plurality of Worlds*, translated by W. Gardiner (1715).

Fox, Caroline, *Memoires* (1882).

The Free-Thinker, nos 1–6, November 1–December 1711.

Gilbert, Ann, *Autobiography and Other Memorials of Mrs Gilbert (formerly Ann Taylor)*, edited by Josiah Gilbert (fourth edition, 1879).

Gildon, Charles, *Miscellaneous Letters on Various Subjects* (1694).

Ginnar, Sarah, *The Women's Almanack* (1659).

Girle, Caroline, *Passages from the Diaries of Mrs Philip Lybbe Powys of Hardwick House. 1756–1808*, edited by Emily J. Climenson (1899).

Godartius, Johannes, *Of Insects*, translated by Martin Lister (York, 1682).

Good News to the Good Women (1700).

Granger, Revd J., *A Biographical History of England* (three volumes, 1779).

The Great Advocate and Oratour for Women (1682).

Gravesande, W.J.S. van's, *Mathematical Elements* (1726).

——*Newtonian Philosophy* (1735).

Gregory, Dr, *A Father's Legacy to his Daughters* (1789).

Grey, Elizabeth, Countess of Kent, *A Choice Manual of Rare and Select Secrets in Physick and Chyrurgery* (1653).

Guardian (two volumes, 1714).

Halkett, Anne, Lady, *Autobiography*, edited by John Gough Nichols, FSA (Camden Society, 1875).

Hamilton, Elizabeth, *Memoirs of Modern Philosophers* (three volumes, 1800).

——*Letters addressed to the Daughter of a Nobleman on the Formation of Religious and Moral Principles* (two volumes, 1806).

Harris, John, *Astronomical Dialogues Between a Gentleman and a Lady* (1719).

Hawkins, Laetitia-Matilda, *Anecdotes, Biographical Sketches and Memoirs* (two volumes, 1822).

——*Memoirs, Anecdotes, Facts and Opinions, Collected and Preserved* (two volumes, 1824).

Haywood, Eliza, *The Female Spectator* (1744, Fifth edition 1755).

Herschel, Caroline, *Memoir and Correspondence of Caroline Herschel*, by Mrs John Herschel (1876).

——*The Herschels*, by Agnes Clerke (1895).

——*The Herschel Chronicle. The Life-Story of William Herschel and His Sister Caroline Herschel*, edited by Constance A. Lubbock (Cambridge, 1933).

Hill, Georgiana, *Women in English Life* (two volumes, 1897).

Holden, Mary, *The Women's Almanack* (1688, 1689).

Hooke, Robert, *Micrographia* (1665).

——*Lectures De Potentia Restitutita or of Spring* (1678).

——*Lectiones Cutlerianae* (1679).

——*Philosophical Experiments and Observations of the Late Eminent Dr. Robert Hooke* (1721).

Hutchinson, Lucy, *Memoirs of the Life of Colonel Hutchinson*, edited by Revd. Julius Hutchinson (1806).

Hume, David, *A Treatise of Human Nature* (1739).

Hutton, Catherine, *Reminiscences of a Gentlewoman of the Last Century*, edited by Mrs C. Hutton Beale (Birmingham, 1891).

——*Catherine Hutton's Friends*, edited by Mrs C. Hutton Beale (Birmingham, 1895).

Johnson, Samuel, *The Rambler* (1750–52).

——*A dictionary of the English Language* (two volumes, 1755).

——*The History of Rasselas Prince of Abissinia. A Tale* (two volumes, 1759).

——*The Letters of Samuel Johnson*, edited by R.W. Chapman (three volumes, Oxford, 1952).

Journal of the Women's Education Union (1873–81).

The Ladies Advocate (1749).

The Ladies Behaviour. A Dialogue written Originally in Italian, Above An Hundred and Fifty Years Agoe (1693).

The Ladies Complete Pocket Book, printed by John Newbery (1759).

The Ladies Diary (1704–1840).

——*A Supplement to the Ladies Diary* (1789–1800).

——*The Mathematical Questions proposed in the Ladies Diary, and their original answers, together with some new solutions. 1704–1816*, edited by Thomas Leybourn (four volumes, 1817).

The Ladies Dictionary (1694).

The Ladies Journal (1694).

The Ladies Journal (1726–7, Dublin, 1727).

The Ladies Library (1714).

The Ladies Magazine: or the Universal Entertainer, by Jasper Goodwill (1749–51).

The Ladies Mercury (1693).

The Ladies Miscellany (1770).

The Ladies Monthly Museum (1798–1800; 1815–23).

The Ladies Own Memorandum Book (1803).

The Ladies Pocket Magazine (1829).

The Ladies Remonstrance (1659).

The Lady's and Gentleman's Scientifical Repository (1783).

Leapor, Mary, *Poems upon Several Occasions* (1748).

Letters on the Improvement of the Mind. By Mrs Chapone. A Father's Legacy to his Daughters by Dr Gregory. A Mother's Advice to her Absent Daughters. By Lady Pennington (Edinburgh, 1821).

Leybourn, William, *Astronomy and Geography* (1675).

——*Arithmetical Recreations* (third edition, 1699).

Locke, John, *Works* (nine volumes, twelveth edition, 1824).

Love Given Over: or a Satyr against … Woman (1686).

Macaulay, Catherine, *Letters on Education with Observations on Religious and Metaphysical Subjects* (1790).

Makin, Bathsua, *An Essay to Revive the Ancient Education of Gentlewomen* (1673).

——'Letter to John Pell', British Library Add. Mss. 4279, f. 103.

Malebranche, Father Nicolas, *Search after Truth* (1674; translated by T. Taylor, 1700).

Marcet, Mrs Jane, *Conversations on Chemistry* (1806).

——*Conservations on Natural Philosophy* (1819).

Martin, Benjamin, *The Description and Use of a New Invented Pocket Reflecting Microscope with a Micrometer* (?1740).

——*A Course of Lectures in Natural and Experimental Philosophy, Geography and Astronomy etc.* (1743).

——*The Young Gentleman and Lady's Philosophy in a continued Survey of the Works of Nature and Art by Way of a Dialogue* (1772).

Martineau, Harriet, *Autobiography* (three volumes, 1877).

Masters, Mary, *Poems on Several Occasions* (1733).

Melmoth, William, the Younger. *Letters on Several subjects. By the Late Sir Thomas Fitzosborne, Bart* (1748).

[Moir, John], *Female Tuiton: or An Address to Mothers on the Education of Daughters* (second edition 1786).

Montaigne, Michel de, *The Essayes or Morall, Politike and Millitarie Discourses*, translated by John Florio (1603).

Montagu, Mrs Elizabeth, *Mrs Montagu 'Queen of the Blues' Her Letters and Friendships from 1762–1800*, edited by Reginald Blunt (two volumes, 1923).

Montague, Elizabeth and Sarah Scott, *A Description of Millenium Hall and the Country Adjacent. By a Gentleman on his Travels* (1762).

Monthly Repository (1823).

More, Hannah, *Essays on various subjects Principally designed for Young Ladies* (1777).

——*Strictures on the Modern System of Female Education with a View of the Principles and Conduct prevalent among Women of Rank and fortune* (two volumes, 1799).

Moxon, Joseph, *Mechanick Dyalling* (1697).

Murch, Jerom, *Mrs Barbauld and her Contemporaries* (1876).

——*Bath in its Relation to Art, Science, Literature and Education* (1888).

Newbery, John, *The Newtonian System of Philosophy explained by Familiar Objects in an Entertaining Manner for the Use of Young Persons* (1812).

Nichols, John, *Minor Lives. A Collection of Biographies*, edited by Edward L. Hart (Cambridge, Mass., 1971).

Now or Never (1656).

Original Weekly Journal (1718).

Oxford Blue v. Drab. By an 'Extensioner' (1892).

Oxford, *Election of School Board* (1871).

Partridge, Dorothy, *The Woman's Almanack* (1694).

Pemberton, Henry, *A View of Sir Isaac Newton's Philosophy* (1728).

Pepys, Samuel, *The Diary of Samuel Pepys*, edited by R.C. Latham and W. Matthews (eleven volumes, 1983).

Philips, Ambrose, *The Free-Thinker* (1718–19).

Philosophical Collections (1681).

Plot, Robert, *The Natural History of Staffordshire* (1686).

——*The Natural History of Oxfordshire* (second Edition. 1705).

Poems by Eminent Ladies (two volumes, 1755).

Pope, Alexander, *The Poems of Alexander Pope*, edited by John Butt (1963).

Power, Henry, *Experimental Philosophy in Three Books: containing New Experiments Microscopical, Mercurial, Magnetical* (1664).

A Present for the Ladies. Being an Historical Vindication of the Female Sex (1692).

Prude, Revd John, *A Sermon at the Funeral of Miss Ann Baynard* (1697).

Radcliffe, Mary Anne, *The Female Advocate or an Attempt to Recover the Rights of Women from Male Usurpation* (1799).

——*The Memoirs of Mrs Mary Anne Radcliffe in Familiar Letters to Her Female Friend* (Edinburgh, 1810).

Report from the Select Committee on Scientific Instruction, chaired by Lord Frederic Cavendish (1868).

[Reynolds, John], *Death's Vision Represented in a Philosophical Sacred Poem* (1709).

Robinson, Mary, *Memoirs of Mary Robinson, 'Perdita'*, Introduction by J. Fitzgerald Molloy (Philadelphia, 1894).

Royal Institution, The, *Managers' Minutes* (1799–).

Life of Mary Anne Schimmelpennick, edited by Christiana C. Hankin (two volumes, 1858).

Schools Inquiry Commission (ten volumes, 1867–8).

Schurmann, Anna Maria von, *The Learned Maid: or Whether a Maid may be a Scholar? A Logick Exercise*, translated by Clement Barksdale (1659).

Scott, Mary, *The Female Advocate. A Poem occasioned by reading Mr Duncombe's Feminead* (1774).

Silvester, Tipping, *Original Poems and Translations consisting of The Microscope, Piscatio, or Angling etc.* (1733).

Somerville, Mary, *On the Connexion of the Physical Sciences* (1834).

——*Personal Recollections from Early Life to Old Age, of Mary Somerville by her Daughter Martha Somerville* (1873).

'Sophia', *Women's Superior Excellence* (1740).

——*Woman not Inferior to Man* (1743).

——*Beauty's Triumph* (1751).

Sprat, Bishop Thomas, *The History of the Royal Society of London, For the Improving of Natural Knowledge* (1667).

Sprint, Revd. John, *The Bride-Woman's Counsellor* (1708).

Steele, Richard, *The Ladies Library* (three volumes, 1714).

Strong, James, *Joanereidos* (1645).

Stuart, James, *On University Extension* (1871).

——*An Inaugural Address* (1892).

——*Reminiscences* (1911).

Swetnam, Joseph, *The Arraignment of Lewd, Idle, Froward and Unconstant Woman* (1637).

Swift, Jonathan, *Journal to Stella*, edited by Harold Williams (Oxford, 1974).

Sylvia's Complaint (1692).

Talbot, Catherine, *Works* (1780).

Tipper, John et al, *The Ladies or, the Womens Almanack Containing many Delightful and Entertaining Particulars, peculiarly adapted for the Use and Diversion of the Fair Sex* (1704ff.).

A Treatise of Feme Coverts: or, the Lady's law, containing All the Laws and Statutes relating to Women, under several Heads (1732).

Trimmer, Mrs Mary, *A Natural History of the Most Remarkable Quadrupeds, Birds, Fishes, Serpents, Reptiles and Insects* (two volumes, 1826).

Triumphs of Female Wit, In Some Pindarick Odes. Or, the Emulation together with an Answer to an Objector against Female Ingenuity, and Capacity of Learning. Also, A Preface to the Masculine Sex. By a Young Lady (1683).

True Taste: or Female Philosophy. Being an Epistle from Sylvia to Libertina (1735).

Turner, Robert, *Botanolgia. The British Physician: or the Nature and Vertues of English Plants* (1664).

Twentieth Report of the Science and Art Department of the committee of Council on Education (1873).

Vesey, Mrs Elizabeth, *The Library of Mrs Elizabeth Vesey 1715–91*, compiled by William H. Robinson (1926).

Victoria Magazine (1862).

Vives and the Renascence Education of Women, edited by Foster Watson (1912).

Voltaire, *The Elements of Sir Isaac Newton's Philosophy*, translated from the French by John Hanna (1738).

Waite, Arthur E., *Lives of Alchemystical Philosophers* (1888).

Wakefield, Mrs Priscilla, *An Introduction to Botany* (second edition 1798).

——*Leisure Hours; or Entertaining Dialogues Between Persons Eminent for Virtue and Magnanimity* (two volumes, fourth edition 1805).

——*Domestic Recreation: or Dialogues Illustrative of Natural and Scientific Subjects* (1805).

——*Reflections on the Present Condition of the Female Sex with Suggestion for its Improvement* (second edition 1817).

[Walker, Anthony], *The Holy Life of Mrs Elizabeth Walker*, Late Wife of A.W.D.D. Rector of Fyfield in Essex (1690).

Watts, Isaac, *A Treatise on the Education of Children and Youth* (second edition, 1769).

Weekly Memorials for the Ingenious or, an Account of Books lately set forth in several Languages with other Accounts Relating to Arts and Sciences (1681–1683).

Wells, Edward, *The Young Gentleman's Astronomy* (1712).

[West, Jane], *The Advantages of Education, or the History of Maria Williams. A Tale for Misses and their Mammas. By Prudentia Homespun* (Two volumes, 1793).

——*Letters to a Young Lady in which the Duties and Characters of Women are considered, chiefly with a Reference to Prevailing Opinion* (1806).

Westminster Review (1852).

Williams, Jane, *The Literary Women of England* (1861).

Williams, L. Pearce, *Michael Faraday* (New York, 1965).

Wilson, David B., 'Experimentalists among the Mathematicians: Physics in the Cambridge Natural Sciences Tripos, 1851–1900', *Historical Studies in the Physical Sciences*, volume 12, 1973.

Wollstonecraft, Mary, *Thoughts on the Education of Daughters with Reflections on Female Conduct in the More Important Duties of Life* (1787).

——*Vindication of the Rights of Woman* (1792).

The Woman of Taste (1733).

Woman Triumphant: Or, the Excellency of the Female Sex. By a Lady of Quality (1721).

Woman's Wit; or A New and Elegant Amusement for the Fair Sex. By a Lady (1780).

Women and the Oxford Examinations (April 1890).

Woolley, Hannah, *The Gentlewoman's Companion; or a Guide to the Female Sex* (1675).

——*The Accomplish'd Lady's Delight* (1675).

Worster, Benjamin, *A Compendious and Methodical Account of the Principles of Natural Philosophy: As they are Explain'd and Illustrated in the Course of Experiments, performed at the Academy in little Tower-Street* (1722).

Secondary Sources

Alic, Margaret, *Hypatia's Heritage: A History of Women in Science from Antiquity to the late Nineteenth Century* (1986).

Allan, D.G.C. and R.E. Schofield, *Stephen Hales: Scientist and Philanthropist* (1980).

Allen, D.E., *The Naturalist in Britain* (1978).

Armytage, W.H.G., *400 Years of English Education* (1970).

Barnard, H.C., *Fenelon on Education* (Cambridge, 1966).

Bell, Alan, *Sidney Smith* (Oxford, 1980).

Bibby, Cyril, *T.H. Huxley: Scientist, Humanist and Educator* (1959).

Birch, Una, *Anna Van Schurmann: Artist, Scholar, Saint* (1909).

Blackman, John, *A Memoir of the Life and Writings of Thomas Day* (1812).

Blakestad, Nancy L., 'The Place of Domestic Subjects in the Curriculum of Girls' Secondary Schools in Late Victorian and Edwardian England' (unpublished M.Phil. thesis, Oxford, 1988).

Blanchet, Jeremy, 'Science, Craft and the State: A Study of English Technical Education and its Advocates 1867–1906' (unpublished D.Phil. thesis, Oxford, 1953).

Boas, Louise S., *Harriet Shelley* (1962).

Boase, Alan M., *The Fortunes of Montaigne* (1935).

Butler, Marilyn, *Maria Edgeworth: A Literary Biography* (Oxford, 1972).

Caroe, Gwendy, *The Royal Institution: An Informal History* (1985).

Chambers, E.K., *Samuel Taylor Coleridge* (1938).

Clark, Donald L., *John Milton at St. Paul's School: A Study of Ancient Rhetoric in English Renaissance Education* (New York, 1948).

Clark, J.W. and Hughes, T.M., *The Life and Letters of the Reverend Adam Sedgwick* (2 volumes, Cambridge, 1890).

Clarke, Desmond, *The Ingenious Mr Edgeworth* (1965).

Clifford, James L., *Hester Lynch Piozzi* (1941, second edition 1952).

Cocking, Helen Muriel, 'Originality and Influence in the Work of Margaret Cavendish, First Duchess of Newcastle' (unpublished M.Phil. thesis, University of Reading, 1972).

Duffy, Maureen, *The Passionate Shepherdess: Aphra Behn 1640–89* (1977).

Eccles, Audrey, 'The Reading Public, the Medical Profession, and the Use of English for Medical Books in the Sixteenth and Seventeenth Centuries', *Neuphilologische Mitteilungen*, vol. 75, 1974, pp. 143–56.

——'The Early Use of English for Midwiferies 1500–1700', *Neuphilologische Mitteilungen*, vol. 78, 1977, pp. 377–85.

Ehrenpreis, Irvin and Robert Halsband, *The Lady of Letters in the Eighteenth Century* (William Andrews Clark Memorial Library, 1969).

Feingold, Mordechai, 'Science, Universities and Society in England 1560–1640' (unpublished D.Phil. thesis, Oxford, 1980).

Fletcher, Sheila, *Feminists and Bureaucrats. A Study in the Development of Girls' Education in the Nineteenth Century* (Cambridge, 1980).

Gardiner, Dorothy, *English Girlhood at School* (1929).

Gerin, Winifred, *Anne Brontë. A Biography* (1959, reprinted 1976).

——*Elizabeth Gaskell* (Oxford, 1976).

Goreau, Angeline, *Reconstructing Aphra* (Oxford, 1980).

Gosden, P.H., *How They Were Taught* (1969).

Goulding, R.W., *Margaret (Lucas) Duchess of Newcastle* (Lincoln, 1925).

Grant, William D.B., *Margaret the First. A Biography of Margaret Cavendish Duchess of Newcastle 1623–1673* (1957).

Green, David, *Queen Anne* (1970).

Griggs, Earl Leslie, *Coleridge Fille: A Biography of Sara Coleridge* (1940).

Haight, Gordon, S., *George Eliot. A Biography* (Oxford, 1968).

Hall, S.M. 'An Investigation of Factors Involved in Girls' Choice of Science Courses in the Sixth Form, and of Scientific Careers' (unpublished B.L. thesis, Oxford, 1965).

Halsband, Robert, *The Life of Lady Mary Wortley Montagu* (Oxford, 1956, reissued 1961).

Hamilton, Lady E.V., *The Mordaunts* (1965).

—— *William's Mary* (1972).

—— *The Illustrious Lady* (1980).

Harte, Negley, *The University of London 1836–1986* (1986).

Hartley, Sir Harold, *Humphrey Davy* (1966).

Health, Medicine and Mortality in the Sixteenth Century, edited by Charles Webster (Cambridge, 1979).

Hemlow, Joyce, *The History of Fanny Burney* (Oxford, 1958).

Holmes, Peggy Preston, 'The Life and Literary Theories of Marie le Jars de Gourney' (unpublished Ph.D. thesis, University of London, 1952).

Ilsley, M.H., *A Daughter of the Renaissance. Marie le Jars de Gourney: Her Life and Works* (The Hague, 1963).

Jacquot, Jean, 'Sir Charles Cavendish and His Learned Friends' in *Annals of Science*, vol. 8, March 1952.

Jones, M.G., *Hannah More* (Cambridge, 1952).

Jones, R.F., *Ancients and Moderns* (St Louis, 1961).

Kaye, Elaine, *A History of Queen's College London 1848–1972* (1972).

Knight, David M., *Natural Science Books in English 1600–1900* (1975).

Maclean, Ian, *The Renaissance Notion of Woman. A Study in the fortunes of scholasticism and medical science in European intellectual life* (Cambridge, 1980).

Manton, Jo, *Elizabeth Garrett Anderson* (1965).

Marshall, Dorothy, *English People in the Eighteenth Century* (1956).

Masson, Flora, *Robert Boyle* (1914).

Mavor, Elizabeth, *The Ladies of Llangollen* (1971).

Meyer, G.D., *The Scientific Lady in England 1650–1760* (Berkeley, 1955).

Millburn, J.R., *Benjamin Martin, Author, Instrument Maker and Country Showman* (Leyden, 1976).

Miller, E.H., *The Professional Writer in Elizabethan England* (Harvard, 1959).

Mintz, S.I., 'The Duchess of Newcastle's Visit to the Royal Society', *Journal of English and Germanic Philology*, 1952, pp. 168–76.

Moore, Doris Langley, *Ada Countess of Lovelace. Byron's Legitimate Daughter* (1977).

Morrell, Jack and Arnold Thackray, *Gentlemen of Science. Early Years of the British Association for the Advancement of Science* (Oxford, 1981).

Mozans, H.T. [J.A. Zahm], *Women in Science* (1913).

McWilliams-Tullberg, Rita, *Women at Cambridge* (1975).

Nicolson, M.H. and Nora M. Mohler, 'The Scientific Background of Swift's *Voyage to Laputa*', *Annals of Science*, 2 (1937), pp. 199–334.

Nicolson, M.H., *Mountain Gloom and Mountain Glory: The Development of the Aesthetics of the Infinite* (Ithaca: NY, 1959).

——*Pepys' Diary and the New Science* (Charlottesville, 1965).

Nixon, Edna, *Mary Wollstonecraft* (1971).

Parker, Irene, *Dissenting Academies in England. Their Rise and Progress and their Place among the Educational Systems of the Country* (Cambridge, 1914).

Patterson, Elizabeth Chambers, *Mary Somerville and the Cultivation of Science 1815–1840* (The Hague, 1983).

Pelling, Margaret, 'Occupational Diversity: Barbersurgeons and the Trades of Norwich 1550–1640', *Bulletin of the History of Medicine*, Volume 56, pp. 484–51.

Perry, H.T.E., *The First Duchess of Newcastle* (1918).

Peterson, R.T., *Sir Kenelm Digby. The Ornament of England 1603–1665* (1956).

Phillips, Patricia, 'The Lady's Journal (1693)', *Studia Neophilogica*, volume 53, 1981.

——*The Adventurous Muse: Theories of Originality in English Poetics 1650–1760* (Uppsala, 1984).

Plumb, J.H., *The Commercialisation of Leisure in the Eighteenth Century* (1973).

Raikes, Elizabeth, *Dorothea Beale* (1908).

Reynolds, Myra, *The Learned Lady in England 1650–1760* (Boston and New York, 1920).

Rice, M.A., *Story of St Mary's Abbots Bromley* (1947).

Schofield, R.E., *The Lunar Society of Birmingham. A Social History of Provincial Science and Industry in Eighteenth Century England* (Oxford, 1963).

Schwartz, Richard B., *Samuel Johnson and the New Science* (1971).

Shuttleworth, Sally, *George Eliot and Nineteenth-Century Science* (Cambridge, 1984).

Sichel, Edith, *Montaigne* (1911).

Small, Mirian Rossiter, *Charlotte Ramsay Lennox. An Eighteenth Century Lady of Letters* (Yale, 1935).

Steadman, F. Cecily, *In the Days of Miss Beale* (1931).

Strachey, Lytton, *Eminent Victorians* (1918, Penguin 1977).

Sturge, H. Winifred and Theodora Clark, *The Mount School York* (1931).

Surtees, Virginia, *Jane Welsh Carlyle* (Wiltshire, 1986).

Sylvester, D.W., *Educational Documents* (1970).

Tabor, M.E., *Pioneer Women* (1925 33).

Trevelyan, Ralph, *A Pre-Raphaelite Circle* (1978).

Turnbull, G.H., *Hartlib, Dury and Comenius. Gleanings from Hartlib's Papers* (1947).

Turner, Barry, *Equality for Some* (1974).

Turner, D.M., *History of Science Teaching in England* (1927).

Tylecote, Mabel, *Women at Manchester University* (1941).

—— *The Mechanics' Institutes* (1957).

The Universities in the Nineteenth Century, edited by Michael Sanderson (1975).

Wardle, Ralph M., *Mary Wollstonecraft: A Critical Biography* (1951).

Woodward, W.H., *Studies in Education during the Age of the Renaissance, 1400–1600* (Cambridge, 1906, reissued 1924).

Index